# Formal Assessment

McDougal Littell

# THE LANGUAGE OF
# LITERATURE

## AMERICAN LITERATURE

**McDougal Littell**
A HOUGHTON MIFFLIN COMPANY
**Evanston, Illinois • Boston • Dallas**

# Acknowledgments

"The Murderer" by Ray Bradbury, from *Argosy* magazine. Copyright © 1953, renewed 1981 by Ray Bradbury. Reprinted by permission of Don Congdon.

ISBN 0-395-96836-4

1 2 3 4 5 6 7 8 9 –MDO – 02 01 00 99

# Contents

# To the Teacher

This Formal Assessment booklet contains the materials described below. For more detailed information, turn to the front of each section.

## Tests for *The Language of Literature*

- **Selection Tests.** A Selection Test is provided for each selection or group of selections in the Pupil's Edition. Each Selection Test may use graphics, multiple-choice items, or essay questions to test students' understanding of vocabulary words, content, major issues, and the literary concepts taught with each selection. Selection Tests should be administered after students have discussed the selection and completed the Responding Options.

- **Part Tests.** Part Tests are open-book tests. Students are directed to answer multiple-choice or short essay questions and complete graphics that require them to discuss or compare a number of selections in terms of themes, characters, and literary concepts.

- **Mid-Year and End-of-Year Tests.** The Mid-Year and End-of-Year Tests are open-book tests designed to check students' understanding of the concepts and skills that were taught in the units preceding the tests. These two tests are similar in format, although the End-of-Year Test is somewhat longer than the Mid-Year Test. Each test consists of a short reading passage followed by several series of multiple-choice questions and short-answer, open-ended questions. These questions test the students' basic understanding of the passage as well as the literary elements and techniques used to write the passage. The writing portion of the tests includes a prompt, which calls for the students to write a short essay applying at least one taught concept or skill. Finally, there is a short activity testing the students' editing and revising skills.

## Additional Test Generator Questions

This section contains a bank of additional questions for each selection, which you can use to create customized tests for your classes. The items in this section of the book are duplicated on the Test Generator software. You are encouraged to scan these items and select the ones that would be most useful for your classes. You can then use the Test Generator software to create tests to suit your students' needs.

## Writing Assessment

This section contains tools to help you conduct holistic evaluations of students' writing, including a general evaluation form and writing assessment prompts to help students prepare for essay tests.

## Standardized Test Practice

This section provides opportunities for students to develop strategies for performing well on standardized tests. Practice items are included for areas typically found on standardized tests. Each section of practice items explains the purpose for those particular items, provides an example, and describes specific strategies students can use to be successful.

## Answer Key

This section includes answer keys for Selection Tests, Part Tests, Mid-Year and End-of-Year Tests, and the Standardized Test Practice.

# Tests for *The Language of Literature*

## Contents

*Answer Key for Selection, Part, Mid-Year, and End-of-Year Tests begins on page 348.

## Unit Three: The Spirit of Individualism

### Part One: Celebrations of the Self

### Part Two: The Dark Side of Individualism

## Unit Four: Conflict and Expansion

### Part One: A House Divided

### Part Two: Tricksters and Trailblazers

*Answer Key for Selection, Part, Mid-Year, and End-of-Year Tests begins on page 348.

*Answer Key for Selection, Part, Mid-Year, and End-of-Year Tests begins on page 348.

| | Tests* | Additional Test Generator Questions |
|---|---|---|

## Unit Seven: War Abroad and Conflict at Home

### Part One: Remembering the Wars

### Part Two: Integration and Disintegration

*Answer Key for Selection, Part, Mid-Year, and End-of-Year Tests begins on page 348.

# To the Teacher

This section contains Selection Tests, Part Tests, the Mid-Year Test, and the End-of-Year Test. The following charts indicate the types of questions and the tested concepts for each type of test in this section. Administer Selection Tests after students have discussed the selection and completed the postreading activities. Tests for poetry should be open-book.

## Selection Tests

| Section | Type of Item | Tested Concepts and Skills from the Selection |
|---------|--------------|-----------------------------------------------|
| A | graphic device (table, chart, diagram, etc.) | selection content or the introduced literary concept |
| B | multiple-choice questions | selection content or the introduced literary concept |
| C* | multiple-choice questions | vocabulary words |
| D** | essay questions | introduced literary concepts |
| E | essay question | how introduced concept relates to student's personal experience |
| F*** | optional | optional |

  * If a selection has no vocabulary words, the item types and tested elements will move up one section. In some tests, a graphic exercise testing a major concept from the selection is inserted in Section C. In this case, the vocabulary questions and/or other items are moved down one section.

 ** The student chooses one of two essay questions to answer.

*** If a graphic exercise is used in Section C and vocabulary is tested in Section D, the remaining sections may be moved down. In this case, Section F is necessary.

## Part Tests

| Section | Type of Item | Tested Concepts and Skills from the Part |
|---------|--------------|------------------------------------------|
| A | multiple-choice or short answer questions | content of selections in the part or the literary concepts that were introduced in those selections |
| B | graphic device (table, chart, diagram, etc.) | compare/contrast elements from one or more selections; analyze elements within a single selection |
| C* | essay questions | students' personal reactions to selections; major ideas, characters, themes, literary concepts |
| D** | graphic device (table, chart, diagram, etc.) | compare/contrast elements from one or more selections; analyze elements within a single selection |

 * The student chooses two of three to four essay questions to answer.

** Included whenever space permits; uses a different graphic device and tests other elements than Section B.

## Mid-Year and End-of-Year Tests*

| Section | Type of Item | Tested Concepts and Skills |
|---------|-------------|---------------------------|
| 1 | multiple-choice questions | basic comprehension of the reading passage |
| 2 | multiple-choice questions | how the literary concepts and skills taught in the preceding units relate the reading passage |
| 3 | short, open-ended essay questions | how the literary concepts and skills taught in the preceding units relate the reading passage |
| 4 | multiple-choice questions | ability to analyze and critically evaluate the reading passage in terms of literary concepts and skills |
| 5 | short, open-ended essay questions | ability to analyze and critically evaluate the reading passage in terms of literary concepts and skills |
| 6 | essay question | writing ability (organization and mechanics) |
| 7 | multiple-choice questions | revising and editing ability (organization and mechanics) |

\* Reading passages for these tests are included in this book.

All questions appearing in this Formal Assessment book, as well as the quizzes printed in the URB, can be found electronically on the Test Generator software.

# The World on the Turtle's Back (page 24)

# Selection Test

**A.** Think about Joseph Campbell's ideas concerning the functions of myths. Then, on the shaded bars below, make a mark in the appropriate spot to show how important you think each function is in this myth. In the box below each bar, write notes explaining your reasons for rating each function's importance as you did. (8 points each)

|  | Not Important | Very Important |
|---|---|---|
| **1. To instill a sense of awe toward the mystery of the universe** | | |
| **2. To explain the workings of the natural world** | | |
| **3. To support and validate social customs** | | |
| **4. To guide people through the trials of living** | | |

**B.** Write the letter of the best answer. This exercise is continued on the next page.
(6 points each)

_____ 1. Which of the following does **not** lead to the pregnant woman's fall from
the sky?
a. fear
b. curiosity
c. disrespect
d. selfishness

........................................................................................................................

_____ 2. According to the myth, what characteristic of the left-handed twin is responsible for the death of his mother?
   a. envy
   b. hatred
   c. despair
   d. stubbornness

_____ 3. The myth implies that, if the right-handed twin had created the world by himself, the world would be
   a. perfect.
   b. unbalanced.
   c. more orderly.
   d. completely peaceful.

**C. Words to Know.** Write the letter of the best answer. (4 points each)

_____ 1. Which would you expect to be described as a void?
   a. outer space          b. a solar system          c. a planet

_____ 2. Which is not a traditional wedding ritual?
   a. exchanging vows      b. a bride and groom       c. exchanging rings

_____ 3. Devious behavior includes
   a. respect.             b. violence.               c. lying.

_____ 4. Where do people regularly contend with one another?
   a. baseball fields      b. birthday parties        c. funerals

_____ 5. If you succumb to your greatest fears, you can expect to become
   a. more powerful.       b. less powerful.          c. all-powerful.

**D.** Answer **one** of the following questions based on your understanding of the selection. Write your answer on a separate sheet of paper. (15 points)

1. Why do you think that the people dance and sing for the left-handed twin? Support your ideas with details from the selection.

2. The myth says that "The right-handed twin made man. The people do not know just how much the left-handed twin had to do with making man." Based on this quotation and the behavior of the twins, what would you say is the Iroquois view of human nature? Support your answer.

**E. Linking Literature to Life.** Answer the following question based on your own experience and knowledge. Write your answer on a separate sheet of paper. (15 points)

In your opinion, are good and evil equally balanced in the world, or is one force more powerful than the other? Explain.

## Song of the Sky Loom
## Hunting Song/Dinni-e Sin (page 33)

# Selection Open-Book Test

**A.** One of the purposes of repetition is to reinforce important ideas and feelings.
In each box at the top, jot down a phrase that is repeated in the poem. In each box
at the bottom, note ideas and feelings that are stressed through the repetition.
(15 points each)

|  | 1. "Song of the Sky Loom" | 2. "Hunting Song" |
|---|---|---|
| **Example of Repetition** |  |  |
| **Ideas or Feelings Stressed** |  |  |

**B.** Write the letter of the best answer. (10 points each)

_____ 1. The speaker of "Song of the Sky Loom" seeks
   a. favors.
   b. knowledge.
   c. forgiveness.
   d. proof of the existence of the Earth and Sky.

_____ 2. In "Hunting Song," the hunter's song
   a. kills the deer.
   b. lulls the deer to sleep.
   c. reassures or attracts the deer.
   d. makes the deer feel suspicious or frightened.

**C.** Answer **one** of the following questions based on your understanding of the poems.
Write your answer on a separate sheet of paper. (25 points)

1. What do you think the "garment of brightness" represents in "Song of the Sky
   Loom"? Explain.

2. What are some reasons that the hunter in "Hunting Song" might feel blessed?

**D. Linking Literature to Life.** Answer the following question based on your own
experience and knowledge. Write your answer on a separate sheet of paper. (25 points)

What is your attitude toward nature? If all people shared your attitude toward nature,
how would nature be affected?

## Coyote and the Buffalo/
## Fox and Coyote and Whale (page 39)

# Selection Test

**A.** Think about folklorist Stith Thompson's ideas about the three roles of tricksters. For each story, make marks in the appropriate small boxes to tell which roles Coyote and Fox play. (They may play more than one role.) Then note details from each story that support your choices. (15 points each)

---

**1. In "Coyote and the Buffalo," Coyote is presented as a**

☐ **helpful culture hero.**   ☐ **clever deceiver.**   ☐ **numskull.**

**Details:**

---

**2. In "Fox and Coyote and Whale," Fox is presented as a**

☐ **helpful culture hero.**   ☐ **clever deceiver.**   ☐ **numskull.**

**Details:**

---

**B.** Write the letter of the best answer. (6 points each)

_____ 1. "Coyote and the Buffalo" explains the reasons that
   a. the Okanogan hunt buffalos.
   b. the Okanogan refuse to hunt buffalos.
   c. buffalos are plentiful on Okanogan lands.
   d. buffalos are not found on Okanogan lands.

_____ 2. Which of the following aids Coyote most in his conflict with Bull Buffalo?
   a. nature
   b. instinct
   c. book learning
   d. the supernatural

_____ 3. The main struggle in "Fox and Coyote and Whale" is between
   a. Fox and Whale.
   b. Fox and Coyote.
   c. Fox and the Water Maidens.
   d. Fox's wife and Whale.

**C.** Think about which characters hold power in the stories. Then, for each story, write notes to answer the questions. (10 points each)

| | **Which character is most powerful?** | **What makes this character more powerful than the other characters?** |
|---|---|---|
| **1. "Coyote and the Buffalo"** | | |
| **2. "Fox and Coyote and Whale"** | | |

**D.** Answer **one** of the following questions based on your understanding of the stories. Write your answer on a separate sheet of paper. (16 points)

1. What character traits are rewarded in "Coyote and the Buffalo"? What character traits are punished? Use details from the story to support your answers.

2. Why do you think "Fox and Coyote and Whale" became part of the oral tradition of Okanogan culture? In your answer, consider the purposes it may have served, the wisdom it may have imparted, and the questions about human life it might have helped to answer.

**E. Linking Literature to Life.** Answer the following question based on your own experience and knowledge. Write your answer on a separate sheet of paper. (16 points)

If you were to create a myth for your peers, what value would you teach or promote? Why?

# The Man to Send Rain Clouds (page 48)

# Selection Test

**A.** Choose an internal and an external conflict in this story that you wish to discuss. Then write notes to answer the questions in the boxes below. (8 points each)

|  | **Internal Conflict** | **External Conflict** |
|---|---|---|
| 1. Who is directly involved with this conflict? |  |  |
| 2. What does the conflict concern? |  |  |
| 3. Why does this conflict exist? |  |  |
| 4. If the conflict is resolved, how is it resolved? If the conflict isn't resolved, why isn't it resolved? |  |  |
| 5. How does the resolution or nonresolution affect those directly involved? |  |  |

**B.** Write the letter of the best answer. This exercise is continued on the next page. (4 points each)

_____ 1. Of the following, which appears to have the least religious value to the Laguna characters in the story?
a. sheep
b. colors
c. cornmeal
d. holy water

_____     2. How do Leon and Ken react to the discovery of Teofilo's body?
           a. calmly
           b. fearfully
           c. scornfully
           d. frantically

_____     3. Once Teofilo is dead, his grandchildren believe that
           a. there is nothing more they can do for him.
           b. there is nothing more that he can do for them.
           c. both they and Teofilo will continue to help each other.
           d. their duties to themselves outweigh their duties to Teofilo.

**C. Words to Know.** Write the letter of the best answer. (4 points each)

_____     1. An arroyo is most similar to a
           a. dry creek bed.      b. grassy meadow.      c. sun-parched desert.

_____     2. From a distance, the top of a mesa appears
           a. jagged.           b. flat.           c. hilly.

_____     3. Who might live in a cloister?
           a. sheep           b. students           c. nuns

_____     4. Who could you expect to wear a cassock?
           a. an infant           b. a dead person      c. a priest

_____     5. Perverse people tend to be
           a. unreasonable.      b. timid.      c. violent.

**D.** Answer **one** of the following questions based on your understanding of the story. Write your answer on a separate sheet of paper. (14 points)

1. What might be some reasons that Leon doesn't reveal the fact of Teofilo's death to Father Paul until after the funeral? Support your ideas with reference to the story.

2. If Father Paul had decided not to sprinkle Teofilo's grave with holy water, what might have been some of the results? In your answer, use details from the story to explain how you think Father Paul, the members of Teofilo's family, the memory of Teofilo, and the community as a whole would have been affected.

**E. Linking Literature to Life.** Answer the following question based on your own experience and knowledge. Write your answer on a separate sheet of paper. (14 points)

What reasons can you think of to make, and **not** to make, compromises? Explain, using real or made-up examples.

## from The Way to Rainy Mountain (page 55)

# Selection Test

**A.** Think about the different settings Momaday describes and the moods that his descriptions evoke. In the boxes below, write notes about the details of each setting Momaday describes, the senses his descriptions appeal to, and the effect of these details on the mood of each setting. (8 points each)

| Details of Setting/Senses Appealed To | Effect of Setting on Mood |
| --- | --- |
| 1. High Country: | |
| 2. Descent to the Plains: | |
| 3. Oklahoma/Rainy Mountain: | |

**B.** Write the letter of the best answer. This exercise is continued on the next page. (5 points each)

_____ 1. The narrator's main reason for going to Rainy Mountain is to
   a. meet his family.
   b. see Fort Sill.
   c. visit his grandmother's grave.
   d. sell his grandmother's house.

_____ 2. Tai-me is
   a. a mountain close to the reservation.
   b. the narrator's grandmother.
   c. the sacred Sun Dance doll.
   d. the Kiowa word for "water."

........_____ 3. The narrator makes a pilgrimage to
........a. trace the migration of the Kiowa.
........b. pay homage to his grandfather.
........c. trace the migration of the Crows.
........d. see what life was like on the plains.

_____ 4. Which sentence best describes the narrator's childhood?
........a. He lived in crippling poverty.
........b. He wanted to leave the plains.
........c. He was very lonely.
........d. He developed a closeness to nature.

**C. Words to Know.** Write the letter of the best answer. (4 points each)

_____ 1. Which person lives in a state of <u>servitude</u>?
........a. a slave ............ b. a ship's captain ............ c. a teacher

_____ 2. A vision of the sun god would most likely <u>engender</u> a
........a. thunderstorm. ............ b. rainbow. ............ c. sense of awe.

_____ 3. A <u>linear</u> progression moves in a
........a. straight line. ............ b. curve. ............ c. circle.

_____ 4. A <u>nomadic</u> tribe is one that
........a. settles down. ............ b. moves around. ............ c. creates farms.

_____ 5. An <u>unrelenting</u> rain is
........a. gentle. ............ b. off and on. ............ c. constant.

**D.** Answer **one** of the following questions based on your understanding of the selection. Write your answer on a separate sheet of paper. (20 points)

1. What does Momaday's description of what he saw as he retraced the migration route of the Kiowas reveal about him and his attitude toward the land? Think about the kinds of details he includes in his description and the details he does not include.

2. What do you learn about the Momaday's grandmother from his description? How do you think he felt about his grandmother? Use details from the selection to support your ideas.

**E. Linking Literature to Life.** Answer the following question based on your own experience and knowledge. Write your answer on a separate sheet of paper. (16 points)

Momaday's descriptions reveal his connection to the land and what it means to him. Describe a place that is important or has special meaning to you. Does nature play an important role in that place? Do you think it would be valuable for people to have a closer relationship with nature? Why or why not?

# Unit One: Origins and Encounters

# Part One Open-Book Test

**A.** Write your answer to each question on the lines. (5 points each)

1. What is "The World on the Turtle's Back" intended to explain?

   _____

   _____

2. What is the setting in the selection from *The Way to Rainy Mountain*, and what is its significance?

   _____

   _____

3. What is the main conflict between Leon and Father Paul in "The Man to Send Rain Clouds"?

   _____

   _____

4. According to the selection from *The Way to Rainy Mountain,* how did the Kiowas come to worship the sun god?

   _____

   _____

**B.** In many of these selections, the writers describe contrasts between two different or opposing things or ideas. Circle the letter of **one** selection you wish to discuss. In the boxes at the top, note two things that are contrasted in the selection. In the box at the bottom, note ideas and feelings that this contrast helps to communicate to the reader. (20 points)

    a. "The World on the Turtle's Back"          d. "The Man to Send Rain Clouds"
    b. "Coyote and the Buffalo"                   e. *The Way to Rainy Mountain*
    c. "Fox and Coyote and Whale"

```
┌─────────────────────────┐                          ┌─────────────────────────┐
│                         │   ➡ is contrasted with ➡ │                         │
│                         │                          │                         │
└─────────────────────────┘                          └─────────────────────────┘
```

**What does this contrast communicate to the reader?**

```
┌──────────────────────────────────────────────────────────────────────────────┐
│                                                                                │
│                                                                                │
│                                                                                │
└──────────────────────────────────────────────────────────────────────────────┘
```

**C.** Answer **two** of the following essay questions based on your understanding of the selections. Write your answers on a separate sheet of paper. (20 points each)

1. Choose a person from the selections who seems to lead a life in harmony with nature and a person who does not. In what ways are their lives affected by their closeness to, or distance from, nature?

2. Choose **one** selection and explain what it reveals about the religious beliefs, political systems, or social values of the culture from which it comes. Support your ideas with details from the selection.

3. If you were designing posters for any **two** of the selections from this unit in order to express the feelings and meanings of the selections, what words would you use for each poster? What one main image would you use for each? Use details from the selections to support your ideas.

4. Describe **one** message or lesson from these selections that you think can be applied to a modern-day situation. How could it be applied to a modern-day situation?

**D.** In many of these selections, the ending or the outcome of the main events determines the lesson or message of the selection. (20 points)

- Choose **one** story from this part that you wish to discuss. **Do not choose a selection that you discussed in Part B on the previous page.**

- Write the name of the story on the blank line below.

- In the box at the top, write notes describing a new ending for that story.

- In the box at the bottom, write notes explaining how your new ending changes the message or lesson of the story.

**Story:** _____

| **New Ending** |
| --- |
| |
| **What message is communicated through your new ending?** |
| |

## *from* La Relación (page 72)

# Selection Test

**A.** In each box on the left, note something that helped Cabeza de Vaca and his crew to survive. In each box on the right, write notes explaining how that thing helped them.
(8 points each)

| 1. A Character Trait of Cabeza de Vaca → | How It Helped Cabeza de Vaca and the Crew to Survive |
|---|---|
| 2. An Action of Cabeza de Vaca → | How It Helped Cabeza de Vaca and the Crew to Survive |
| 3. A Character Trait of the Karankawas → | How It Helped Cabeza de Vaca and the Crew to Survive |
| 4. An Action of the Karankawas → | How It Helped Cabeza de Vaca and the Crew to Survive |

**B.** Write the letter of the best answer. This exercise is continued on the next page.
(6 points each)

_____ 1. Because his audience was the king of Spain, Cabeza de Vaca's main
purpose in writing *La Relación* was to relate his
a. feelings.
b. experiences.
c. political beliefs.
d. private thoughts.

_____ 2. Which of the following is **not** a feeling toward the Karankawas expressed in Cabeza de Vaca's writing?
   a. fear
   b. hatred
   c. gratitude
   d. superiority

_____ 3. Why did the Spanish agree to act as physicians for the Karankawas?
   a. They had to do so, or starve.
   b. They hoped to trick the Karankawas.
   c. They wanted to learn the Karankawas's treatments.
   d. They wanted to repay the Karankawas for helping them.

**C. Words to Know.** Write the letter of the best answer. (4 points each)

_____ 1. When people <u>lament</u> about an event, they express
   a. amusement.         b. sadness.            c. scorn.

_____ 2. Which of the following is evidence of a possible <u>infirmity</u>?
   a. fear                b. thunder             c. nausea

_____ 3. If you were unable to <u>placate</u> someone, that person would remain
   a. sick.               b. disinterested.      c. upset.

_____ 4. When an order is given, the people who <u>comply</u> are those who
   a. obey.               b. rebel.              c. issue it.

_____ 5. Which word would you use to <u>beseech</u> someone?
   a. "Welcome!"          b. "Please!"           c. "Thanks!"

**D.** Answer **one** of the following questions based on your understanding of the selection. Write your answer on a separate sheet of paper. (15 points)

1. Why do you think the Karankawas welcomed and aided Cabeza de Vaca and his crew? Use details from the selection to support your answer.

2. In what ways did the Karankawas and Cabeza de Vaca's crew benefit from their relationship? What were the drawbacks of this relationship for each group? Use details from the selection to support your answers.

**E. Linking Literature to Life.** Answer the following question based on your own experience and knowledge. Write your answer on a separate sheet of paper. (15 points)

If you were free to explore any place or subject, what would you choose to explore, and why? What significant challenges would you face? Explain.

# *from* Of Plymouth Plantation (page 81)

# Selection Test

**A.** Think about the differences between the two accounts: the primary source by William Bradford and the secondary source by Alicia Crane Williams. In the boxes below, write notes explaining how and why the two accounts differ in content, biases or opinions, tone, and points of view. (8 points each)

| Bradford's Account | Williams's Account |
|---|---|
| 1. Content | |
| 2. Biases or Opinions | |
| 3. Tone | |
| 4. Points of View | |

**B.** Write the letter of the best answer. This exercise is continued on the next page. (6 points each)

_____ 1. Throughout this selection, Bradford views God's actions mainly as providing
      a. challenge.
      b. protection.
      c. punishment.
      d. enlightenment.

_____ 2. Which of the following is the **greatest** danger to the Pilgrims during their early months at Plymouth?
a. disease
b. starvation
c. Indian attack
d. lack of leadership

_____ 3. *Of Plymouth Plantation* is considered a primary source because it
a. is a historical document.
b. is written in the third person.
c. is the first document written about these events.
d. was written by someone who actually took part in these events.

**C. Words to Know.** Write the letter of the best answer. (4 points each)

_____ 1. Which of the following is another name for a desolate town?
a. campground          b. community          c. ghost town

_____ 2. What is the hue of the pure white Pascali variety of rose?
a. pure white          b. Pascali          c. rose

_____ 3. A common household sentinel is the
a. oven.          b. family dog.          c. family car.

_____ 4. Which of the following is a commodity?
a. a river          b. an anthill          c. a sack of flour

_____ 5. A feigned smile is one that is
a. concealed.          b. insincere.          c. very noticeable.

**D.** Answer **one** of the following questions based on your understanding of the selection. Write your answer on a separate sheet of paper. (15 points)

1. Do you think that the selection supports Bradford's claim that the Native Americans were "savage barbarians"? Why do you think Bradford felt this way? Support your answers with details from the selection and your own ideas.

2. What do you think of the compact between the Puritans and the Native Americans? Was it fair to both parties? Support your answers with references to the selection.

**E. Linking Literature to Life.** Answer the following question based on your own experience and knowledge. Write your answer on a separate sheet of paper. (15 points)

With what social, political, religious, or other groups do you most closely identify? What are some ways in which your ties to those groups affect your behavior, beliefs, opportunities, and perception of the world?

## from **The Interesting Narrative of the Life of Olaudah Equiano (page 93)**

# Selection Test

**A.** Equiano uses sensory details in his narration to vividly convey his feelings about his experiences. In the boxes on the left are sensory images used by Equiano. In the boxes in the middle, identify the sense or senses to which the image appeals. In the boxes on the right, note emotions felt by Equiano that the sensory image conveys. (10 points each)

| Sensory Imagery | Senses Appealed To | Conveys Equiano's Feeling Of |
|---|---|---|
| 1. "The stench of the hold was so intolerably loathsome . . ." | | |
| 2. ". . . those white men with horrible looks, red faces, and long hair . . ." | | |
| 3. "The shrieks of the women and the groans of the dying . . ." | | |

**B.** Write the letter of the best answer. This exercise is continued on the next page. (6 points each)

_____ 1. When Equiano is taken aboard the slave ship, his main reaction is one of
   a. anger.
   b. terror.
   c. frustration.
   d. pity for other victims.

_____ 2. Equiano relates how the crew deals with the fish they have caught in order to emphasize the crew's
   a. greed.
   b. cruelty.
   c. practicality.
   d. seemingly magical powers.

_____ 3. In his description of the slave sale, Equiano shows the most concern for
      a. his own fate.
      b. the souls of the buyers.
      c. the future of Christianity.
      d. those who are separated from loved ones.

**C. Words to Know.** Write the letter of the best answer. (4 points each)

_____ 1. Which is a mild form of anguish?
      a. unhappiness      b. snobbery      c. compassion

_____ 2. When people encounter a stench, they tend to
      a. close their eyes.      b. hold their noses.      c. become confused.

_____ 3. Most people have apprehensions about
      a. death.      b. independence.      c. wealth.

_____ 4. If you had a copious supply of something, you would have
      a. plenty.      b. just enough.      c. not enough.

_____ 5. A person's countenance is usually a good indication of his or her
      a. upbringing.      b. ability to learn.      c. mood.

**D.** Answer **one** of the following questions based on your understanding of the selection. Write your answer on a separate sheet of paper. (16 points)

1. How do you account for the attitude and behavior of the Europeans toward the Africans as described in this selection?

2. Some of the Africans described in this selection prefer death to slavery, while others do not. Give at least two reasons for each of these attitudes.

**E. Linking Literature to Life.** Answer the following question based on your own experience and knowledge. Write your answer on a separate sheet of paper. (16 points)

Is there anything more precious to you than your freedom? Give at least **two** reasons for your answer.

## *from* **Blue Highways (page 100)**

# Selection Test

**A.** Fill in the bar graph to show how important you think each purpose was to Heat-Moon when he wrote about his conversation with Fritz. Then, in the boxes at the bottom, write notes explaining your reasons. (12 points each)

**1.**                                    **Not Important**                                         **Very Important**

| | |
|---|---|
| **To Inform the Reader** | |
| **To Entertain the Reader** | |
| **To Express Himself** | |
| **To Persuade the Reader** | |

| **2. Briefly explain why you rated each purpose as you did in the bar graph above.** | | | |
|---|---|---|---|
| To Inform the Reader | To Entertain the Reader | To Express Himself | To Persuade the Reader |
| | | | |

**B.** Write the letter of the best answer. This exercise is continued on the next page. (5 points each)

_____   1. Fritz believes that very few white Americans view Native Americans
        a. negatively.
        b. realistically.
        c. suspiciously.

_____   2. Hopi legends are full of migrations **most** probably because the Hopi
        a. feel pressured by the Navajo to give up their land.
        b. have always lived on land they could call their own.
        c. believe that human existence is a series of journeys.

_____ 3. According to the Hopi Way, the human being's greatest task is to
        a. look to the future.
        b. be at one with the world.
        c. honor and obey one's elders.

_____ 4. According to Fritz, the Hopi Way encourages
        a. harmony.
        b. individuality.
        c. constant sacrifice.

**C. Words to Know.** Write the letter of the best answer. (4 points each)

_____ 1. As a general rule, whose actions reveal <u>contempt</u> for the law?
        a. judges'        b. criminals'        c. legislators'

_____ 2. A book dealing with the <u>emergence</u> of a people would be about their
        a. beginnings.        b. social structure.        c. recent history.

_____ 3. An idea that <u>evolves</u> is one that
        a. develops slowly.        b. never develops.        c. is rejected.

_____ 4. A person who is <u>receptive</u> to new ideas
        a. fears them.        b. rejects them.        c. welcomes them.

_____ 5. To solve simple <u>ethical</u> problems, most people consult their
        a. doctors.        b. consciences.        c. lawyers.

**D.** Answer **one** of the following questions based on your understanding of the selection. Write your answer on a separate sheet of paper. (18 points)

1. Why do you think Fritz insists that Heat-Moon eat piki before telling him about the Hopi Way?

2. What might Heat-Moon have been looking for as he traveled the United States? Why do you think he traveled the back roads instead of using interstate highways? Use details from the selection to support your ideas.

**E. Linking Literature to Life.** Answer the following question based on your own experience and knowledge. Write your answer on a separate sheet of paper. (18 points)

Fritz relates the Hopi belief that humanity has evolved through four worlds. He says, "In the fourth and present world, life is difficult for mankind, and he struggles to remember his source because materialism and selfishness block a greater vision." Does this seem to you an accurate description of the human condition today? Why or why not?

## My Sojourn in the Lands of My Ancestors (page 109)

# Selection Test

**A.** After passing Cape Coast Castle, Angelou pulls off the road and watches "a troupe of tragic players enter and exit the stage." Think about Angelou's reasons for including this vision of the past and the effect it had on you. Then write notes to answer the questions in the boxes below. (12 points each)

| 1. Why do you think Angelou interrupts the action of the narrative with this description? | 2. What effect does this flashback have on the reader? |
|---|---|
|  |  |

**B.** Write the letter of the best answer. This exercise is continued on the next page. (8 points each)

_____ 1. The **main** purpose of Angelou's journey from Accra to Dunkwa is to
    a. trace the origins of her ancestors.
    b. practice using the local language.
    c. escape from the city to the countryside.
    d. confront the ghosts of slavery that haunt her.

_____ 2. The people of Dunkwa don't consider Angelou a stranger because they believe that she
    a. is white.
    b. is from Dunkwa.
    c. is the descendant of slaves.
    d. belongs to an African clan.

_____ 3. The main reason Angelou doesn't tour the Cape Coast and Elmina castles
is that she
a. can't bear to.
b. is the kind of person who never looks backward.
c. doesn't have enough gas in her car to get there.
d. doesn't like to go to places where everyone else goes.

## C. Words to Know. Write the letter of the best answer. (4 points each)

_____ 1. When does the appearance of the moon <u>wane</u>?
a. before a full moon    b. during a full moon    c. after a full moon

_____ 2. If blood were to <u>suffuse</u> your face more than is normal, you would
a. blush.              b. become pale.        c. require stitches.

_____ 3. A person who was <u>impervious</u> to the crying of a baby would probably
a. become impatient.    b. ignore it.          c. comfort it.

_____ 4. In which occupation would a person be required to be <u>surreptitious</u>?
a. secret agent         b. astronaut           c. writer

_____ 5. A noise that <u>reverberates</u> can be heard
a. only once.          b. at least twice.      c. only close up.

**D.** Answer **one** of the following questions based on your understanding of the
selection. Write your answer on a separate sheet of paper. (16 points)

1. How do Angelou's memories of Stamps, Arkansas, influence her feelings and
   behavior in Dunkwa? How does this flashback affect your understanding of what
   happens to her in Dunkwa?

2. What does Angelou gain by not telling the people of Dunkwa that she is an
   American? Does she lose anything by not revealing this fact? Use details from
   the selection to support your answers.

**E. Linking Literature to Life.** Answer the following question based on your own
experience and knowledge. Write your answer on a separate sheet of paper. (16 points)

To what extent do you think that America as a nation has come to terms with its past
history as a slave nation? Do you think that further action is needed? If so, why? If not,
why not?

# Unit One: Origins and Encounters

# Part Two Open-Book Test

**A.** Write the letter of the best answer to each question. (5 points each)

_____ 1. In *La Relación,* Cabeza de Vaca describes the Karankawas as
      a. remarkably skilled healers.   c. wealthy and cultured.
      b. inferior to Christians.        d. adventurous and bold.

_____ 2. In *Of Plymouth Plantation,* Bradford attributes the Pilgrims' safe arrival to
      a. the Indians' help.        c. the strength of the women.
      b. his own leadership.      d. their faith in God.

_____ 3. The selection from *Blue Highways* is mostly about trying to
      a. survive the cold at the top of the mountain.
      b. understand why Kendrick Fritz does not have a Hopi name.
      c. find a way of life that combines Indian and Anglo traditions.
      d. persuade readers that the Hopi Way is better than Anglo ways.

_____ 4. In the slave narrative by Olaudah Equiano, the sensory details
      in the phrase "the galling of the chains" appeal to what sense?
      a. touch
      b. hearing
      c. smell
      d. sight

**B.** Think about the journeys undertaken in these selections. Choose one individual or group from each of **two** selections. In the boxes below, write the name of each individual or group and write notes describing each journey, its purpose, and how the traveler(s) were affected by it. (20 points)

| Individual/Group | | |
| --- | --- | --- |
| **The Journey** | | |
| **Its Purpose** | | |
| **How It Affected the Traveler(s)** | | |

**C.** Answer **two** of the following essay questions based on your understanding of the selections. Write your answers on a separate sheet of paper. (20 points each)

1. In many of the selections, the writers address—either directly or indirectly—the issue of oppression. Choose **two** of these selections and explain the reasons for the writers' interest in the issue of oppression. What do the writers conclude about the results of oppression and the benefits of freedom? Use details from the selections to support your answers.

2. Many of the selections emphasize the connection between people and a greater power such as nature or God. Choose any **two** individuals from the selections and compare how they view this connection with a greater power. Use details from the selections to support your opinions.

3. Which individual in the selections do you think is most able to determine his or her own destiny? Which is least able? Use details from the selections to explain how and why each individual is or is not able to control his or her destiny.

**D.** Think about the cultural, religious, and philosophical clashes described in the selections. (20 points)
- Circle the letter of **one** individual or group from Group A that you wish to discuss.
- Circle the letter of **one** individual or group from Group B that you wish to compare with the person or group from Group A.
- In the box on the left, note ways in which your two choices are similar.
- In the box on the right, note ways in which your two choices are different.

**Group A**
a. the Spanish *(La Relación)*
b. the Karankawas *(La Relación)*
c. Olaudah Equiano ("The Interesting Narrative . . .")
d. Fritz *(Blue Highways)*

**Group B**
e. the Pilgrims *(Of Plymouth Plantation)*
f. Squanto *(Of Plymouth Plantation)*
g. Maya Angelou ("My Sojourn . . .")
h. the people of Dunkwa ("My Sojourn . . .")

| Similarities: | Differences: |
|---|---|
|  |  |

# Selected Poems by Bradstreet (page 138)

# Selection Open-Book Test

**A.** Think about the different ways in which the Bradstreet poems appeal to the reader's intellect, senses, and emotions. In the box on the left, write the **one** element to which each poem appeals the most. Then, in the box on the right, make notes explaining how the poem appeals to that element. (15 points each)

| Poem/Element | How It Appeals to Intellect, Senses, or Emotions |
|---|---|
| 1. "To My Dear and Loving Husband"  Element: | |
| 2. "Upon the Burning of Our House, July 10, 1666"  Element: | |

**B.** Write the letter of the best answer. This exercise is continued on the next page. (5 points each)

_____ 1. "To My Dear and Loving Husband" could best be described as a tribute to
   a. youth.
   b. God.
   c. marriage.
   d. faith.

_____ 2. Which of the following **best** restates the last two lines of "To My Dear and Loving Husband"?
   a. As long as we live, we'll love each other.
   b. As long as one of us lives, our love will live.
   c. Let's love each other so well that we live on after death.
   d. If we're very determined, we'll be able to love each other until we die.

_____ 3. Which of the following **best** restates lines 19 and 20 of "Upon the Burning of Our House"?
a. I forgive Him for taking everything we had.
b. He might have abandoned us and yet He stayed with us.
c. He had the right to take everything and instead he left us enough.
d. We deserved to lose everything we had and we lost hardly anything.

_____ 4. Which of the following does the speaker hold responsible for the burning of her house?
a. God's will
b. human frailty
c. human greed
d. human vanity

_____ 5. Each foot in a poem is one
a. stressed syllable.
b. unstressed syllable.
c. line of the poem.
d. unit of rhythmic pattern.

_____ 6. What is the meter used in "Upon the Burning of Our House"?
a. iambic pentameter
b. iambic tetrameter
c. trochaic pentameter
d. trochaic tetrameter

**C.** Answer **one** of the following questions based on your understanding of the poems. Write your answer on a separate sheet of paper. (20 points)

1. Identify **three** words or phrases you would use to describe the relationship between the speaker of "To My Dear and Loving Husband" and her husband. Explain your choices.

2. Why doesn't the speaker of "Upon the Burning of Our House" feel anger toward God for her misfortune? Support your answer with details from the poem.

**D. Linking Literature to Life.** Answer the following question based on your own experience and knowledge. Write your answer on a separate sheet of paper. (20 points)

What, in your opinion, are some healthy or productive ways to respond to misfortune? What are some unhealthy or unproductive responses? Explain.

# The Examination of Sarah Good (page 144)

# Selection Test

**A.** Think about the uses of loaded language and loaded questions in this document. What biases or assumptions do they reveal? In the boxes below, write five examples of loaded language and loaded questions from the document. Then write notes explaining the biases or assumptions each example reveals. (15 points each)

| Language | Bias or Assumption |
|---|---|
| 1. | |
| 2. | |
| 3. | |

**B.** Write the letter of the best answer. This exercise is continued on the next page. (5 points each)

_____ 1. Which of the following statements from "The Examination of Sarah Good" is **least** objective?
a. "Her answers were in a very wicked spiteful manner."
b. "Sarah Osborne was then under Custody and not in the house."
c. "Sarah Good, the wife of William Good of Salem Village, Laborer."
d. "We Asked her who it was: She then answered and said it was Sarah Osborne."

_____ 2. To which of the following does Good admit?
a. practicing witchcraft
b. hurting her accusers
c. visiting the homes of her accusers
d. having knowledge of the existence of a witch

_____ 3. The prosecutors associate Good's habit of muttering with
                a. evil.
                b. insanity.
                c. spirituality.
                d. innocence.

_____ 4. Which of the following questions is Good **most** reluctant to answer?
                a. "Why do you hurt these children?"
                b. "Who do you employ then to do it?"
                c. "Have you made no contract with the devil?"
                d. "What is it you say when you go muttering away from persons' houses?"

_____ 5. The **strongest** evidence against Good is
                a. her testimony.
                b. her past behavior.
                c. her behavior in the courtroom.
                d. the testimony and behavior of her accusers.

**C.** Answer **one** of the following questions based on your understanding of the selection. Write your answer on a separate sheet of paper. (15 points)

1. Based on your understanding of these court documents, what do you suppose it was like to live in Salem during the time of the trials? Support your ideas with reference to the selection.

2. How do you think the people involved in the Salem witchcraft trials defined justice? How is their definition of justice different from the one used in the American court system today?

**D. Linking Literature to Life.** Answer the following question based on your own experience and knowledge. Write your answer on a separate sheet of paper. (15 points)

In your opinion, does religious belief have too little or too great an influence on public life in America today? Explain.

Name _____   Date _____

# *from* **Sinners in the Hands of an Angry God (page 152)**

# Selection Test

**A.** Think about the emotional appeals and loaded language Edwards uses in this sermon to persuade his listeners. For each of the three parts of this selection, choose one quotation that makes an emotional appeal or uses loaded language. In the boxes below, write the quotation from each part. Then write notes explaining the intended effect of the quotation and what Edwards is trying to persuade listeners to believe in that part of the sermon. (10 points each)

| Quotation | Intended Effect | Edwards's Goal |
|---|---|---|
| 1. | | |
| 2. | | |
| 3. | | |

**B.** Write the letter of the best answer. This exercise is continued on the next page. (6 points each)

_____ 1. Which of the following **best** states the main idea of the sermon?
   a. People can count on God's protection from the torments of hell.
   b. People are in terrible danger from the anger of God unless they are "born again."
   c. God hates to see people suffer for their sins, but he is powerless to stop their suffering.
   d. There is nothing people can do to save themselves from the terrible punishments that await sinners.

........................................................................................................................................

_____ 2. Which of the following was **most** probably Edwards's main purpose in writing this sermon?
  a. to seek God's help
  b. to praise and glorify God
  c. to persuade his listeners to seek spiritual rebirth in God
  d. to encourage in his listeners goodness and kindness toward others

_____ 3. According to Edwards, which of the following can protect people from the miseries of Hell?
  a. God
  b. fear
  c. good works
  d. virtuous behavior

**C. Words to Know.** Write the letter of the best answer. (4 points each)

_____ 1. The best way to <u>appease</u> someone who is angry with you is to
  a. issue a warning.        b. apologize.            c. pretend you don't care.

_____ 2. If something is <u>loathsome</u> to you, it is
  a. terrifying.              b. mysterious.           c. disgusting.

_____ 3. You would be in need of <u>deliverance</u> if you were
  a. endangered.            b. fulfilled.              c. very serious.

_____ 4. If a person's beliefs <u>incense</u> you, you most probably find them
  a. persuasive.            b. offensive.             c. inspirational.

_____ 5. A doctor would <u>ascribe</u> the common cold to
  a. bed rest.               b. viruses.              c. fever and chills.

**D.** Answer **one** of the following questions based on your understanding of the selection. Write your answer on a separate sheet of paper. (16 points)

  1. Do you think that Edwards's sermon appeals primarily to the intellect, the senses, or the emotions? Support your answer with reference to the sermon.

  2. What does this sermon ask of its audience? What does it offer to the audience in exchange for these things?

**E. Linking Literature to Life.** Answer the following question based on your own experience and knowledge. Write your answer on a separate sheet of paper. (16 points)

  What do you think America is most in need of "re-awakening" today? How would such a re-awakening affect Americans as individuals and America as a nation? Explain.

# The Crucible: Act One (page 166)

# Selection Test

**A.** The first act of *The Crucible* takes place in Betty Parris's bedroom, and the stage directions include details that help to set the mood, or atmosphere. Think about the stage directions for this act. Then write notes in the boxes below that describe the setting and how it helps to create the mood of the play. (10 points each)

| Stage Directions | |
|---|---|
| **1. Details of Setting** | **2. Mood** |
| | |

**B.** Write the letter of the best answer. This exercise is continued on the next page. (5 points each)

_____  1. Which of the following seems to foreshadow the real cause of the frightening events to come?
   a. Parris's concern over firewood
   b. Parris's call for Reverend Hale
   c. the relationship between Goody Osburn and Giles
   d. the relationship between Abigail and John Proctor

_____  2. Thomas Putnam can best be described as
   a. kindhearted.
   b. vindictive.
   c. sympathetic.
   d. rational.

_____  3. Parris is reluctant to tell anyone that Betty may be bewitched because he
   a. fears that Betty's reputation will be destroyed.
   b. knows that the idea of witchcraft will cause mass hysteria.
   c. fears that his enemies will destroy his reputation.
   d. firmly believes that witches do not exist.

........................................................................................................................................

_____ 4. Thomas Putnam's attitude toward Reverend Parris can best be described as
        a. respectful.
        b. contemptuous.
        c. indifferent.
        d. fearful.

**C. Words to Know.** Write the letter of the best answer. (4 points each)

_____ 1. A person with a predilection for mystery novels is likely to
        a. dislike them.      b. criticize them.      c. prefer them.

_____ 2. A fanatic is best described as
        a. solemn.      b. honest.      c. irrational.

_____ 3. People who arbitrate disputes are most like
        a. employers.      b. judges.      c. executioners.

_____ 4. If you and a friend earn disproportionate amounts of money for a day's
        work, the amounts are
        a. balanced.      b. unequal.      c. not enough.

_____ 5. Who is most likely to try to ascertain the truth?
        a. a detective      b. a criminal      c. a bystander

**D.** Answer **one** of the following questions based on your understanding of Act One of *The Crucible.* Write your answer on a separate sheet of paper. (20 points)

1. How do Rebecca Nurse's and John Proctor's views differ from those of the other villagers? Support your ideas with details from the play.

2. Compare your feelings and thoughts about Reverend Parris in the first part of Act One with your feelings toward him by the end of Act One. Support your ideas with details from the play.

**E. Linking Literature to Life.** Answer the following question based on your own experience and knowledge. Write your answer on a separate sheet of paper. (20 points)

Arthur Miller says, "A political policy is equated with moral right, and opposition to it with diabolical malevolence." Do you agree or disagree with his statement? Include in your response examples from recent history (such as the war with Iraq or political campaigns) that support or call into question Miller's belief.

# The Crucible: Act Two (page 191)

# Selection Test

**A.** In addition to factual information, dialogue often provides clues about characters' motives, feelings, and relationships. Read the dialogue from the play in the box on the left. Then, in the boxes on the right, write notes explaining what the dialogue reveals about each character. (10 points each)

| Dialogue | What is revealed about the character? |
|---|---|
| **Mary Warren.** . . . I'm—I am an official of the court, they say, and I—<br><br>**Proctor.** I'll official you! (*He strides to the mantel, takes down the whip . . .*)<br><br>**Mary Warren** (*terrified, but coming erect, striving for her authority*). I'll not stand whipping any more!<br><br>**Elizabeth** (*hurriedly, as* Proctor *approaches*). Mary, promise now you'll stay at home—<br><br>**Mary Warren** (*backing from him, but keeping her erect posture, striving, striving for her way*). The Devil's loose in Salem, Mr. Proctor; we must discover where's he's hiding!<br><br>**Proctor.** I'll whip the Devil out of you! (*With whip raised he reaches out for her, and she streaks away and yells.*)<br><br>**Mary Warren** (*pointing at Elizabeth*). I saved her life today!<br><br>(*Silence. His whip comes down.*)<br><br>**Elizabeth** (*softly*). I am accused? | **1. Mary Warren:**<br><br><br><br><br>**2. Proctor:**<br><br><br><br><br>**3. Elizabeth:** |

**B.** Write the letter of the best answer. This exercise is continued on the next page. (5 points each)

_____ 1. Elizabeth urges John to go to Salem to
  a. protect Mary Warren.
  b. tell the court that Abigail's story is a hoax.
  c. announce publicly that he believes in witchcraft.
  d. ask the court for forgiveness.

_____  2. People "part like the seas" for Abigail because they
        a. love and admire her.
        b. believe her to be honest.
        c. respect her devotion and faith.
        d. fear her power to accuse them.

_____  3. By the end of Act Two, Reverend Hale has begun to worry that
        a. the villagers might rebel against his authority.
        b. perhaps innocent people are being accused.
        c. Rebecca Nurse did murder Goody Putnam's babies.
        d. most of the villagers are in league with the devil.

**C. Words to Know.** Write the letter of the best answer. (5 points each)

_____  1. A person who is <u>indignant</u> most likely feels
        a. cheerful.          b. very angry.         c. bored.

_____  2. Which of these events would likely bring about a <u>calamity</u>?
        a. a hurricane        b. a lunar eclipse       c. a frost

_____  3. Who would most likely act in a <u>subservient</u> way?
        a. a judge           b. a principal        c. a butler

_____  4. A person accused of <u>iniquity</u> is accused of
        a. theft.            b. wickedness.      c. fraud.

**D.** Answer **one** of the following questions based on your understanding of the second act of *The Crucible*. Write your answer on a separate sheet of paper. (20 points)

1. Proctor accuses Hale of being a "Pontius Pilate" and a coward, but Proctor could be considered a coward, too. How might both men be considered guilty of cowardice? Use details from the play to support your ideas.

2. Mary Warren has allowed herself to be talked into doing something dishonest and dangerous. What factors cause her to continue to accuse people? Use details from the play to support your ideas.

**E. Linking Literature to Life.** Answer the following question based on your own experience and knowledge. Write your answer on a separate sheet of paper. (15 points)

Both Ezekiel Cheever and Marshal Herrick arrest innocent people, yet both say they are only following orders and doing their jobs. Do you think that this is a defensible reason for what they do? Why or why not?

# The Crucible: Act Three (page 207)

# Selection Test

**A.** Think about how Mary Warren serves as a foil to Abigail in Act Three of *The Crucible*. In the boxes below, write notes giving examples from this act that demonstrate each of Abigail's character traits and explaining how Mary's personality contrasts with or emphasizes each trait. (6 points each)

| Abigail's Character Traits | Example | How Mary Serves as a Foil |
| --- | --- | --- |
| 1. Self-confident | | |
| 2. Manipulative | | |
| 3. Vindictive | | |
| 4. Arrogant | | |

**B.** Write the letter of the best answer. This exercise is continued on the next page. (5 points each)

_____ 1. In Act Three, the details of the setting create a mood that is
    a. gloomy and forbidding.
    b. airy and hopeful.
    c. sad and dispirited.
    d. strange and mysterious.

_____ 2. When Abigail says to Danforth, "Think you be so mighty that the power of Hell may not turn your wits? Beware of it!" she is
    a. asking Danforth to help her.
    b. saying that she regrets accusing innocent people.
    c. asking Danforth for forgiveness.
    d. using her power to threaten him.

_____ 3. What can you conclude about Parris from Act Three?
  a. He truly fears for his life.
  b. He is a tremendous help to the proceedings.
  c. He is a wretched, cowardly person.
  d. He is fighting hard to get at the truth.

_____ 4. Elizabeth Proctor did not tell Danforth that Abigail was a harlot because she
  a. wanted John to be arrested.
  b. feared that John might be hanged for adultery.
  c. wanted to save John's reputation.
  d. did not want to hurt Abigail's reputation.

**C. Words to Know.** Write the letter of the best answer. (4 points each)

_____ 1. Contentious people are most likely to
  a. compromise.          b. agree.          c. argue.

_____ 2. A person of immaculate character is
  a. dishonest.          b. pure.          c. confused.

_____ 3. Who would most likely make a deposition?
  a. a witness          b. a teacher          c. a writer

_____ 4. The plaintiff in a court trial is the person who makes the
  a. defense.          b. complaint.          c. judgment.

_____ 5. Effrontery involves behavior that is
  a. adoring.          b. disrespectful.          c. submissive.

**D.** Answer **one** of the following questions based on your understanding of Act Three. Write your answer on a separate sheet of paper. (20 points)

1. What concerns Danforth most about the interruptions and accusations made by Giles and Proctor? How does Danforth handle their accusations? Use details from the play to support your answer.

2. Some people believe that indifference to evil is even worse than the evil itself. John Proctor would probably agree with this statement. How does he act on his beliefs? Use examples from the play to support your answer.

**E. Linking Literature to Life.** Answer the following question based on your own experience and knowledge. Write your answer on a separate sheet of paper. (16 points)

John Proctor is reluctant to become involved with the trials because he does not want to damage his reputation. Do you think people should risk their personal reputations for a greater good? Explain why or why not. Can you think of any situations where people should take this step?

# The Crucible: Act Four (page 229)

# Selection Test

**A.** Think about Danforth's struggle with external and internal conflicts. In the boxes below, write notes explaining his external conflict with Hale, his external conflict with society, and his own internal conflict. (8 points each)

| 1. Conflict with Hale | 2. Conflict with Society | 3. Internal Conflict |
| --- | --- | --- |
|  |  |  |

**B.** Write the letter of the best answer. This exercise is continued on the next page.
(5 points each)

_____ 1. What can you conclude from the references made to Andover?
a. Andover has been purged of all witches.
b. The people of Andover are demanding new trials.
c. There will be many more deaths in Andover.
d. The people have rebelled and overthrown the court.

_____ 2. Why is it important to Danforth and Parris that Proctor confess?
a. His confession will prove that Abigail is a fraud.
b. His confession will convince people the court has been just.
c. They truly want to save Proctor's soul.
d. Elizabeth has pleaded for Proctor's life.

_____ 3. Why does Elizabeth say of John, "He have his goodness now"?
a. He deserves to hang for the sins he has committed against her.
b. He has self-respect and knows there is some goodness in him.
c. She would rather have him confess to a lie than be hanged.
d. Abigail has left the village and freed John from guilt.

_____ 4. The climax of Act Four occurs when
    a. Hale says it is better to live than to die unjustly.
    b. Rebecca realizes that John Proctor is confessing.
    c. Proctor rips up his confession.
    d. Parris admits that Abigail is gone.

**C. Words to Know.** Write the letter of the best answer. (4 points each)

_____ 1. A person who receives excommunication from the church is
    a. banished.      b. asked to repent.      c. forced to confess.

_____ 2. If you empower a person, you give that person
    a. pride.      b. cooperation.      c. authority.

_____ 3. Which person would most likely receive an indictment?
    a. a professor      b. an editor      c. a criminal

_____ 4. A person who is afflicted would most likely to visit a
    a. doctor.      b. barber.      c. supermarket.

_____ 5. An unintelligible remark cannot be
    a. translated.      b. understood.      c. altered.

**D.** Answer **one** of the following questions based on your understanding of Act Four. Write your answer on a separate sheet of paper. (20 points)

1. A *crucible* is "a severe test or trial." What test did the characters in this play have to face? Which characters do you believe failed the test, and which passed? Use examples from the play to support your answers.

2. Both Parris and Hale try to persuade Proctor to make a false confession. How are Hale's motivations different from Parris's? What justification does Hale use to attempt to persuade Proctor to confess? Use examples from the play to support your answers.

**E. Linking Literature to Life.** Answer the following question based on your own experience and knowledge. Write your answer on a separate sheet of paper. (16 points)

Do you think John Proctor should have made a false confession and lived, or do you agree with his decision to die? What do you think you would do if you faced a similar situation?

# Unit Two: From Colony to Country

## Part One Open-Book Test

**A.** Write the letter of the best answer to each question. (5 points each)

_____ 1. In Bradstreet's "Upon the Burning of Our House," the "house on high
erect / Framed by that mighty Architect" refers to
   a. her home.                          c. the governor's house.
   b. heaven.                            d. hell.

_____ 2. In "Sinners in the Hands of an Angry God," Edwards's primary goal is to
persuade his congregation to
   a. accept the idea that they will all end up in hell.
   b. question the beliefs of Christianity.
   c. confess that they have made pacts with the devil.
   d. repent and accept Christ before it is too late.

_____ 3. In both "The Examination of Sarah Good" and *The Crucible,* the judges
assume that
   a. a woman accused of witchcraft is guilty.
   b. a person is innocent until proven guilty.
   c. a Christian woman cannot become a witch.
   d. everyone is guilty until purified by confession.

_____ 4. The real cause of the troubles in *The Crucible* was
   a. Tituba's curse.                    c. an adulterous affair.
   b. Elizabeth's jealousy.              d. Hale's interference.

**B.** The Puritans are known for being intolerant of beliefs and ideas different from their
own. Circle the letter of **one** selection you wish to discuss. In the box on the left, write
notes describing a character from the selection who shows intolerance and an example
of how he or she shows it. In the box on the right, write notes explaining the reasons
for that intolerance. (20 points)

   a. "The Examination of Sarah Good"
   b. "Sinners in the Hands of an Angry God"
   c. *The Crucible*

| Character Who Shows Intolerance | Reasons for That Intolerance |
|---|---|
|  |  |

**C.** Answer **two** of the following essay questions based on your understanding of the selections. Write your answers on a separate sheet of paper. (20 points each)

1. Think about the distinguishing characteristics of the women in these selections. What do they reveal about Puritan ideals of womanhood? Use details from at least three selections to support your ideas.

2. What are some distinguishing characteristics of the Puritans' views of their relationship to God? Use details from at least two selections to support your ideas.

3. Which selection do you think presents the Puritans in the most favorable light? Which selection do you think presents the Puritans in the least favorable light? Support your opinions with references to the selections and your own ideas.

**D.** Think about what the selections reveal about the early Anglo-American colonists and their way of life. (20 points)

- Circle the letter of **one** selection you wish to discuss. **Do not choose a selection that you discussed in Part B on the previous page.**
- In the top box, write notes describing the events or activities recorded in that selection.
- In the bottom box, write notes describing the ideas expressed in that selection.

a. "Upon the Burning of Our House, July 10, 1666"      c. "Sinners in the Hands of an Angry God"
b. "The Examination of Sarah Good"                       d. *The Crucible*

---

**Events or Activities Recorded**




---

**Ideas Expressed**

# Speech in the Virginia Convention (page 262)

# Selection Test

**A.** Think about how Patrick Henry uses allusions in this speech. Then, in the boxes below, write notes explaining the general lesson of the allusion and how it relates to the specific situation of the colonists. (8 points each)

| Allusion | What it refers to | 1. General lesson of the allusion | 2. How it relates to the colonists' situation |
|---|---|---|---|
| "Mr. President, it is natural to man to indulge in the illusions of hope. We are apt to shut our eyes against a painful truth, and listen to the song of that siren, till she transforms us into beasts." | Homer's *Odyssey:* The sirens' seductive song lured sailors to their deaths. The goddess Circe lured men to her island and then magically transformed them into pigs. | | |

| Allusion | What it refers to | 3. General lesson of the allusion | 4. How it relates to the colonists' situation |
|---|---|---|---|
| "The battle, sir, is not to the strong alone; it is to the vigilant, the active, the brave." | Ecclesiastes 9:11: "the race is not to the swift, nor the battle to the strong." | | |

**B.** Write the letter of the best answer. This exercise is continued on the next page. (6 points each)

_____ 1. The **main** idea of this speech is that
   a. the British are evil.
   b. the Convention is cowardly.
   c. it is time for the colonists to fight for freedom.
   d. war is the best way to solve conflicts between peoples.

........ 2. Henry believes that the time for negotiation
  a. is at hand.
  b. has passed.
  c. may still come.
  d. has never and will never exist.

........ 3. What human weakness does Henry associate with the colonists who
  oppose his position?
  a. disloyalty
  b. cowardice
  c. selfishness
  d. self-deception

**C. Words to Know.** Write the letter of the best answer. (4 points each)

........ 1. If your offer of friendship is spurned, it is
  a. welcomed.    b. considered.    c. rejected.

........ 2. A formidable enemy is
  a. all-powerful.    b. difficult to defeat.    c. wicked.

........ 3. Who is your adversary on a softball field?
  a. your coach    b. your teammates    c. the opposing team

........ 4. An invincible enemy cannot be
  a. overcome.    b. reasoned with.    c. confronted.

........ 5. If you are vigilant, you are difficult to
  a. trust.    b. surprise.    c. get along with.

**D.** Answer **one** of the following questions based on your understanding of the speech. Write your answer on a separate sheet of paper. (15 points)

1. What does Henry seem to feel are the colonists' greatest strengths and weaknesses?

2. What are some of the reasons that Henry sees only one possible course of action for the colonists? Use details from the speech to support your answer.

**E. Linking Literature to Life.** Answer the following question based on your own experience and knowledge. Write your answer on a separate sheet of paper. (15 points)

How does emotional language tend to affect you? To what extent does it interfere with your ability to make a reasonable decision? Explain, citing examples.

# Declaration of Independence (page 270)

# Selection Test

**A.** Think about Jefferson's uses of parallelism in the Declaration of Independence. Then read the excerpt below. In the first column, underline the parallel phrases. Then, in the other columns, write notes explaining what ideas are connected by the parallel phrases and the overall effects of the parallelism. (8 points each)

| 1. Parallel Phrases | 2. Ideas Being Connected | 3. Overall Effect |
|---|---|---|
| Nor have we been wanting in our attentions to our British brethren. We have warned them, from time to time, of attempts by their legislature to extend an unwarrantable jurisdiction over us. We have reminded them of the circumstances of our emigration and settlement here. We have appealed to their native justice and magnanimity; and we have conjured them . . . to disavow these usurpations. . . . | | |

**B.** Write the letter of the best answer. This exercise is continued on the next page. (6 points each)

_____ 1. According to the Declaration, a government should derive its power from
   a. the politicians.
   b. the educated class.
   c. a carefully selected few.
   d. those it governs.

_____ 2. The Declaration states that it is right to overthrow a government when it
   a. becomes a strong central government.
   b. becomes a weak central government.
   c. no longer represents the people.
   d. is obvious that political change is needed.

_____ 3. The ultimate goal of the Declaration of Independence was to
      a. plead with the British not to declare war.
      b. absolve the colonies of any allegiance to Britain.
      c. ask the British to grant some powers to the colonies.
      d. force the British to deal with the colonies' complaints.

**C. Words to Know.** Write the letter of the best answer. (4 points each)

_____ 1. To impel a man to testify in court means to
      a. ask him.        b. arrest him.        c. force him.

_____ 2. An arbitrary ruler is **most** likely to have
      a. unlimited power.    b. strong allies.      c. religious faith.

_____ 3. When King Edward VIII abdicated the throne in 1936, he
      a. resented it.      b. took office.      c. gave it up.

_____ 4. A mercenary is a soldier who serves for
      a. patriotism.      b. payment.        c. glory.

_____ 5. An insurrection is a
      a. surrender.       b. rebellion.      c. compromise.

**D.** Answer **one** of the following questions based on your understanding of the Declaration of Independence. Write your answer on a separate sheet of paper. (20 points)

1. Jefferson stated that the king of Great Britain had long worked toward "the establishment of an absolute tyranny over these states." What had the British government done that seemed oppressive and unjust to the colonists?

2. Before the American Revolution, how did the American colonies try to settle peacefully their differences with Great Britain? Use examples from the Declaration to support your answers.

**E. Linking Literature to Life.** Answer the following question based on your own experience and knowledge. Write your answer on a separate sheet of paper. (18 points)

The Declaration of Independence states that "all men are created equal." Do you think this is true? Do citizens of the United States live as if this statement were true? How might you change the wording of this sentence if you had an opportunity to do so? Why?

## Letter to the Rev. Samson Occom/
## Letter to John Adams (page 282)

# Selection Test

**A.** Think about how these two letters are alike and how they are different. Then, in each box below, write notes describing each aspect of the letters. (12 points each)

|  | **Wheatley's Letter** | **Adams's Letter** |
|---|---|---|
| **1. Tone or general attitude** | | |
| **2. Writer's purpose** | | |

**B.** Write the letter of the best answer. (6 points each)

_____ 1. Wheatley believes that Christianity
      a. opposes slavery.
      b. encourages slavery.
      c. is responsible for slavery.
      d. has little to say about slavery.

_____ 2. Adams believes that the colonists should
      a. cooperate with British rule.
      b. oppose British rule in nonviolent ways.
      c. forcefully declare their independence to the world.
      d. keep their desire for independence a secret for the time being.

_____ 3. Adams believes that the lack of generosity shown to "the ladies" by her husband and his colleagues is
      a. forgivable.
      b. deliberate.
      c. necessary.
      d. reasonable.

**C.** In the boxes below, identify the two things that figurative language is used to compare in the quotation below. On the line between the two boxes, note how those two things are alike. (8 points)

"I fear a fatal security has taken possession of [our leaders]. Whilst the building is in flames they tremble at the expense of the water to quench it. In short, two months have elapsed since the evacuation of Boston, and very little has been done in that time to secure it."

```
┌─────────────────┐                              ┌─────────────────┐
│                 │──────────────────────────────│                 │
│                 │                              │                 │
└─────────────────┘                              └─────────────────┘
```

**D. Words to Know.** Write the letter of the best answer. (4 points each)

_____ 1. When you countenance the actions of another, you give that person your
        a. approval.        b. criticism.        c. advice.

_____ 2. If you spent the afternoon ruminating, you were
        a. resting.        b. writing.        c. thinking.

_____ 3. A person seized by lethargy lacks
        a. integrity.        b. energy.        c. self-confidence.

_____ 4. Whom did President Lincoln emancipate?
        a. his wife        b. slaves        c. the Confederacy

_____ 5. What is a precept?
        a. a demand        b. a request        c. a guiding principle

**E.** Answer **one** of the following questions based on your understanding of the letters. Write your answer on a separate sheet of paper. (15 points)

1. What does Wheatley think will be the fate of the slavery system? Why does she think that?

2. In what ways does Adams's life and the way she feels contrast with the life and feelings of her husband? Support your ideas with details from the letter.

**F. Linking Literature to Life.** Answer the following question based on your own experience and knowledge. Write your answer on a separate sheet of paper. (15 points)

Why, do you think, is power so often abused? What advice would you offer to modern America's leaders concerning the proper use of their power?

# What Is an American? (page 289)

# Selection Test

**A.** In the box on the left, jot down what you think the theme of the letter is. In the box on the right, write notes supporting your answer. (40 points)

| Theme | | Support |
|---|---|---|
|  | ➡ |  |

**B.** Circle the letter of the best answer. (8 points)

Throughout the letter, Crèvecoeur describes America by
a. criticizing it.                c. comparing it to Europe.
b. comparing it to its past.      d. creating sensory images.

**C. Words to Know.** Write the letter of the best answer. (4 points each)

_____ 1. Your <u>kindred</u> includes all of the people whom you
a. are related to.        b. consider heroic.        c. live near.

_____ 2. Which would be used as an <u>allurement</u> for a fish?
a. a worm                b. a net                c. an aquarium

_____ 3. <u>Despotic</u> rulers tend to be
a. weak.                b. powerful.                c. fair.

_____ 4. A person's <u>servile</u> attitude reflects a **lack** of
a. understanding.        b. self-respect.        c. humility.

_____ 5. A grocery store provides <u>subsistence</u> for
a. vegetables.        b. families.        c. cashiers.

**D.** Answer **one** of the following questions based on your understanding of the letter.
Write your answer on a separate sheet of paper. (16 points)

1. Does Crèvecoeur believe that poor people should love their country? Explain.

2. What do you think Crèvecoeur would have thought of the modern tendency to use
   phrases such as "Italian American" and "African American"? Explain.

**E. Linking Literature to Life.** Answer the following question based on your own
experience and knowledge. Write your answer on a separate sheet of paper. (16 points)

What, in your opinion, are the distinguishing characteristics of an American? Explain.

# Lecture to a Missionary (page 295)

# Selection Test

**A.** Circle words and phrases in the excerpt from the selection below that you think **convey** the tone. Then, in the box, jot down words or phrases that **describe** the tone. (30 points)

"Brother, the Great Spirit has made us all, but He has made a great difference between his white and red children. He has given us different complexions and different customs. To you He has given the arts. To these He has not opened our eyes. We know these things to be true. Since He has made so great a difference between us in other things, why may we not conclude that He has given us a different religion according to our understanding? The Great Spirit does right. He knows what is best for his children; we are satisfied."

**B.** Write the letter of the best answer. (15 points each)

_____ 1. According to Red Jacket, which of the following is a way in which his religion differs from that of the missionary?
   a. Red Jacket's religion is much older.
   b. Red Jacket's people agree on one set of religious beliefs.
   c. Red Jacket's people believe in more than one Great Spirit.

_____ 2. Near the end of the selection, Red Jacket
   a. rejects the missionary's religion for all of time.
   b. reconsiders his feelings about the missionary's religion.
   c. leaves open the possibility of reconsidering in the future.

**C.** Answer **one** of the following questions based on your understanding of the selection. Write your answer on a separate sheet of paper. (20 points)

1. What effect does the history of relations between Native Americans and white settlers have on Red Jacket's decision? Why does it have this effect? Use details from the selection to support your answers.

2. What can you tell from this selection about the kind of person Red Jacket was? Identify at least three personality traits of Red Jacket's and support them with details from the selection.

**D. Linking Literature to Life.** Answer the following question based on your own experience and knowledge. Write your answer on a separate sheet of paper. (20 points)

   If you could convince a group of people of one thing, what group of people would you choose, and what would you convince them of? How might you convince them?

## *from* Stride Toward Freedom/ Necessary to Protect Ourselves (page 300)

# Selection Test

**A.** Think about the structure of King's argument that "Oppressed people deal with their oppression in three characteristic ways." In each box below, identify one of those ways and jot down a reason that King either approves or disapproves of it. Then, in the box at the bottom, write notes to answer the question. (8 points each)

| King's Ways of Dealing with Oppression | | |
|---|---|---|
| 1. What is one way?<br><br>▼<br><br>Why he approves or disapproves. | 2. What is another way?<br><br>▼<br><br>Why he approves or disapproves. | 3. What is a third way?<br><br>▼<br><br>Why he approves or disapproves. |

| |
|---|
| 4. Does Malcolm X advocate dealing with oppression in any of these ways? If you think so, tell which ones and support your choices. If you don't think so, explain why. |
| <br><br><br><br> |

**B.** Write the letter of the best answer. This exercise is continued on the next page. (5 points each)

_____ 1. Which phrase in this statement is the **worst** example of loaded language: "Well, it sounds as though you could be preaching a sort of anarchy"?
   a. "it sounds as though"
   b. "you could be preaching"
   c. "a sort of anarchy"

_____ 2. In *Stride Toward Freedom,* King's diction does **not** show the influence of
   a. formal education.
   b. familiarity with street slang.
   c. familiarity with the Christian Bible.

_____ 3. Imagine that you've discovered your best friend supports a group that advocates hatred and violence. The excerpt from *Stride Toward Freedom* suggests that King would advise you to
a. avoid your friend.
b. explain to your friend why you object to the group.
c. join the group and give them a fair chance to change your views.

_____ 4. In the interview, Malcolm X implies that the solution to racial injustice will most probably come from actions taken by
a. individuals.
b. the federal government.
c. local governments in the South.

**C. Words to Know.** Write the letter of the best answer. (4 points each)

_____ 1. Which is an <u>oppressed</u> person?
a. a slave                  b. a judge                  c. a minister

_____ 2. When you <u>tacitly</u> agree with another person's ideas, you do so
a. with enthusiasm.       b. without thinking.       c. without saying so.

_____ 3. <u>Anarchy</u> is a situation in which political authority is
a. absolute.              b. limited.                c. nonexistent.

_____ 4. If you choose <u>indiscriminately</u>, your choice is made
a. with prejudice.        b. at random.              c. thoughtfully.

_____ 5. If you <u>repudiate</u> violence, you
a. ignore it.             b. support it.             c. oppose it.

**D.** Answer **one** of the following questions based on your understanding of the selections. Write your answer on a separate sheet of paper. (14 points)

1. In the excerpt from *Stride Toward Freedom,* King says, "Nonviolent resistance is not aimed against oppressors but against oppression." What does he mean, and why do you think he makes this distinction? Explain your answer.

2. On the basis of your understanding of "Necessary to Protect Ourselves," under what conditions do you think Malcolm X would condone violence? Support your answer with reference to the selection.

**E. Linking Literature to Life.** Answer the following question based on your own experience and knowledge. Write your answer on a separate sheet of paper. (14 points)

In *Stride Toward Freedom,* King writes, "To accept passively an unjust system is to cooperate with that system; thereby the oppressed become as evil as the oppressor." To what extent do you agree or disagree with this statement? Why?

## *from* I Am Joaquín/Yo Soy Joaquín (page 309)

# Selection Open-Book Test

**A.** At the end of the poem, the speaker says, "I SHALL ENDURE! / I WILL ENDURE!" In each box on the left, note one way in which the speaker implies that he will endure or one thing that will help him to endure. In each box on the right, write notes explaining how that way or thing might help a person endure what Joaquín must. (10 points each)

| **1. How will he endure, or what will help him to endure?** | → | **How might this help a person endure what Joaquín must?** |
| --- | --- | --- |
| | | |
| **2. How will he endure, or what will help him to endure?** | → | **How might this help a person endure what Joaquín must?** |
| | | |
| **3. How will he endure, or what will help him to endure?** | → | **How might this help a person endure what Joaquín must?** |
| | | |

**B.** Write the letter of the best answer. (6 points each)

_____  1. Joaquín's past includes all of the following **except**
        a. conflict.
        b. anguish.
        c. defiance.
        d. surrender.

_____  2. Which of the following does Joaquín call for?
        a. violent revolution
        b. popular revolution
        c. peaceful negotiation
        d. gradual change for the better

**C.** Typical characteristics of an epic poem are noted in the boxes on the left. In the boxes on the right, write notes explaining how the excerpt from this poem appears to conform to or depart from typical epic poems in each respect. (6 points each)

| | |
|---|---|
| **1. It is a long narrative poem. (A narrative poem tells a story.)** | |
| **2. It has a serious subject.** | |
| **3. It has an elevated or formal style.** | |
| **4. It traces the adventures of a hero whose actions consist of courageous, even superhuman, deeds.** | |
| **5. The deeds of the hero represent the ideals and values of a group of people, such as a nation or race.** | |

**D.** Answer **one** of the following questions based on your understanding of the poem. Write your answer on a separate sheet of paper. (14 points)

1. In your opinion, do all Americans face the choice that Joaquín faces (line 14), or just certain types of Americans? In your answer, describe the choice and tell why it applies to the Americans that you think it applies to.

2. What are some of the things that Joaquín associates with "gringo society" (line 4)? What does he associate with the society of his ancestors? In your answers, note the lines from the poem in which he makes these associations.

**E. Linking Literature to Life.** Answer the following question based on your own experience and knowledge. Write your answer on a separate sheet of paper. (14 points)

Do you approve of the use of such terms as "African American" and "Mexican American"? Why or why not?

# Unit Two: From Colony to Country

# Part Two Open-Book Test

**A.** Write your answer to each question on the lines. (5 points each)

1. Give an example of a rhetorical question used in Patrick Henry's "Speech in the Virginia Convention."

   _____

   _____

2. Briefly paraphrase the preamble to the Declaration of Independence.

   _____

   _____

3. Give an example of figurative language from Wheatley's letter to the Reverend Occom or Adams's letter to John Adams and explain its meaning.

   _____

   _____

4. State the main idea of Red Jacket's "Lecture to a Missionary."

   _____

   _____

**B.** Think about the strong emotions expressed in these selections. Write the title of one selection you wish to discuss on the line below. In the box on the left, identify a strong emotion expressed in the selection. In the box on the right, give some possible reasons for the expression of that emotion. (20 points)

**Selection:** _____

| Strong Emotion | Reasons for That Emotion |
|---|---|
|  |  |
|  |  |
|  |  |
|  |  |

**C.** Answer **two** of the following essay questions based on your understanding of the selections. Write your answers on a separate sheet of paper. (20 points each)

1. Choose **one** of the writers from this part and tell whether you think he or she would make a good modern-day president of the United States. Support your opinion with reference to the selection by that writer.

2. Choose any **two** people from different selections in the part and tell how you think they would fill in the blanks in this sentence about the Americans of their own time: "What Americans really need is _____, _____, and _____." Why did they think that Americans were in need of these things?

3. Choose a pair of selections from the part. Discuss any similarity or difference they have in one of the following literary categories. (Suggested selections follow the categories, but you are free to choose any pair of selections from the part.)
   • Allusion ("Speech in the Virginia Convention" and "I Am Joaquín")
   • Theme ("Letter to John Adams" and Declaration of Independence)
   • Tone ("Lecture to a Missionary" and *Stride Toward Freedom*)

**D.** All the selections in this part are concerned with obtaining freedom. Choose one selection you wish to discuss. **Do not choose the same selection you discussed in Part B.** In the boxes below, write notes to identify the group whose freedom is the concern of the selection, explain why the group is not free, and explain how the group's freedom can be won. (20 points)

| Group: | |
|---|---|
| **Why They Are Not Free:** | **How the Group's Freedom Can Be Won:** |
| | |

# A Psalm of Life (page 344)

# Selection Open-Book Test

**A.** Think about the attitude toward life and death expressed by the speaker in "A Psalm of Life." Then make a mark in the box next to a quotation that you think reflects or supports the speaker's attitude. In the box at the bottom, write notes explaining your choice. (40 points)

☐ "I postpone death by living, by suffering, by error, by risking, by giving, by losing."
   —Anaïs Nin

☐ "The end of man is an action, and not a thought, though it were the noblest."
   —Thomas Carlyle

| **Explain your choice.** |
| --- |
| |

**B.** Write the letter of the best answer. This exercise is continued on the next page. (4 points each)

_____ 1. What is the rhyme scheme of each stanza in "A Psalm of Life"?
   a. *aabb*
   b. *abab*
   c. *abba*
   d. *abcb*

_____ 2. It is most important to the speaker that life be
   a. exciting.
   b. enjoyed.
   c. meaningful.
   d. long-lasting.

_____ 3. Which of these words is one of the rhyming words in this poem?
   a. dust
   b. art
   c. hearts
   d. time

_____    4. In the meter of the poem, the second and fourth lines of each stanza
           end with
           a. stressed syllables.
           b. long *a* sounds.
           c. unstressed syllables.
           d. long *o* sounds.

_____    5. Which is generally true of the first and third lines of each stanza?
           a. Each line has internal rhymes.
           b. Only the first two words are stressed.
           c. Each line has eight syllables.
           d. The last syllable is emphasized.

**C.** Answer **one** of the following questions based on your understanding of the poem.
Write your answer on a separate sheet of paper. (20 points)

  1. Do you agree with the philosophy of life presented in the poem? Explain your answer,
     noting at least **two** specific points of agreement or disagreement.

  2. At what type of event do you think it would be especially appropriate to read aloud
     this poem? Support your idea with reference to the poem.

**D. Linking Literature to Life.** Answer the following question based on your own
experience and knowledge. Write your answer on a separate sheet of paper. (20 points)

   Do you think that living in the present without giving thought to the past or future is
possible? Is it desirable? Explain.

# The Devil and Tom Walker (page 349)

# Selection Test

**A.** Read the quotations below and think about the information conveyed in Irving's imagery. In each box on the left, note words or phrases describing the thing that is noted in the box. In each box on the right, identify the one feeling that you think the imagery in the quotation most conveys. (10 points each)

> "... [Tom] met the black man one evening in his usual woodsman's dress, with his ax on his shoulder, sauntering along the swamp, and humming a tune."

➡ **1. Old Scratch**                                                                 ➡

> "As [Tom] scrambled up the tree, the vulture spread its wide wings, and sailed off screaming into the deep shadows of the forest. Tom seized the checked apron, but, woeful sight! found nothing but a heart and liver tied up in it!"

➡ **2. The Mood of This Passage**                                    ➡

> "Some say that Tom grew a little crackbrained in his old days, and that fancying his end approaching, he had his horse new shod, saddled and bridled, and buried with his feet uppermost; because he supposed that at the last day the world would be turned upside down; in which case he should find his horse standing ready for mounting. . . ."

➡ **3. Tom Walker**                                                                   ➡

**B.** Write the letter of the best answer. This exercise is continued on the next page. (4 points each)

_____ 1. An important condition of Tom's deal with Old Scratch that is not directly
stated in the story is that Tom will
a. lose his soul.                    c. become a moneylender.
b. gain great wealth.          d. act on behalf of Old Scratch.

_____ 2. After Tom makes his deal with Old Scratch, his name is most probably recorded
    a. in an account book.    c. on a tree in the swamp.
    b. on Old Scratch's ax.    d. on a skull in the swamp.

**C.** In each box below, make notes describing the attitude of the omniscient narrator toward the character. (4 points each)

| | |
|---|---|
| **1. Tom Walker** | |
| **2. Tom's wife** | |
| **3. Old Scratch** | |

**D. Words to Know.** Write the letter of the best answer. (4 points each)

_____ 1. One would **most** expect to find respect for piety in a
    a. stadium.    b. temple.    c. theater.

_____ 2. One is **most** likely to find a melancholy house to be
    a. dirty.    b. haunted.    c. depressing.

_____ 3. A truly singular activity would be playing golf
    a. very badly.    b. by oneself.    c. on the moon.

_____ 4. Farmers are **most** likely to see dark clouds as propitious during
    a. a drought.    b. harvest time.    c. flood season.

_____ 5. When you surmise the ending of a movie, you do it
    a. before the end.    b. at the end.    c. after the end.

**E.** Answer **one** of the following questions based on your understanding of the story. Write your answer on a separate sheet of paper. (15 points)

1. What do you think was the original purpose of this story? Does it still serve the same purpose today? Explain your answers.

2. Do you think the characters in the story are believable? Pick one of the three main characters and use details from the story to support your answer.

**F. Linking Literature to Life.** Answer the following question based on your own experience and knowledge. Write your answer on a separate sheet of paper. (15 points)

Identify at least two actions that might bring a person temporary happiness or success but have harmful consequences in the long term. Explain.

## *from* Self-Reliance (page 363)

# Selection Test

**A.** Think about Emerson's aphorism, "A foolish consistency is the hobgoblin of little minds." What does he mean by "a foolish consistency"? What might he consider a *wise* consistency? In the box on the left, note an example from everyday life of what Emerson might consider foolish consistency. In the box on the right, note an example of what he might consider wise consistency. In each box at the bottom, write notes explaining how the selection supports your examples. (15 points each)

| 1. Example of Foolish Consistency | 2. Example of Wise Consistency |
|---|---|
| | |
| **Explain.** | **Explain.** |

**B.** Write the letter of the best answer. This exercise is continued on the next page. (6 points each)

_____ 1. With which of the following aphorisms would Emerson **most** probably disagree?
   a. "No man is wise enough by himself."—Titus Maccius Plautus
   b. "You don't need a weatherman to know which way the wind blows." —Bob Dylan
   c. "No one can make you feel inferior without your consent." —Eleanor Roosevelt
   d. "The whole of science is nothing more than a refinement of everyday thinking."—Albert Einstein

_____  2. According to Emerson, what is the main source of greatness in a person?
        a. God
        b. nature
        c. one's individuality
        d. one's reputation among the people

_____  3. Which of the following is an essential part of Emerson's definition of integrity?
        a. devoting oneself to social progress
        b. faithfully following one's conscience
        c. holding reliable thoughts and opinions
        d. doing all that one can to ensure the happiness of others

**C. Words to Know.** Write the letter of the best answer. (4 points each)

_____  1. An aversion to gossip makes you want to
        a. hear it.        b. repeat it.        c. avoid it.

_____  2. Something that could absolve a suspect is his or her
        a. alibi.        b. confession.        c. suspicious behavior.

_____  3. Knowledge bestowed is information
        a. misused.        b. shared.        c. withheld.

_____  4. The team that predominates in the league is **most** probably in
        a. first place.        b. second place.        c. last place.

_____  5. Compared to others, nonconformists are **more** often considered
        a. kind.        b. logical.        c. different.

**D.** Answer **one** of the following questions based on your understanding of the selection. Write your answer on a separate sheet of paper. (16 points)

1. Is self-reliance as Emerson describes it difficult to obtain? Support your opinion with reference to the selection and your own ideas.

2. Do you think it is easier for a wealthy person or a poor person to be self-reliant in the way that Emerson describes it? Support your answer with details from the selection and your own ideas.

**E. Linking Literature to Life.** Answer the following question based on your own experience and knowledge. Write your answer on a separate sheet of paper. (16 points)

What forces, factors, trends, and institutions in the modern world do you think encourage self-reliance? What might discourage it? Explain.

## *from* Civil Disobedience (page 369)

# Selection Test

**A.** Think about the characteristics of an essay. Write a brief description of these characteristics in the boxes on the left. In the boxes on the right, explain how these characteristics apply to this essay from "Civil Disobedience." (8 points each)

| Characteristics of a Personal Essay | How They Apply to "Civil Disobedience" |
|---|---|
| **1.** | |
| **2.** | |
| **3.** | |

**B.** Write the letter of the best answer. This exercise is continued on the next page. (5 points each)

_____ 1. According to Thoreau, the majority generally rules in a democracy because it is the
   a. most intelligent.
   b. strongest.
   c. most expedient.
   d. fairest.

_____ 2. In Thoreau's view, which man exemplifies "undue respect for law"?
   a. a soldier
   b. a farmer
   c. a reformer
   d. a martyr

_____ 3. Practically speaking, Thoreau would most likely want
   a. no government.
   b. a totalitarian government.
   c. a strong central government.
   d. a weak central government.

_____ 4. Thoreau says that the only obligation he has to assume is to
  a. support the government.
  b. obey all laws.
  c. do what he thinks is right.
  d. accept the majority rule.

**C. Words to Know.** Write the letter of the best answer. (4 points each)

_____ 1. <u>Unscrupulous</u> people are people without
  a. anger.          b. principles.          c. goals.

_____ 2. To <u>endeavor</u> to complete all your homework is to
  a. make an effort.     b. decide against it.     c. fail.

_____ 3. Whom would you <u>confront</u> in a debate?
  a. your team          b. the judge          c. the opponents

_____ 4. To <u>conclude</u> that an answer is correct, you must
  a. make a mistake.     b. ask your teacher.     c. make a judgment.

_____ 5. A vegetable garden will most likely <u>flourish</u> if it
  a. is watered.        b. dries out.          c. is planted in shade.

**D.** Answer **one** of the following questions based on your understanding of "Civil Disobedience." Write your answer on a separate sheet of paper. (20 points)

1. Thoreau's "Civil Disobedience" has influenced generations of people—from Mohandas Gandhi to Martin Luther King, Jr., to the protesters of the Vietnam War. What ideas from this essay do you think would be most useful and effective in protesting a war?

2. In his book *On the Mexican War,* John Jordan Crittenden, a 19th-century senator from Kentucky, wrote, "I hope to find my country in the right; however, I will stand by her, right or wrong." Briefly summarize how you think Thoreau might have responded to Crittenden's statement.

**E. Linking Literature to Life.** Answer the following question based on your own experience and knowledge. Write your answer on a separate sheet of paper. (16 points)

The government of the United States is based on the rule of the majority. Do you think there are times when the majority rule might be in conflict with the individual's conscience? What would you do if there were a law you strongly disagreed with?

## *from* Walden (page 381)

# Selection Test

**A.** How well does your life agree with Thoreau's idea of the way people should live? In the box on the left, note something that you did in the last year that fits Thoreau's philosophy of life. In the box on the right, note something you did that does not fit Thoreau's philosophy. In the boxes at the bottom, write notes explaining how your examples fit or don't fit Thoreau's philosophy. (15 points each)

| 1. Fits Thoreau's philosophy | 2. Doesn't Fit Thoreau's Philosophy |
|---|---|
| | |
| **Explain how this action fits Thoreau's philosophy.** | **Explain how this action doesn't fit Thoreau's philosophy.** |

**B.** Write the letter of the best answer. This exercise is continued on the next page. (4 points each)

_____ 1. Thoreau went to Walden Pond because he
 a. had given up on life at that time.
 b. needed to hide from life for awhile.
 c. wanted to lead a more meaningful life.
 d. hoped to discover what in life serves to glorify God.

_____ 2. Thoreau would **most** probably describe "details" as
 a. distractions from life.        c. humanity's greatest allies.
 b. nature's building blocks.     d. efforts to lead a spiritual life.

_____ 3. Thoreau learned from his stay at Walden Pond that people who pursue their dreams
 a. must give them up in the end.
 b. must be careful not to reach too high.
 c. will meet with unexpected success.
 d. will be ridiculed by practical people.

_____ 4. To Thoreau, the incident of the insect emerging from the leg of a wooden table years after it had been laid in a tree is a symbol of human
   a. greed.
   b. vanity.
   c. failure.
   d. potential.

_____ 5. Thoreau's essay would probably be described **least** as
   a. narrative.
   b. sarcastic.
   c. persuasive.
   d. descriptive.

**C. Words to Know.** Write the letter of the best answer. (4 points each)

_____ 1. If you do something deliberately, you act
   a. carefully.          b. quickly.          c. spitefully.

_____ 2. In a state of perturbation, one feels
   a. anxiety.          b. joy.          c. nothing.

_____ 3. An act of magnanimity involves
   a. pride.          b. giving.          c. wealth.

_____ 4. People often indicate that they feel resignation by
   a. fighting.          b. sighing.          c. pleading.

_____ 5. A perennial problem for many modern American cities is
   a. crime.          b. smallpox.          c. a heat wave.

**D.** Answer **one** of the following questions based on your understanding of the selection. Write your answer on a separate sheet of paper. (15 points)

 1. Imagine that you were to visit Thoreau at his cabin for an hour or two. Do you think you would enjoy the visit? Give at least three reasons for your answer.

 2. How would you summarize what Thoreau learned from his stay at Walden Pond?

**E. Linking Literature to Life.** Answer the following question based on your own experience and knowledge. Write your answer on a separate sheet of paper. (15 points)

   List the machines, modern conveniences, and types of technology that you used yesterday. Which ones complicated your life more than they simplified it? Explain.

# Selected Poems by Whitman (page 396)

# Selection Open-Book Test

**A.** Think about how these poems use three devices of free verse: catalog, repetition, and parallelism. For each poem, write notes describing one of these devices that is used in the poem and how it is used. In the boxes on the right, describe the effect or the meaning suggested by the device. (10 points each)

| Device and How It Is Used | Effect or Suggested Meaning |
|---|---|
| 1. "I Hear America Singing" | |
| 2. "I Sit and Look Out" | |
| 3. *from* "Song of Myself" | |

**B.** Write the letter of the best answer. This exercise is continued on the next page. (6 points each)

_____ 1. In "I Hear America Singing," all the people referred to are
    a. poor.
    b. male.
    c. young.
    d. working.

_____ 2. All the following are true of "I Hear America Singing" except that it
    a. is written in free verse.
    b. consists of several long sentences.
    c. associates occupations with singing.
    d. contains a catalog of people and things.

_____ 3. In "I Sit and Look Out," the images could **best** be described as
   a. colorful.
   b. hopeful.
   c. religious.
   d. distressing.

_____ 4. The speakers of "I Sit and Look Out" and "Song of Myself" are alike in that both
   a. love nature.
   b. are observant.
   c. feel closely tied to humanity.
   d. have little interest in life's mysteries.

_____ 5. Line 7 of "Song of Myself" suggests that the speaker sees himself as
   a. a superior being.
   b. part of a cycle of life.
   c. deserving a better existence.
   d. one whose life will be short but meaningful.

_____ 6. Lines 17–19 of "Song of Myself" suggest that the purpose of grass is to
   a. perfume the world.
   b. inspire life by hiding death.
   c. remind people that God made it.
   d. provide protection for God's children.

**C.** Answer **one** of the following questions based on your understanding of the poems. Write your answer on a separate sheet of paper. (20 points)

1. In "I Hear America Singing," what is suggested by the fact that the people are "singing"? Identify and support at least two things that are suggested.

2. How do you account for the speaker's silence at the end of "I Sit and Look Out"? Support your answer with reference to the poem.

**D. Linking Literature to Life.** Answer the following question based on your own experience and knowledge. Write your answer on a separate sheet of paper. (14 points)

Traditionally, a person is thought to have a body, a mind, and a soul. In what ways—if at all—do you think the body, mind, and soul "live on" after death? Explain.

# Danse Russe/anyone lived in a pretty how town (page 410)

## Selection Open-Book Test

**A.** In each box at the top, write notes to describe the people in the "pretty how town" and comment on what they seem to be like. Note a line or lines from the poem that support your descriptions. Then, in the box at the bottom, write notes to answer the question. (8 points each)

| 1. "anyone" | 2. "noone" | 3. "women and men" | 4. "children" |
|---|---|---|---|
| | | | |
| Line Numbers: | Line Numbers: | Line Numbers: | Line Numbers: |

**5. What do you think is the main difference between those people who are referred to in the singular and those who are referred to in the plural?**

**B.** Write the letter of the best answer. This exercise is continued on the next page. (6 points each)

_____ 1. In "Danse Russe," the speaker suggests that he can regard himself as the "happy genius" of his household **mainly** because
a. his talent for dancing is unsurpassed.
b. there is no one present to contradict him.
c. he can express himself with genuine artistry.
d. no one else in the family shares his passion for dancing.

_____ 2. In "anyone lived in a pretty how town," the townspeople **least** consider "anyone" to be
a. inferior.
b. strange.
c. likeable.
d. undignified.

_____ 3. In "anyone lived in a pretty how town," "noone" expresses her love for "anyone" by

    a. quietly pining away for him.

    b. telling others about her feelings.

    c. sharing the ups and downs of his life.

    d. teaching others to care for him the way she does.

**C.** Consider how the styles of William Carlos Williams and E. E. Cummings contribute to your appreciation of the poems. Then, circle the letter of one set of lines from the poems you wish to discuss. In the box on the left, rewrite the set of lines, using everyday language. In the box on the right, write notes to answer the question. (12 points)

a. "and the sun is a flame-white disc
   in silken mists
   above shining trees,—"

b. "someones married their everyones
   laughed their cryings and did their
   dance (sleep wake hope and then) they
   said their nevers they slept their dream"

| Rewrite in everyday language. | What ideas and feelings conveyed by the poet's style are lost in your rewrite? |
| --- | --- |
| | |

**D.** Answer **one** of the following questions based on your understanding of the poems. Write your answer on a separate sheet of paper. (15 points)

1. In "Danse Russe," why do you think the speaker dances alone? Support your opinion with details from the poem.

2. In "anyone lived in a pretty how town," what impact does "anyone" have on most of the townspeople? How is it different from his impact on "noone"? Support your answer with details from the poem.

**E. Linking Literature to Life.** Answer the following question based on your own experience and knowledge. Write your answer on a separate sheet of paper. (15 points)

In what ways are young people today pressured to "fit in"? In what ways is individuality encouraged in young people?

# Ending Poem/Tía Chucha (page 416)

# Selection Open-Book Test

**A.** Think about the sense of identity celebrated in each of the poems. Draw a line from the title of each poem to the place on the bar where you think that poem belongs. (If, for example, you think the two values are equally important in a poem, draw a line from that title to the center of the bar.) Then, in each box under the bar, write notes explaining why you placed the poem where you did. (15 points each)

**Value of
Cultural Identity**                                                                                          **Value of
Individual Identity**

"Ending Poem"
"Tía Chucha"

| 1. Why did you place "Ending Poem" where you did on the bar? |
|---|
|  |

| 2. Why did you place "Tía Chucha" where you did on the bar? |
|---|
|  |

**B.** Write the letter of the best answer. This exercise is continued on the next page.
(10 points each)

_____ 1. In "Ending Poem," the speaker **most** probably represents
      a. all women.
      b. one individual woman.
      c. only Hispanic-American women.
      d. American women of many different cultures.

_____ 2. The speaker of "Tía Chucha" would **most** probably describe Tía Chucha's
      visits to the family as
      a. exceptions to the usual chaos.
      b. painful episodes of family conflict.
      c. enjoyable disruptions of family routine.
      d. unremarkable and ordinary occurrences.

........

_____     3. The tone of "Tía Chucha" could best be described as one of
a. dismay.
b. admiration.
c. amusement.
d. embarrassment.

**C.** Choose **one** of the following examples of figurative language used in the poems. Circle the example you have chosen. Then, in the box, write notes explaining what you think the speaker means by the statement. (10 points)

| **"Ending Poem"** |
| --- |
| "Africa waters the roots of my tree, but I cannot return." |
| "They have kept it all going / All the civilizations erected on their backs." |

| **"Tía Chucha"** |
| --- |
| "Tía Chucha would visit the family / in a tornado of song . . ." |
| "To me, she was the wisp / of the wind's freedom . . ." |

| **What the Speaker Means:** |
| --- |
|  |

**D.** Answer **one** of the following questions based on your understanding of the poems. Write your answer on a separate sheet of paper. (15 points)

1. In "Ending Poem," what do think the speaker means when she says, "History made us" (line 44)? Support your answer with details from the poem.

2. What can you tell about the speaker of "Tía Chucha" by reading the poem? Support your answer with details from the poem.

**E. Linking Literature to Life.** Answer the following question based on your own experience and knowledge. Write your answer on a separate sheet of paper. (15 points)

American society has been referred to as a "melting pot," in which the cultural identities of many people blend together to produce "Americans." Do you think this is an accurate description? Why or why not?

# Gary Keillor (page 424)

## Selection Test

**A.** Think about what Gary learns during the course of the story. In each box on the left is a description of a key event in Gary's life. In each box on the right, write notes explaining what the event teaches Gary about himself and about life. (14 points each)

| | |
|---|---|
| 1. When Gary volunteers to participate in the talent show, Dede Petersen responds by saying, *"You?"* | |
| 2. Gary puts his finger on the record during Bill Swenson's performance of "Vaya con Dios" at the talent show. | |
| 3. Gary performs "O Captain! My Captain!" at the talent show. | |

**B.** Write the letter of the best answer. This exercise is continued on the next page.
(5 points each)

_____ 1. Gary gets an invitation to Colorado because
       a. he is the oldest child.
       b. he works hard to obtain it.
       c. he is in the right place at the right time.
       d. his aunt and uncle feel sorry for him.

_____ 2. Gary likes the photograph of himself in Colorado because it makes him
       look like a
       a. clown.
       b. criminal.
       c. passionate young man.
       d. nice young man from Minnesota.

_____ 3. When Gary first recites "O Captain! My Captain!" in class, the other
students respond with
a. ridicule.
b. sympathy.
c. admiration.
d. disappointment.

_____ 4. At the talent show, Gary recites the poem
a. carelessly.
b. humorously.
c. sentimentally.
d. quietly and quickly.

_____ 5. The students find Gary's performance at the talent show
a. boring.
b. inspiring.
c. disgusting.
d. entertaining.

_____ 6. When Miss Rasmussen questions Gary about his performance at the talent
show, she expresses
a. alarm.
b. anger.
c. delight.
d. puzzlement.

**C.** Answer **one** of the following questions based on your understanding of the story.
Write your answer on a separate sheet of paper. (14 points)

1. When Gary suggests to Miss Rasmussen that "O Captain! My Captain!" may not be
appropriate for the talent show, she tells him, "Never compromise your standards
out of fear that someone may not understand." Why do you think Gary considers
this advice useless?

2. How does Gary's relationship to the other students change during the course of
the story? In your opinion, is the change a positive one? Support your answers
with details from the story and your own ideas.

**D. Linking Literature to Life.** Answer the following question based on your own
experience and knowledge. Write your answer on a separate sheet of paper. (14 points)

What are some of the challenges faced by high school students who want to be
accepted by their peers? Explain.

# Unit Three: The Spirit of Individualism

# Part One Open-Book Test

**A.** Write the answer to each question on the lines. (5 points each)

1. In "A Psalm of Life," what does the speaker mean when he says we can leave our "footprints on the sands of time"?

_____

_____

2. In "The Devil and Tom Walker," how do both Tom and his wife bring about their own demise?

_____

_____

3. Give an example of an aphorism from "Civil Disobedience" or *Walden* and explain what it means.

_____

_____

4. Describe the speaker's tone in either "anyone lived in a pretty how town" or "Tía Chucha."

_____

_____

---

**B.** In several of these selections, the writers express—either directly or indirectly—a criticism of society. Circle the letter of **one** selection you wish to discuss. Write notes explaining what the writer criticizes and what the writer says about that thing or aspect of society. (20 points)

a. "The Devil and Tom Walker"      c. "Civil Disobedience"

b. "Self-Reliance"      d. *from* "Walden"

| What the Writer Criticizes | What the Writer Says About It |
|---|---|
| | |
| | |
| | |
| | |
| | |

**C.** Answer **two** of the following essay questions based on your understanding of the selections. Write your answers on a separate sheet of paper. (20 points each)

1. One meaning of the word *romantic* is "not practical; idealistic." Which of the selections in this part do you think best reflects this meaning of *romantic*? Which one do you think least reflects it? Use details from the selections and your own ideas about life to support your opinions.

2. Think about the selections that express insights that you find particularly interesting. Choose **one** selection that expresses an insight into love, **one** that expresses an insight into human nature, and **one** that expresses an insight into the natural world. What are the insights and how are they communicated?

3. Many of the speakers of the poems in this part reveal a great deal about themselves. Choose the speakers from **two** of these poems—one speaker who you think is like you and one who is not at all like you. What do you find out about the speakers in the poems? In what ways are they similar to you, and in what ways are they different? Explain.

**D.** The theme of a poem most often concerns the writer's views about life or humanity. Choose any two poems from this part. For each one, write the title of the poem and explain what you think the theme of the poem is. In the box on the right, note some images from the poem that communicate or support this theme. (20 points)

| Title and Theme | Images That Support the Theme |
|---|---|
| **1.** | |
| **2.** | |

# The Masque of the Red Death (page 454)

# Selection Test

**A.** Think about this story as an allegory. Then, for each thing from the story noted at the top, circle one abstract quality that it might represent in the story. In each box at the bottom, note a reason that supports your choice. (6 points each)

| 1. Prince Prospero | 2. The Ebony Clock | 3. The Red Death |
|---|---|---|
| prosperity      privilege<br>evil               selfishness | mortality        poverty<br>guilt             time | revenge          fear<br>wisdom           fate |
| **Reason:** | **Reason:** | **Reason:** |

**B.** Write the letter of the best answer. (4 points each)

_____ 1. Prince Prospero's name is ironic in that
      a. no one calls him by it.     c. he leads a carefree life.
      b. he isn't really wealthy.     d. he dies a horrible death.

_____ 2. Once they have retreated to Prince Prospero's abbey, the general attitude of
      the courtiers toward the Red Death is one of
      a. guilt.              c. mild fear.
      b. terror.           d. carefree disregard.

_____ 3. The appearance of the Red Death in Prince Prospero's abbey is ironic in that
      a. it disturbs the revelers.
      b. it angers Prince Prospero.
      c. so many people have died from it.
      d. great precautions have been taken to keep it out of the abbey.

**C.** Think about how Prince Prospero and his courtiers respond to the Red Death before the masque, the possible reasons for their response, and what their response shows about them. Also consider how other kinds of people might have responded. Then, on a separate sheet of paper create a chart like the one below, and write notes reflecting your thoughts. (6 points each)

| Prince Prospero/Courtiers | Other People |
|---|---|
| 1. Responses | 4. Responses |
| 2. Reasons | 5. Who would respond in this way? |
| 3. What Responses Show | |

**D. Words to Know.** Write the letter of the best answer. (4 points each)

_____ 1. A movie featuring one or more <u>grotesque</u> characters is **most** likely to be
  a. a romance.          b. a war story.          c. science fiction.

_____ 2. If your parents give you <u>license</u>, they take away their
  a. limits.          b. approval.          c. expectations.

_____ 3. A <u>dauntless</u> journalist has
  a. courage.          b. consistency.          c. writing skills.

_____ 4. An act of <u>impetuosity</u> is always
  a. dangerous.          b. unplanned.          c. unreliable.

_____ 5. Which would be <u>tangible</u> in a haunted house?
  a. fear          b. a ghost          c. the house

**E.** Answer **one** of the following questions based on your understanding of the story. Write your answer on a separate sheet of paper. (10 points)

1. How did you feel about the death of the revelers at the masque? Did you feel sorry for them, or did you feel they deserved their fate? Explain.

2. What is the most important lesson Poe teaches in the story? Explain how you think this lesson applies to the situation with AIDS in America today.

**F. Linking Literature to Life.** Answer the following question based on your own experience and knowledge. Write your answer on a separate sheet of paper. (10 points)

Do you feel an individual responsibility toward the needy people of the world? If so, what does that sense of responsibility compel you to do? If not, why not?

# The Raven (page 466)

## Selection Open-Book Test

**A.** Think about the effect that the raven has on the speaker. Then, in the boxes below, write notes reflecting your thoughts. (10 points each)

| 1. What is the speaker feeling and doing at the beginning of the poem, and why? | 3. What is the speaker feeling and doing at the end of the poem? |
|---|---|

2. How does the raven affect the speaker, and why does it affect him in these ways?

**B.** Write the letter of the best answer. This exercise is continued on the next page. (1 points each)

_____ 1. In lines 91–95, what is the main thing that the speaker seeks from the raven?
   a. reason to hope
   b. reason to believe the raven
   c. an explanation for Lenore's death
   d. an explanation for the raven's appearance

_____ 2. By the end of the poem, where does the speaker assume that the raven has come from?
   a. hell
   b. Eden or heaven
   c. the shores of a nearby sea
   d. the home of an unhappy master

_____ 3. In the poem, the bust of Pallus is most probably intended to represent
   a. death.
   b. sorrow.
   c. reason.
   d. romantic love.

_____ 4. What is the end-of-line rhyme scheme of the poem?
        a. *abcbbb*
        b. *abcbbc*
        c. *abcccb*
        d. *abcccc*

_____ 5. Which lines of each stanza contain internal rhyme?
        a. the first and second
        b. the first and third
        c. the second and third
        d. the second and fourth

**C. Words to Know.** Write the letter of the best answer. (4 points each)

_____ 1. In grade school, a respite would be
        a. recess.        b. a fistfight.        c. homework.

_____ 2. Which kind of movie is **most** likely to be described as beguiling?
        a. suspense thriller        b. action-adventure        c. romantic comedy

_____ 3. A placid expression reflects a person's
        a. fear.        b. excitement.        c. peace of mind.

_____ 4. During a tempest, you are **most** likely to hear
        a. snoring.        b. thunder.        c. applause.

_____ 5. One is likely to find the **most** decorum at a
        a. ball game.        b. school picnic.        c. formal dinner.

**D.** Answer **one** of the following questions based on your understanding of the poem. Write your answer on a separate sheet of paper. (15 points)

1. What do you think it means that the raven is still present at the end of the poem? Use details from the poem and your own ideas to support your opinion.

2. What do you think the raven represents in this poem? Use details from the poem to support your answer.

**E. Linking Literature to Life.** Answer the following question based on your own experience and knowledge. Write your answer on a separate sheet of paper. (15 points)

Identify **three** healthy ways to cope with grief. Support your ideas with real or made-up examples.

# The Fall of the House of Usher (page 473)

# Selection Test

**A.** Many Gothic stories take place in huge, dark castles or mansions. Think about the setting of this story and how it conveys atmosphere and mood. For each element of the setting listed in the boxes on the left, write notes describing what it looks like and how it contributes to the atmosphere and mood of the story. (8 points each)

| Element of Setting | Description and Contribution to Atmosphere and Mood |
|---|---|
| **1. Exterior of house** | |
| **2. Interior of house** | |
| **3. Physical surroundings** | |

**B.** Write the letter of the best answer. This exercise is continued on the next page. (5 points each)

_____ 1. The narrator's first glimpse of the House of Usher gives him a feeling of
   a. excitement.          c. depression.
   b. numbness.           d. anticipation.

_____ 2. The fact that Usher hears his sister's struggles before the narrator does reinforces the
   a. terror created by the storm on the last night.
   b. closeness between the brother and sister.
   c. fact that the house will fall.
   d. the narrator's fears.

_____ 3. Which description of Usher best foreshadows his death?
   a. "His air appalled me. . . ."
   b. ". . . an eye large, liquid, and luminous. . . ."
   c. "The silken hair, too, had been suffered to grow. . . ."
   d. "His countenance was . . . cadaverously wan. . . ."

_____ 4. The mood of the story can best be described as
       a. terrifying.                   c. revolting.
       b. melancholy.             d. cheerless.

**C. Words to Know.** Write the letter of the best answer. (4 points each)

_____ 1. An insoluble problem is one that cannot be
       a. postponed.        b. overlooked.       c. solved.

_____ 2. If soldiers annihilate a city, the city is
       a. destroyed.        b. under siege.       c. captured.

_____ 3. Vivacious people are best described as
       a. idle.               b. lively.          c. sluggish.

_____ 4. If you sleep fitfully, you will most likely feel
       a. contented.        b. energized.       c. exhausted.

_____ 5. Which animal is generally thought of as being obstinate?
       a. fox              b. rabbit         c. mule

**D.** Answer **one** of the following questions based on your understanding of "The Fall of the House of Usher." Write your answer on a separate sheet of paper. (20 points)

1. Poe believed that all elements of a story must contribute to a single unified effect. What unified effect does Poe strive for in this story, and how do the different elements—setting, action, characters, and dialogue—contribute to that effect?

2. There are many interpretations of "The Fall of the House of Usher." One interpretation suggests that Usher's nervousness and weakness are the results of Madeline Usher's being a vampire. Using details from the story, write an analysis of the story that supports this interpretation.

**E. Linking Literature to Life.** Answer the following question based on your own experience and knowledge. Write your answer on a separate sheet of paper. (16 points)

In many of Poe's stories, he focuses on the imagination and how it can overpower even the most logical minds. Do you think it is possible for people's imaginations to control their lives and overcome their common sense? Explain.

# Dr. Heidegger's Experiment (page 500)

# Selection Test

**A.** Several clues and hints in this story foreshadow what happens later. In the boxes on the left, write notes describing four of these clues or hints and what they foreshadow. In the boxes on the right, describe what happens later in the story that fulfills the prediction suggested by each clue or hint. (6 points each)

| Clues or Hints | Events That Happen Later in the Story |
|---|---|
| **1.** | |
| **2.** | |
| **3.** | |
| **4.** | |

**B.** Write the letter of the best answer. This exercise is continued on the next page. (5 points each)

_____ 1. The narrator implies that Dr. Heidegger's guests are
    a. brilliant.          c. fascinating.
    b. pathetic.          d. dangerous.

_____ 2. If you interpret this story as an allegory, what does Dr. Heidegger represent?
    a. science or wisdom
    b. youthful lust
    c. loss of beauty
    d. ignorance or superstition

_____ 3. In allegorical terms, which character represents greed?
   a. Widow Wycherly
   b. Mr. Gascoigne
   c. Mr. Medbourne
   d. Colonel Killigrew

_____ 4. How did the four guests feel when the experiment was over?
   a. relieved
   b. humiliated
   c. excited
   d. frustrated

**C. Words to Know.** Write the letter of the best answer. (4 points each)

_____ 1. A <u>decrepit</u> building is one that is
   a. being built.　　　　b. fully occupied.　　　　c. run-down.

_____ 2. One could expect the **most** <u>deferential</u> treatment to be given to a
   a. pet.　　　　b. guest.　　　　c. burglar.

_____ 3. A <u>transient</u> feeling is one that lasts
   a. briefly　　　　b. a long time.　　　　c. forever.

_____ 4. Trees become <u>tremulous</u>
   a. in the wind.　　　　b. as they grow.　　　　c. when they die.

_____ 5. <u>Exhilaration</u> is a feeling that involves
   a. pain.　　　　b. pleasure.　　　　c. indifference.

**D.** Answer **one** of the following questions based on your understanding of the story. Write your answer on a separate sheet of paper. (20 points)

1. Do you think that this story is more of a tribute to science or an attack on science? Use details from the story to support your opinion.

2. Why won't Dr. Heidegger participate in the experiment? Identify and support at least two reasons.

**E. Linking Literature to Life.** Answer the following question based on your own experience and knowledge. Write your answer on a separate sheet of paper. (16 points)

As a young person, would you say that youthfulness is overrated in American culture? Give at least **three** reasons for your opinion.

# A Rose for Emily (page 516)

# Selection Test

**A.** Think about how the narrator characterizes Miss Emily. Then, for each passage of narration on the left, jot down in each box on the right what it suggests about Miss Emily's appearance, personality, standing in the community, state of mind, situation in life, or effect on others. (8 points each)

| | |
|---|---|
| 1. "But garages and cotton gins had encroached and obliterated even the august names of that neighborhood; only Miss Emily's house was left, lifting its stubborn and coquettish decay above the cotton wagons and gasoline pumps—an eyesore among eyesores." → | |
| 2. "We had long thought of them as a tableau, Miss Emily a slender figure in white in the background, her father a spraddled silhouette in the foreground, his back to her and clutching a horsewhip, the two of them framed by the back-flung front door." → | |
| 3. "[Miss Emily] was over thirty then, still a slight woman, though thinner than usual, with cold, haughty black eyes in a face the flesh of which was strained across the temples and about the eye-sockets as you imagine a lighthouse-keeper's face ought to look." → | |
| 4. "Now and then we would see [Miss Emily] in one of the downstairs windows—she had evidently shut up the top floor of the house—like the craven torso of an idol in a niche, looking or not looking at us, we could never tell which." → | |

**B.** Write the letter of the best answer. This exercise is continued on the next page. (6 points each)

_____ 1. Which quotation does not foreshadow the ending of the story?

    a. "When [Miss Emily] opened the package at home there was written on the box, under the skull and bones: 'For rats.' "

    b. "When the town got free postal delivery, Miss Emily alone refused to let them fasten the metal numbers above her door and attach a mailbox to it."

    c. "We remembered all the young men her father had driven away, and we knew that with nothing left, she would have to cling to that which had robbed her, as people will."

    d. "So when [Miss Emily] got to be thirty and was still single, we were not pleased exactly, but vindicated; even with insanity in the family she wouldn't have turned down all of her chances if they had really materialized."

_____ 2. The narrator implies that Miss Emily's father tended to do all of the
        following **except**
        a. trust her.
        b. spoil her.
        c. control her.
        d. overprotect her.

_____ 3. When the smell developed around Miss Emily's home, the older aldermen
        were reluctant to ask her about it because they
        a. were afraid of her temper.
        b. were afraid of what they might discover.
        c. didn't want to embarrass or humiliate her.
        d. knew she would be too ill to do anything about it.

**C. Words to Know.** Write the letter of the best answer. (4 points each)

_____ 1. It is easiest to <u>obliterate</u> writing done with
        a. chalk.              b. a pen.                c. a chisel.

_____ 2. A <u>pallid</u> person would be most likely to be described as looking like a
        a. stick.             b. ghost.               c. tomato.

_____ 3. An example of an <u>edict</u> would be when a king gives
        a. an invitation.      b. an interview.         c. a command.

_____ 4. During a <u>tedious</u> speech, the audience would be **most** likely to
        a. yawn.              b. laugh.               c. get worked up.

_____ 5. A person engages in <u>coquettish</u> behavior in an attempt to seem
        a. polite.            b. attractive.          c. unconcerned.

**D.** Answer **one** of the following questions based on your understanding of the story.
Write your answer on a separate sheet of paper. (15 points)

1. Identify at least **two** feelings that the townspeople have had for Miss Emily over the
   years. Explain how those feelings have affected how the townspeople relate to Miss
   Emily.

2. Why do you think Miss Emily's crime goes undetected until her death? Identify at
   least **three** contributing factors and support them with reference to the story.

**E. Linking Literature to Life.** Answer the following question based on your own
experience and knowledge. Write your answer on a separate sheet of paper. (15 points)

   What are, in your opinion, the pros and cons of living in a tight-knit family or
community? Explain your ideas.

# The Life You Save May Be Your Own (page 528)

# Selection Test

**A.** Think about what Mr. Shiftlet and Mrs. Crater want and what they actually get. Then, in the boxes below, write notes reflecting your thoughts. (10 points each)

| | What the Character Wants | | What the Character Gets |
|---|---|---|---|
| **1. Mr. Shiftlet** | | → | |
| **2. Mrs. Crater** | | → | |

**B.** Write the letter of the best answer. (4 points each)

_____  1. Mrs. Crater has to talk Mr. Shiftlet into
      a. leaving.               c. taking her money.
      b. fixing the car.     d. marrying Lucynell.

_____  2. Immediately after the wedding ceremony, Mr. Shiftlet feels
      a. bitter.               c. terrified.
      b. happy.             d. satisfied.

_____  3. The hitchhiker's rejection of him makes Mr. Shiftlet feel
      a. guilty.               c. carefree.
      b. humble.            d. hopeless.

_____  4. The storm that overtakes Mr. Shiftlet at the end of the story is an indication that he
      a. has been saved.    c. plans to return for Lucynell.
      b. has been forgiven.  d. is part of the "slime" of this earth.

_____  5. O'Connor **most** probably intended the name *Crater* to suggest to the reader that the lives of Mrs. Crater and young Lucynell are
      a. empty.               c. colorful.
      b. strange.           d. satisfying.

_____  6. O'Connor **most** probably intended the name *Shiftlet* to suggest to the reader that Mr. Shiftlet is
      a. unhappy.           c. idealistic.
      b. practical.         d. untrustworthy.

**C.** Think about the irony in the story as you read the quotations on the left. Then, in each box on the right, write notes explaining how the quotation is ironic. (6 points each)

| | |
|---|---|
| 1. "Mr. Shiftlet said that the trouble with the world was that nobody cared, or stopped and took any trouble. He said he never would have been able to teach Lucynell to say a word if he hadn't cared and stopped long enough." ➡ | |
| 2. "There were times when Mr. Shiftlet preferred not to be alone. He felt too that a man with a car had a responsibility to others, and he kept his eye out for a hitchhiker." ➡ | |

**D. Words to Know.** Write the letter of the best answer. (4 points each)

_____    1. A person who is <u>gaunt</u> **most** resembles a
　　　　　　　a. whale.　　　　　　　b. string bean.　　　　　c. weight lifter.

_____    2. A <u>composed</u> attitude suggests that a person feels
　　　　　　　a. smart.　　　　　　　b. tranquil.　　　　　　c. physically fit.

_____    3. A boy would be **most** likely to look <u>morose</u> if he had lost
　　　　　　　a. weight.　　　　　　　b. his pursuers.　　　　c. his best friend.

_____    4. If you <u>rue</u> something you have said or done, you are **most** likely to
　　　　　　　a. laugh.　　　　　　　b. apologize.　　　　　c. do it again.

_____    5. A ship is **most** likely to <u>list</u> when it is in a
　　　　　　　a. storm.　　　　　　　b. hurry.　　　　　　　c. harbor.

**E.** Answer **one** of the following questions based on your understanding of the story. Write your answer on a separate sheet of paper. (12 points)

　1. In your opinion, which characters in this story need to be saved? From whom or what do they need to be saved? Support your answers.

　2. O'Connor said that the hitchhiker Mr. Shiftlet picks up at the end "makes the story work." How do you think the episode with the hitchhiker does this?

**F. Linking Literature to Life.** Answer the following question based on your own experience and knowledge. Write your answer on a separate sheet of paper. (12 points)

　Identify an example of a "false savior" in real life. What are some reasons that you think of this person or thing as a false savior as opposed to a true one?

# Unit Three: The Spirit of Individualism

# Part Two Open-Book Test

**A.** Write the letter of the best answer to each question. (5 points each)

_____ 1. The shriveling of the rose in "Dr. Heidegger's Experiment" foreshadows
   a. an early autumn.
   b. the death of Madame Wycherly.
   c. the failure of the potion.
   d. a swarm of aphids.

_____ 2. In "The Fall of the House of Usher," the collapse of the house represents the
   a. end of the Usher family.
   b. resurrection of Madeline.
   c. narrator's effort to destroy evil.
   d. final phase of Roderick's growing insanity.

_____ 3. In the poem "The Raven," the line "Ah, distinctly I remember it was in the bleak December;" includes an example of
   a. allegory.
   b. internal rhyme.
   c. end rhyme.
   d. foreshadowing.

_____ 4. Which sentence from "The Life You Save May Be Your Own" best reveals Mr. Shiftlet's true character?
   a. "The tramp stood looking at her and didn't answer."
   b. "He held the burning match as if he were studying the mystery of flame while it traveled dangerously toward his skin."
   c. "Lady . . . there ain't a broken thing on this plantation that I couldn't fix for you, one-arm jackleg or not."
   d. "In the darkness, Mr. Shiftlet's smile stretched like a weary snake waking up by a fire."

**B.** Think about the the mood, or the feeling or atmosphere, of the selections in this part of the unit. Choose **one** selection you wish to analyze, and then on a separate sheet of paper, make a two-column chart. In the lefthand column, write five examples of sensory details that helped create the mood in that selection. In the righthand column, write notes explaining how each example affected you as you read the selection. (20 points)

**C.** Answer **two** of the following essay questions based on your understanding of the selections. Write your answers on a separate sheet of paper. (20 points each)

1. In general, when Gothic writers looked at the individual, they saw potential evil. Which selection from this part seems to present the darkest view of the individual? Support your choices with reference to the selections.

2. Choose **two** selections from this part in which the writers express—either directly or indirectly—a criticism of human nature. Explain what each writer criticizes about human nature, and how he or she communicates this criticism to the reader. Do the writers you chose have similar attitudes toward human nature? Explain.

3. Think about the roles played by the female characters in these Gothic selections. Choose any **two** of these selections and discuss any similarities you see between the lives and roles of the female characters in those selections.

**D.** Many of these selections concern death in either a literal sense—as the actual loss of life—or in a figurative sense—as the loss of meaning or hope. (20 points)

- In the boxes at the top, jot down the titles of two selections you wish to discuss. **Do not choose a selection that you discussed in Part B on the previous page.**
- Then fill in the remaining boxes with notes to answer the questions about those selections.

|  | **Selection:** | **Selection:** |
|---|---|---|
| Who or what dies? | | |
| Is the death literal or figurative? | | |
| What is communicated to the reader through this death? | | |

# The Language of Literature: American Literature

# Mid-Year Test

**Directions:** Read the short essay below. Then answer the questions that follow.

### *from* The Crisis, Number 1
*Thomas Paine*

These are the times that try men's souls. The summer soldier and the sunshine patriot will, in this crisis, shrink from the service of their country; but he that stands it *now,* deserves the love and thanks of man and woman. Tyranny, like hell, is not easily conquered; yet we have this consolation with us, that the harder the conflict, the more glorious the triumph. What we obtain too cheap, we esteem too lightly; it is dearness only that gives everything its value. Heaven knows how to put a proper price upon its goods, and it would be strange indeed if so celestial an article as *freedom* should not be highly rated. Britain, with an army to enforce her tyranny, had declared that she has a right not only to *tax,* but "to *bind* us in *all cases whatsoever"*; and if being *bound in that manner* is not slavery, then is there not such a thing as slavery upon earth. Even the expression is impious, for so unlimited a power can belong only to God. . . .

I have as little superstition in me as any man living, but my secret opinion has ever been, and still is, that God Almighty will not give up a people to military destruction, or leave them unsupportedly to perish, who have so earnestly and so repeatedly sought to avoid the calamities of war, by every decent method which wisdom could invent. Neither have I so much of the infidel in me as to suppose that He has relinquished the government of the world, and given us up to the care of devils; and as I do not, I cannot see on what grounds the king of Britain can look up to heaven for help against us: a common murderer, a highwayman, or a housebreaker has as good a pretense as he. . . .

I once felt all that kind of anger which a man ought to feel against the mean[1] principles that are held by the Tories.[2] A noted one, who kept a tavern at Amboy, was standing at his door, with as pretty a child in his hand, about eight or nine years old, as I ever saw, and after speaking his mind as freely as he thought was prudent, finished with this unfatherly expression, "Well! give me peace in my day." Not a man lives on the continent, but fully believes that a separation must sometime or other finally take place, and a generous parent should have said, "If there must be trouble, let it be in my day, that my child may have peace"; and this single reflection, well applied, is sufficient to awaken every man to duty. Not a place upon earth might be so happy as America. Her situation is remote from all the wrangling world, and she has nothing to do but to trade with them. A man can distinguish

---

[1]*small-minded*

[2]*those colonists who sympathized with the British*

himself between temper and principle, and I am as confident as I am that God governs the world, that America will never be happy till she gets clear of foreign dominion. Wars, without ceasing, will break out till that period arrives, and the continent must in the end be conqueror; for though the flame of liberty may sometimes cease to shine, the coal can never expire. . . .

The heart that feels not now is dead; the blood of his children will curse his cowardice who shrinks back at a time when a little might have saved the whole, and made *them* happy. I love the man that can smile in trouble, that can gather strength from distress, and grow brave by reflection. 'Tis the business of little minds to shrink; but he whose heart is firm, and whose conscience approves his conduct, will pursue his principles unto death. My own line of reasoning is to myself as straight and clear as a ray of light. Not all the treasures of the world, so far as I believe, could have induced me to support an offensive war, for I think it murder; but if a thief breaks into my house, burns and destroys my property, and kills or threatens to kill me, or those that are in it, and to "bind me in all cases whatsoever" to his absolute will, am I to suffer it? What signifies it to me whether he who does it is a king or a common man; my countryman or not my countryman; whether it be done by an individual villain, or an army of them? If we reason to the root of things we shall find no difference; neither can any just cause be assigned why we should punish in the one case and pardon in the other. . . .

**A.** The following items test your understanding of the selection. Circle the letter of the response that best completes the sentence.

1. In this essay, "the times" Paine refers to are the years just before the
   a. Civil War.
   b. establishment of slavery.
   c. arrival of the Pilgrims.
   d. American Revolution.

2. According to Paine, being bound by Britain's laws "in all cases whatsoever" is the same as
   a. slavery.
   b. rebellion.
   c. murder.
   d. liberty.

3. As used in the first paragraph, the word *impious* means
   a. related to the supernatural.
   b. confusing.
   c. without respect for God.
   d. dishonest.

4. Paine compares the king's actions to those of
   a. a housebreaker.
   b. Satan in hell.
   c. a summer soldier.
   d. God in heaven.

5. In Paine's view, the Colonies will not be happy until they are
   a. trading with Britain.
   b. ruled by a different king.
   c. involved in a war.
   d. free of foreign control.

6. Paine thinks that the colonists should rebel against Britain in order to
   a. increase trade with other countries.
   b. set an example for others.
   c. make things better for their children.
   d. enforce their own laws.

**B.** The following items check your understanding of the way in which the selection is written. Circle the letter of the response that best completes the sentence.

7. The main purpose of this essay is to
   a. persuade readers to fight for freedom.
   b. describe the many injustices committed by Britain.
   c. compare Britain and the Colonies.
   d. explain the meaning of bravery.

8. In this essay, Paine expresses his ideas mainly through
   a. allusions.
   b. the use of irony.
   c. persuasive argument.
   d. the use of allegory.

9. Stating that a line of reasoning is "as straight and clear as a ray of light" is an example of
   a. irony.
   b. hyperbole.
   c. simile.
   d. personification.

10. In this essay, Paine reveals his own bias against
    a. soldiers.
    b. children.
    c. patriots.
    d. loyalists.

........................................................................................................................................

**C.** The following items check your understanding of the way in which the selection is written. Write your response after each item.

11. Write a brief analysis of how Paine organizes and presents ideas in this essay.

_____

_____

_____

12. Explain why the author relates the anecdote about the tavern owner in the third paragraph.

_____

_____

_____

13. How does the author use references to God to strengthen his argument? Give examples from the essay.

_____

_____

_____

**D.** The following items check your ability to analyze and evaluate the selection. Circle the letter of the response that best completes the sentence or answers the question. This exercise is continued on the next page.

14. Which proverb best states a theme expressed in the first paragraph of this essay?
    a. A fool and his money are soon parted.
    b. That is best which costs the most.
    c. Nothing succeeds like success.
    d. A bird in the hand is worth two in the bush.

15. In the second paragraph, Paine implies that the colonists have the right to rebel because
    a. they have tried every reasonable way to avoid war.
    b. Britain has sent murderers and highwaymen to the Colonies.
    c. they are destined to be free.
    d. the people of Britain are infidels.

16. Which word best describes the tone of this essay?
    a. resentful                    c. righteous
    b. cautious                     d. enthusiastic

17. In which statement does Paine use an emotional appeal to a person's conscience rather than an appeal to reason?
    a. "I love the man that can smile in trouble. . . ."
    b. ". . . the blood of his children will curse his cowardice who shrinks back . . ."
    c. "What signifies it to me whether he who does it is a king or a common man . . . ?"
    d. "If we reason to the root of things we shall find no difference. . . ."

**E.** The following items check your ability to analyze and evaluate the selection. Write your response after each item.

18. According to Paine, what kind of relationship should the Colonies have with the rest of the world?

    _____

    _____

    _____

    _____

    _____

19. Why, do you think, does the author draw a comparison between Britain and a house thief in the last paragraph?

    _____

    _____

    _____

    _____

    _____

20. In your opinion, how persuasive is Paine's argument in this essay? Explain why you think it is persuasive or not.

    _____

    _____

    _____

    _____

    _____

**Writing Exercise**  The following activity is designed to assess your writing ability. The prompt asks you to explain something. Think of your audience as being any reader other than yourself.

When scorers evaluate your writing, they will look for evidence that you can:

- respond directly to the prompt;

- make your writing thoughtful and interesting;

- organize your ideas so that they are clear and easy to follow;

- develop your ideas thoroughly by using appropriate details and precise language;

- stay focused on your purpose for writing by making sure that each sentence you write contributes to your composition as a whole; and

- communicate effectively by using correct spelling, capitalization, punctuation, grammar, usage, and sentence structures.

Prompt: According to Paine, ". . . he whose heart is firm, and whose conscience approves his conduct, will pursue his principles unto death." How might this quotation apply to one of the writers or characters you have read about?

Choose one of the characters or writers you have read about, such as Jonathan Edwards; John Proctor, Giles Corey, or Rebecca Nurse in *The Crucible;* Patrick Henry; or Henry David Thoreau. Or think about a time in your own life when conscience and principles affected what you did. Write a short essay explaining how this quotation might apply to the character or writer you choose or to your own life. Use the bottom of the page to organize your ideas. Then write your essay on a separate sheet of paper.

_____

_____

_____

_____

_____

_____

_____

_____

_____

_____

_____

**Revising/Editing** The purpose of the following exercise is to check your ability to proofread and revise a piece of writing in order to improve its readability and presentation of ideas. Read the following paragraph. Then, for each underlined section, circle the letter of the revision below that most improves the writing. Or, if the section is best left as it is, circle letter *d.*

In our modern world, it is difficult to understand how early colonists in

Salem massachusetts, could have executed people for witchcraft. In 1692,
      1.

for example, 20 people <u>was convicted</u> of being witches and put to death.
           2.

<u>How did the judges try these cases? How did the judges decide who was</u>
           3.

<u>guilty?</u> One method of evaluating women suspected of being witches was

<u>to tie them</u> to the "dunking stool." <u>The suspect then lowered into the water.</u>
  4.                              5.

If she drowned, she was innocent. <u>Those</u> who survived was declared a
                      6.

witch and executed. Either way, the end result was the same.

1. a. Salem, massachusetts
   b. Salem Massachusetts
   c. Salem, Massachusetts
   d. Correct as is

2. a. is convicted
   b. were convicted
   c. been convicted
   d. Correct as is

3. a. How did the judges try these cases, and how
      did they decide who was guilty?
   b. How did the judges try these cases and how
      did they decide who were guilty?
   c. How did the judges try these cases, but how
      did they decide who was guilty?
   d. Correct as is

4. a. to be tied
   b. to tie her
   c. to have tied
   d. Correct as is

5. a. The suspect then lowering into the water.
   b. The suspect was then lowered into
      the water.
   c. The suspect, then lowered, was into
      the water.
   d. Correct as is

6. a. Them
   b. All
   c. Anyone
   d. Correct as is

## *from* **Narrative of the Life of Frederick Douglass, an American Slave (page 562)**

# Selection Test

**A.** Think about the different styles of writing used in this selection. Read the quotations below. In the boxes, write notes about each quotation. Tell whether the language used in the quotation is mainly **objective** or **subjective** and why you think it is one or the other. Then write notes telling whether you think the style is effective or not and why. (15 points each)

| 1. "I had been at my new home but one week before Mr. Covey gave me a very severe whipping, cutting my back, causing the blood to run, and raising ridges on my flesh as large as my little finger." | |
|---|---|
| **Description of Style** | **Is it effective or not? Why?** |
| | |

| 2. "My long-crushed spirit rose, cowardice departed, bold defiance took its place; and I now resolved that, however long I might remain a slave in form, the day had passed forever when I could be a slave in fact." | |
|---|---|
| **Description of Style** | **Is it effective or not? Why?** |
| | |

**B.** Write the letter of the best answer. (5 points each)

_____ 1. After the first six months at Covey's farm, Douglass was
   a. determined to avenge himself on Covey.
   b. determined to gain freedom or die trying.
   c. reduced to an unthinking, uncaring brute.
   d. reduced to a ball of rage waiting to explode.

_____ 2. In this selection, what does Douglass seek from his owner, Master Thomas?
   a. liberty          c. vengeance
   b. justice          d. forgiveness

_____ 3. Which of the following involves the **greatest** exercise of free will by Douglass?
   a. standing up to Covey     c. working in Covey's fields
   b. being beaten by Covey     d. returning to Covey's farm

**C. Words to Know.** Write the letter of the best answer. (4 points each)

_____ 1. Which is **most** likely to cause a houseplant to <u>languish</u>?
     a. fertilizer           b. repotting           c. lack of water

_____ 2. If you have a <u>faculty</u> for playing the piano, you have a
     a. love of it.          b. talent for it.        c. teacher for it.

_____ 3. To <u>intimate</u> something is to communicate it
     a. in a low voice.      b. in precise terms.      c. through suggestions.

_____ 4. A person who <u>interposes</u> habitually is **most** likely to be called a
     a. bully.            b. busybody.          c. scaredy cat.

_____ 5. Which is the **best** expression for referring to a group of <u>sundry</u> items?
     a. a mixed bag       b. a baker's dozen      c. a barrel of monkeys

**D.** Answer **one** of the following questions based on your understanding of the selection. Write your answer on a separate sheet of paper. (20 points)

1. Identify at least **two** reasons that the fight with Covey is a turning point in Douglass's life. You may refer to the selection and your own ideas.

2. What actions does Douglass take to try to improve his situation at Covey's farm? What do these actions say about Douglass as a person?

**E. Linking Literature to Life.** Answer the following question based on your own experience and knowledge. Write your answer on a separate sheet of paper. (15 points)

What group of people in the modern world do you think is in a situation closest to that of people in slavery? Discuss at least **two** ways in which the situations of the two groups are similar and at least **two** ways in which they are different.

## Stanzas on Freedom/Free Labor (page 574)

# Selection Open-Book Test

**A.** Think about the use of symbols in these poems. Find one symbol in "Stanzas on Freedom" and two symbols in "Free Labor." In each box on the left, identify a symbol and tell what it represents. In each box on the right, write notes to support your interpretation of the symbol. (10 points each)

| Symbol and Its Meaning | Support for Your Interpretation |
|---|---|
| 1. "Stanzas on Freedom" | |
| 2. "Free Labor" | |
| 3. "Free Labor" | |

**B.** Write the letter of the best answer. (5 points each)

_____ 1. The tone of the questions asked by the speaker of "Stanzas on Freedom" could **best** be described as
       a. tender.                c. insistent.
       b. spiteful.              d. gracious.

_____ 2. Which of the following abilities does the speaker of "Free Labor" attribute to his or her garment?
       a. the ability to forgive
       b. the ability to take revenge
       c. the ability to predict the future
       d. the ability to bear witness against the wearer

_____ 3. In "Free Labor," the speaker's garment doesn't "cry to God" (line 6) or "pierce the sky" with its voice (line 24) because it
       a. lacks faith.          c. has no need to.
       b. is too proud.       d. has been forsaken by God.

Name _____ Date _____

C. Think about the kind of person who, according to "Stanzas on Freedom," is truly a slave. Then, in each box on the left, restate in your own words the point made in the set of lines. In each box on the right, identify a historical or present-day situation, either political or personal, that you think illustrates that point. (10 points each)

| 1. "They are slaves who fear to speak<br>   For the fallen and the weak;" | |
| --- | --- |
| Restatement: | Example: |

| 2. "They are slaves who dare not be<br>   In the right with two or three." | |
| --- | --- |
| Restatement: | Example: |

D. Answer **one** of the following questions based on your understanding of the poems. Write your answer on a separate sheet of paper. (20 points)

1. What do you think is the central message of "Stanzas on Freedom"? Is this message still important today? Use details from the poem and your own ideas to support your answers.

2. What do you think is the central message of "Free Labor"? Is this message still important today? Use details from the poem and your own ideas to support your answers.

E. Linking Literature to Life. Answer the following question based on your own experience and knowledge. Write your answer on a separate sheet of paper. (15 points)

The speaker of "Stanzas on Freedom" asks, "If there breathe on earth a slave, / Are ye truly free . . . ?" What is your personal response to this question? Give at least three reasons for your opinion.

# An Occurrence at Owl Creek Bridge (page 580)

# Selection Test

**A.** Think about how the reader is affected by the way that narrative point of view is used in this story. Then, in the boxes below, write notes to answer the questions.
(12 points each)

| | Third-Person Omniscient Point of View | Third-Person Limited Point of View |
|---|---|---|
| **1. How does the point of view tend to affect the reader's attitude toward Farquhar, and why?** | | |
| | **The Shift in Point of View** | |
| **2. What role does the shift in point of view play in creating suspense for the reader? Explain.** | | |

**B.** Write the letter of the best answer. This exercise is continued on the next page.
(8 points each)

_____ 1. How much time passes in Farquhar's life between the end of section I and the end of the last section, section III?
   a. his entire lifetime
   b. just a few seconds
   c. about one afternoon
   d. about one day and one night

_____ 2. Which of the following aspects of Farquhar is **most** responsible for the predicament he finds himself in?
   a. his desire to live          c. his love for his family
   b. his wild imagination        d. his devotion to the South

_____ 3. Farquhar believes that the soldier who stops for a drink of water is a
     a. Federal spy.             c. Confederate soldier.
     b. Federal scout.           d. Confederate deserter.

_____ 4. In this story, all of the following exists only in Farquhar's imagination **except**
     a. his wife's outstretched arms.
     b. the soldiers' shooting at him.
     c. his body's falling into the water.
     d. the noose's tightening around his neck.

**C. Words to Know.** Write the letter of the best answer. (4 points each)

_____ 1. Ineffable feelings are those that you
     a. keep secret.       b. can't explain.       c. write about.

_____ 2. To apprise someone of a problem is to
     a. solve it.       b. cause it.       c. tell about it.

_____ 3. A goal is inaccessible if it
     a. isn't achieved.       b. can't be achieved.       c. is easily achieved.

_____ 4. An accident that you evade is one that you end up
     a. causing.       b. being part of.       c. not having.

_____ 5. One would be **most** likely to describe a movie as interminable if it is
     a. boring.       b. exciting.       c. popular.

**D.** Answer **one** of the following questions based on your understanding of the story. Write your answer on a separate sheet of paper. (12 points)

1. In your opinion, is Farquhar a hero? Use details from the story and your own ideas about heroism to support your answer.

2. In your opinion, would the story have been more enjoyable or less enjoyable if the last two sentences were cut—that is, if Farquhar had, in real life, reached home? Explain.

**E. Linking Literature to Life.** Answer the following question based on your own experience and knowledge. Write your answer on a separate sheet of paper. (12 points)

What do you think are the **two** most important functions—or benefits—of the human imagination? Explain.

# A Mystery of Heroism (page 593)

# Selection Test

**A.** Think about how this story exemplifies the characteristics of naturalism. The chart below lists four characteristics of naturalism. For each characteristic, write notes explaining how the characteristic applies to this story. Give examples from the story to support your ideas. (6 points each)

| Characteristic of Naturalism | How does the characteristic apply to the story? |
|---|---|
| 1. Common people and ordinary life | |
| 2. Accuracy of details | |
| 3. Effects of natural and social forces | |
| 4. Fate beyond individual's control | |

**B.** Write the letter of the best answer. This exercise is continued on the next page. (5 points each)

_____ 1. Collins decides to go to the well mostly because
   a. the men will die soon without water.
   b. he wants to help the dying officer.
   c. the captain orders him to go.
   d. his comrades have dared him to go.

_____ 2. The mood of the story suggests
   a. a sense of excitement.
   b. disillusionment.
   c. a melancholy gloom.
   d. a feeling of pride.

3. Once Collins is in the meadow, he begins to
   a. realize that there is no water in the well.
   b. feel that he can easily accomplish his task.
   c. wonder why he agreed to get the water.
   d. swell with courage and determination.

4. What did the men discover when Collins got back from the well?
   a. The bucket was empty.
   b. The captain was dead.
   c. Collins was wounded.
   d. No one was thirsty.

**C. Words to Know.** Write the letter of the best answer. (4 points each)

1. An incessant noise is one that
   a. is very loud.          b. does not stop.          c. is hard to hear.

2. To make a hand signal precisely, the movement must be
   a. exact.                 b. rapid.                  c. complex.

3. A man who answers sullenly is expressing his
   a. resentment.            b. satisfaction.           c. self-esteem.

4. The subject of a retraction is something that has been
   a. frightened.            b. withdrawn.              c. confirmed.

5. A futile effort is
   a. determined.            b. skillful.               c. useless.

**D.** Answer **one** of the following questions based on your understanding of "A Mystery of Heroism." Write your answer on a separate sheet of paper. (20 points)

1. Crane's stories often focus on a single ironic incident and a character who must deal with a moral problem of conduct. What ironic incident is the focus of this story, and what moral problems of conduct does Collins struggle with?

2. Since Collins's companions do not really need the water, why does he risk his life to go to the well? Use details from the story to support your answer.

**E. Linking Literature to Life.** Answer the following question based on your own experience and knowledge. Write your answer on a separate sheet of paper. (16 points)

Crane never explains what the "mystery" of heroism is. What do you think the "mystery" is? Do you think Collins is a heroic figure?

# Gettysburg Address (page 605)

# Selection Test

**A.** Think about the elements that make up a writer's style. For each element of style below, write a description of how that element applies to Lincoln's Gettysburg Address.
(6 points each)

| Element of Style | How does it apply to the Gettysburg Address? |
|---|---|
| 1. Word choice and sentence length | |
| 2. Tone | |
| 3. Imagery | |
| 4. Repetition and parallelism | |

**B.** Write the letter of the best answer. This exercise is continued on the next page.
(8 points each)

_____ 1. The tone of Lincoln's speech can best be described as
   a. critical.
   b. subjective.
   c. casual.
   d. sincere.

_____ 2. Lincoln says that the men who lost their lives on the battlefield died to
   a. prolong the practice of slavery.
   b. hold a nation and its people together.
   c. maintain the independence of the United States.
   d. preserve the Confederacy.

_____  3. What does Lincoln's speech emphasize most?
        a. the idea of strong independent states
        b. the defeat of the Confederacy
        c. the idea of one strong nation
        d. the abolition of slavery

**C. Words to Know.** Write the letter of the best answer. (4 points each)

_____  1. Which people have most likely conceived new ideas?
        a. manufacturers      b. employers      c. inventors

_____  2. Which would most detract from a person's reputation?
        a. bad manners      b. honesty      c. attention to detail

_____  3. Baseball fans who have a devotion to a particular team are
        a. loyal.      b. upset.      c. discouraged.

_____  4. If you resolve to get better grades, you are
        a. resentful.      b. determined.      c. pessimistic.

_____  5. Which person would most likely consecrate something?
        a. a policeman      b. a teacher      c. a priest

**D.** Answer **one** of the following questions based on your understanding of the Gettysburg Address. Write your answer on a separate sheet of paper. (20 points)

1. One of Lincoln's great talents was the ability to take difficult, profound, or highly emotional thoughts and express them in simple words. What two sentences from the Gettysburg Address best exemplify this talent? Why do you think people so easily remember these sentences?

2. The Gettysburg Address, though brief, tells you a great deal about Lincoln the man. How does this address reveal Lincoln's determination to do the right thing, his responsibility, and his devotion to the men who lost their lives on the battlefield?

**E. Linking Literature to Life.** Answer the following question based on your own experience and knowledge. Write your answer on a separate sheet of paper. (12 points)

   In Lincoln's second inaugural address, delivered as the war was coming to an end, he said, "With malice toward none; with charity for all; with firmness in the right . . . let us strive on to finish the work we are in; to bind up the nation's wounds; to care for him who shall have borne the battle . . . to do all which may achieve and cherish a just and lasting peace among ourselves, and with all nations." Do you think his words are just as applicable today as they were in the 1800s, or does the United States need to deal with its enemies of today in a different manner?

## *from* Coming of Age in Mississippi (page 609)
## Selection Test

**A.** Think about the characteristics of eyewitness accounts. For each characteristic listed below, write notes describing how it applies to this selection. Give examples from the selection to support your ideas. (6 points each)

| Characteristic | How It Applies to "Coming of Age in Mississippi" |
| --- | --- |
| 1. Objective facts | |
| 2. Chronological order | |
| 3. Sensory details | |
| 4. Direct quotations | |
| 5. Subjective feelings | |

**B.** Write the letter of the best answer. This exercise is continued on the next page. (6 points each)

_____ 1. How does Moody get involved in the sit-in?
   a. She volunteers.
   b. She happens upon it by accident.
   c. She is pushed into it by people at her school.
   d. She is obligated to participate as a member of a civil rights organization.

_____ 2. When Moody sits down at the lunch counter, her **main** goal is to
   a. eat lunch.
   b. challenge segregation.
   c. prove something to her mother.
   d. make the white customers angry.

_____ 3. Moody implies that the store manager's **main** reason for trying to empty the store of people is to
  a. appear to be a hero.
  b. protect the protesters.
  c. prevent his store and goods from being damaged.
  d. prevent the police from arresting people in the crowd.

_____ 4. Who initiates the violence at the sit-in?
  a. the police
  b. white onlookers
  c. the store's employees
  d. supporters of Moody and the other "sit-inners"

_____ 5. When violence erupts inside the store, the police force outside
  a. arrests the mob for violating the law.
  b. arrests the protesters for their own protection.
  c. does nothing because it isn't aware that a problem exists.
  d. does nothing even though it is aware that a problem exists.

_____ 6. Which of the following is changed **most** significantly by the sit-in?
  a. Moody's views toward herself
  b. Moody's views toward Mississippi whites
  c. Moody's views toward Mississippi blacks
  d. Moody's views toward the Mississippi police

_____ 7. At the beauty salon, Moody is treated with
  a. indifference.
  b. shy curiosity.
  c. kindly respect.
  d. fearful respect.

**C.** Answer **one** of the following questions based on your understanding of the selection. Write your answer on a separate sheet of paper. (14 points)

 1. How does participating in the sit-in change Moody's perception of whites in Mississippi? How might this change in perception affect her work in the movement? Explain your answers.

 2. What kind of person is Moody? Support your description of her character with details from the selection.

**D. Linking Literature to Life.** Answer the following question based on your own experience and knowledge. Write your answer on a separate sheet of paper. (14 points)

   What do you see as the main benefits and drawbacks of nonviolent protest? Explain your ideas.

# Ballad of Birmingham (page 618)

# Selection Open-Book Test

**A.** Traditionally, ballads depict tragic events that befall ordinary people, include supernatural elements, and treat themes related to love, adventure, and bravery. Make marks in the small boxes next to elements of traditional ballads found in this ballad. Then, in the box, write notes supporting your answers. (40 points)

☐ **tragic events**

☐ **ordinary people**

☐ **supernatural elements**

☐ **theme related to love, adventure, and bravery**

**Supporting Notes:**

**B.** Write the letter of the best answer. (10 points each)

_____ 1. The image of the little girl in the fifth stanza conveys a feeling of
       a. heroism.
       b. violence.
       c. innocence.

_____ 2. When the mother hears the explosion, her first thought is for
       a. her daughter.
       b. the marchers.
       c. the cause of freedom.

**C.** Answer **one** of the following questions based on your understanding of the ballad. Write your answer on a separate sheet of paper. (20 points)

1. What does this ballad say to you about freedom? Explain.

2. A martyr is someone who dies or suffers greatly, often unwillingly, for the sake of a principle or a cause. Do you think the little girl in this ballad is a martyr? Is her mother a martyr? Explain your answers.

**D. Linking Literature to Life.** Answer the following question based on your own experience and knowledge. Write your answer on a separate sheet of paper. (20 points)

Is there any principle or cause for which you would approve or promote the use of violence? Explain.

# Unit Four: Conflict and Expansion

# Part One Open-Book Test

**A.** Write the answer to each question on the lines. (5 points each)

1. As described in his *Narrative,* what does Frederick Douglass accomplish as a result
   of his fight with Mr. Covey?

   _____

   _____

2. Describe the speaker's purpose in "Stanzas on Freedom" or "Free Labor."

   _____

   _____

3. Explain the title of "A Mystery of Heroism."

   _____

   _____

4. Describe the terrible irony of the ending of "Ballad of Birmingham."

   _____

   _____

**B.** Think about the motivations of the people in this part. Choose **two** people from
two different selections in this part that you wish to discuss. In the box on the left, write
notes describing something the person says or does. In the boxes on the right, explain
the person's motivations—or reasons—for saying or doing that thing. (20 points)

| Person and Selection:<br><br>Action/Statement: | Motivations: |
|---|---|
| Person and Selection:<br><br>Action/Statement: | Motivations: |

**C.** Answer **two** of the following essay questions based on your understanding of the selections. Write your answers on a separate sheet of paper. (20 points each)

1. Many of these selections deal with the theme of personal responsibility. Compare and contrast **two** people from different selections in terms of responsibility. Which of the two do you think acts more responsibly? Explain.

2. Choose **two** selections from this part—one in which you think justice is served and one in which it isn't. Use details from the selections to support your choices.

3. Choose **two** selections from this part in which the tables are turned—that is, when people's fortunes or roles are reversed. Explain how the tables are turned in each selection and what results from this reversal.

4. From these selections, choose the person who you think was most victimized and the one you think won the greatest victory. (You may decide that both things are true of **one** person.) Support your choices with details from the selections.

**D.** Read the quotation below and think about what it says about courage. On the line above each box, write the name of a person from one of the selections that you wish to discuss. **Do not choose a person you discussed in Part B on the previous page.** In the box below each name, write notes to explain whether the person reveals this type of "real" courage and why you think so. (20 points)

"I wanted you to see what real courage is, instead of getting the idea that courage is a man with a gun in his hand. It's when you know you're licked before you begin but you begin anyway and you see it through no matter what." —Harper Lee

**Person:** _____    **Person:** _____

| **Does the person show this type of real courage? Explain.** | **Does the person show this type of real courage? Explain.** |
| --- | --- |
| | |

# The Indian and the Hundred Cows/
# El indito de las cien vacas (page 638)

## Selection Test

**A.** Think about the misunderstanding between the Indian and the priest. Then, in the box on the left, jot down what the priest means by what he says. In the box on the right, jot down what the Indian thinks the priest means. (20 points each)

**"You know that when you make a donation to God, He returns it a hundredfold."**

| 1. The priest | 2. The Indian |
|---|---|
|  |  |
|  |  |

**B.** Write the letter of the best answer. (10 points each)

_____ 1. The Indian takes the priest's cows because the Indian feels that
   a. the priest lied to him.
   b. the priest won't notice.
   c. the cows belong to him.
   d. the cows belong to the church, not the priest.

_____ 2. The priest lets the Indian keep the cows because the priest realizes that
   a. they belong to the Indian.
   b. God is punishing him for lying.
   c. the Indian needs them more than he does.
   d. the Indian isn't going to be peacefully persuaded.

_____ 3. Who learns a lesson in this *cuento*?
   a. the priest alone           c. both the priest and the Indian
   b. the Indian alone           d. neither the priest nor the Indian

**C.** Answer **one** of the following questions based on your understanding of the *cuento*. Write your answer on a separate sheet of paper. (15 points)

1. Do you think that justice is served in this *cuento*? Support your opinion with reference to the story and your own ideas about justice.

2. What purpose does this *cuento* serve as a folk tale—that is, what does it reveal about the values of the culture from which it comes? Support your ideas.

**D. Linking Literature to Life.** Answer the following question based on your own experience and knowledge. Write your answer on a separate sheet of paper. (15 points)

What are some clues that a statement is meant to be taken literally, and what are some clues that it isn't? Explain, using real or made-up examples.

# High Horse's Courting
## *from* Black Elk Speaks (page 645)

# Selection Test

**A.** Each of the characters in this folk tale is determined to get or accomplish something. In each box below, note what the character wants. (40 points)

**High Horse**

|  |
|--|
|  |

**Red Deer**

|  |
|--|
|  |

**The Girl**

|  |
|--|
|  |

**The Girl's Father**

|  |
|--|
|  |

**B.** Write the letter of the best answer. (10 points each)

_____ 1. The **best** clue that "High Horse's Courting" has its roots in oral literature is that it has a
   a. narrator.
   b. happy ending.
   c. humorous tone.
   d. conversational style.

_____ 2. High Horse's attraction to the girl is **mainly** based on her
   a. character.
   b. family background.
   c. physical appearance.
   d. abilities and achievements.

**C.** Answer **one** of the following questions based on your understanding of the folk tale. Write your answer on a separate sheet of paper. (20 points)

1. How would you describe the personality of High Horse? What elements in his personality do you think contribute to the humor of the story of his courting? Support your answers with details from the folk tale and your own ideas about him and his situation.

2. What values and beliefs of the Sioux are communicated through this example of their oral literature? Support your ideas with details from the folk tale.

**D. Linking Literature to Life.** Answer the following question based on your own experience and knowledge. Write your answer on a separate sheet of paper. (20 points)

How would you describe the difference between pursuing someone you are romantically interested in and harassing or stalking him or her? Explain.

Name _____  Date _____

# *from* **The Autobiography of Mark Twain (page 658)**

# Selection Test

**A.** Think about the situational ironies in this selection. For each situation listed below, Twain's expectations were quite different from the outcome. In each row, write notes describing what Twain expected and what actually happened. (7 points each)

| Situation | What Twain Expected | What Actually Happened |
|---|---|---|
| 1. When he first went to the mesmerizer's show | | |
| 2. When he pretended to receive a mental suggestion | | |
| 3. When he tried to convince Dr. Peake | | |
| 4. When he confessed to his mother | | |

**B.** Write the letter of the best answer. (4 points each)

_____ 1. Which of the following **least** describes Twain as a teenager?
   a. daring
   b. secure
   c. imaginative
   d. competitive

_____ 2. When Twain's mother refuses to believe his confession, he feels
   a. justified.
   b. relieved.
   c. satisfied.
   d. offended.

_____ 3. In this excerpt from his autobiography, Twain stresses that one's most memorable achievements
   a. make life worth living.
   b. are rarely noticed by others.
   c. can come back to haunt one.
   d. usually come too early in life.

**C.** As a local color realist, Twain based a good deal of his fiction on his own life experiences. Based on this excerpt from his autobiography, what types of settings and characters could you expect to find in his fictional works? In the boxes below, write notes reflecting your thoughts. (6 points each)

| 1. Settings | 2. Characters |
| --- | --- |
|  |  |

**D. Words to Know.** Write the letter of the best answer. (4 points each)

_____ 1. A <u>gullible</u> person is someone who is easily
      a. hurt.             b. fooled.           c. frightened.

_____ 2. In crime stories, <u>confederates</u> are **most** likely to be referred to as
      a. victims.          b. villains.          c. accomplices.

_____ 3. To <u>dissemble</u> is to behave in a way that is
      a. phony.           b. daring.          c. destructive.

_____ 4. Which **always** involves <u>collusion</u>?
      a. a lie             b. a trick         c. a conspiracy

_____ 5. A <u>rapt</u> audience indicates to a speaker that it is
      a. bored.           b. confused.        c. interested.

**E.** Answer **one** of the following questions based on your understanding of the selection. Write your answer on a separate sheet of paper. (14 points)

1. What do you think are the most important factors involved in the young Twain's fooling the townspeople? Explain.

2. What evidence do you see in the young Twain that he would grow up to become a great American writer? Support your ideas with details from the selection.

**F. Linking Literature to Life.** Answer the following question based on your own experience and knowledge. Write your answer on a separate sheet of paper. (14 points)

Mark Twain wrote, "How easy it is to make people believe a lie and how hard it is to undo that work again!" Does your personal experience support this idea? Explain.

# *from* **Life on the Mississippi (page 669)**

# Selection Test

**A.** Descriptive images help the reader visualize a scene. In addition, specific verbs often suggest more than what is stated, such as how the narrator feels about what he describes. Read each of the examples below. In the boxes on the right, write notes explaining what the sentence describes and what unstated feelings or ideas are suggested by the underlined verb(s). (8 points each)

| Example | Explanation |
| --- | --- |
| 1. "Mr. Bixby, my chief, 'straightened her up,' <u>plowed</u> her along past the sterns of the other boats . . ." | |
| 2. "I held my breath and began to <u>claw</u> the boat away from danger. . . ." | |
| 3. ". . . Mr. Bixby was going into danger again and <u>flaying</u> me alive with abuse of my cowardice." | |
| 4. "He [Mr. Bixby] would boil awhile to himself, and then <u>overflow</u> and scald me again. . . ." | |

**B.** Write the letter of the best answer. This exercise is continued on the next page. (7 points each)

_____ 1. At first, Twain thought that piloting the river would be
     a. challenging.
     b. a little difficult.
     c. impossible.
     d. easy.

_____ 2. Twain thought that Mr. Bixby was pointing out certain spots in the river to
     a. demonstrate his vast knowledge.
     b. teach an important lesson.
     c. be entertaining.
     d. confuse his apprentice.

_____ 3. Twain's view of his experiences as a steamboat pilot can best be
described as
a. naive.
b. wistful.
c. disdainful.
d. critical.

_____ 4. What did Twain lose by mastering the river?
a. his appreciation for its beauty
b. his respect and admiration for Mr. Bixby
c. any desire to travel to the Amazon
d. a love for steamboats

**C.** Answer **one** of the following questions based on your understanding of this excerpt
from *Life on the Mississippi.* Write your answer on a separate sheet of paper. (20 points)

1. At the beginning of this selection, Twain said he took on the task of learning the river
"with the easy confidence of my time of life." How did his views of the river and of
himself change as a result of his experiences? Use details from the selection to
support your ideas.

2. Descriptive writing helps you to picture scenes, events, and characters in your mind.
Think about Twain's description of the scene where Mr. Bixby got so upset with
Twain that he ran over the steering oar of a trading scow. What words or phrases
help you visualize the exchange between Mr. Bixby and the traders? What does
this scene reveal about Mr. Bixby's character?

**D. Linking Literature to Life.** Answer the following question based on your own
experience and knowledge. Write your answer on a separate sheet of paper. (20 points)

At the end of this selection, Twain stated that after his days as a steamboat pilot, he
pitied doctors. He suspected that doctors couldn't appreciate a woman's beauty because
they viewed everyone professionally. Do you think that too much knowledge can
sometimes ruin a thing, as it did for Twain? Have you—or has someone you know—
ever had a similar experience?

# The Notorious Jumping Frog of Calaveras County (page 679)

# Selection Test

**A.** Think about the characteristics of a tall tale. For each literary element below, write a brief description of its characteristics in a tall tale. Then explain how these characteristics apply to "The Notorious Jumping Frog of Calaveras County." (8 points each)

| Literary Element | Characteristics in a Tall Tale | In "The Notorious Jumping Frog of Calaveras County" |
|---|---|---|
| 1. Characters | | |
| 2. Plot | | |
| 3. Local color | | |

**B.** Write the letter of the best answer. This exercise is continued on the next page. (5 points each)

_____    1. When the narrator describes Simon Wheeler and his tall tale, he appears to be
          a. transfixed.         c. amused.
          b. unimpressed.     d. shocked.

_____    2. According to Jim Smiley, a frog can become a great jumper if it is
          a. well fed.           c. shown affection.
          b. educated.         d. pampered.

_____  3. The example that best shows Smiley's addiction to gambling with disregard
        for anything else is the bet he places on
        a. Dan'l Webster.              c. the mare.
        b. Andrew Jackson.             d. Parson Walker's wife.

_____  4. The stranger got the best of Jim Smiley by
        a. stepping on Dan'l Webster.
        b. feeding Dan'l Webster a load of flies.
        c. filling Dan'l Webster with lead.
        d. pretending that his frog was sick.

**C. Words to Know.** Write the letter of the best answer. (4 points each)

_____  1. Which is most likely to seem <u>interminable</u>?
        a. a two-minute talk     b. a five-hour movie     c. a half-hour sitcom

_____  2. If you <u>conjecture</u>, you are making a
        a. profit                b. mistake.              c. guess.

_____  3. Which person is most likely to be <u>infamous</u>?
        a. a bank robber         b. a magician            c. a singer

_____  4. A <u>garrulous</u> man is one who
        a. eats too much.        b. talks too much.       c. laughs too much.

_____  5. Which activity generally requires the most <u>finesse</u>?
        a. playing pool          b. hitchhiking           c. gardening

**D.** Answer **one** of the following questions based on your understanding of "The
Notorious Jumping Frog of Calaveras County." Write your answer on a separate
sheet of paper. (20 points)

1. One of the elements of a tall tale is the use of dialect, or local speech. How does Twain
   use dialect in "The Notorious Jumping Frog . . ."? How does dialect help underscore the
   differences in the personalities of the narrator and of Simon Wheeler and add to the
   humor of the story? Use examples from the story to support your ideas.

2. How does Twain personify Andrew Jackson and Dan'l Webster, and how does this
   personification influence your feelings toward Jim Smiley and the two animals?
   Use details from the story to support your ideas.

**E. Linking Literature to Life.** Answer the following question based on your own
experience and knowledge. Write your answer on a separate sheet of paper. (16 points)

In his novel *Pudd'nhead Wilson,* Twain wrote, "One of the most striking differences
between a cat and a lie is that a cat has only nine lives." What do you think Twain meant
by this remark? Do you agree or disagree?

# A Wagner Matinee (page 688)

# Selection Test

**A.** Think about the contrasting settings—the city of Boston and a farm in Nebraska—as described by Clark, who has strong feelings for both places. In the boxes at the top, describe the settings as Clark sees them. Then imagine how someone who loved the life of a frontier farmer might describe the two settings. In the boxes at the bottom, describe the settings as that farmer would probably see them. (8 points each)

|  | **Boston** | **Nebraska** |
|---|---|---|
| **1. Clark** | | |
| **2. Frontier Farmer** | | |

**B.** Write the letter of the best answer. This exercise is continued on the next page. (10 points each)

_____ 1. When Clark remembers his Aunt Georgiana's efforts to educate him, he feels
   a. grateful.
   b. unworthy.
   c. self-pitying.
   d. bitter and angry.

_____ 2. When Aunt Georgiana arrives in Boston, she is **most** concerned about
   a. recapturing her past.
   b. appearing sophisticated.
   c. her responsibilities at home.
   d. Clark's life since he left Nebraska.

......................................................................................................................................

_____ 3. The concert's effect on Aunt Georgiana could be described as all of the
following **except**
a. soothing.
b. inspiring.
c. depressing.
d. overwhelming

_____ 4. This story specifically makes the point that hopes and dreams
a. can come true.
b. can change over time.
c. can be denied but not forgotten.
d. usually have little to do with reality.

**C. Words to Know.** Write the letter of the best answer. (4 points each)

_____ 1. An example of <u>pious</u> behavior is
a. praying.　　　　b. playing.　　　　c. disobeying.

_____ 2. A parent is **most** likely to use <u>reproach</u> if a child has been
a. sick.　　　　b. rude.　　　　c. well-behaved.

_____ 3. At which age is a person **most** likely to be described as <u>callow</u>?
a. 15　　　　b. 35　　　　c. 55

_____ 4. To understand something <u>superficially</u> is to know it
a. slightly.　　　　b. fairly well.　　　　c. thoroughly.

_____ 5. A dog sounds **most** <u>pathetic</u> when it
a. yaps.　　　　b. growls.　　　　c. whimpers.

**D.** Answer **one** of the following questions based on your understanding of the story.
Write your answer on a separate sheet of paper. (12 points)

1. How do you think Aunt Georgiana feels about her life after the concert? Do you
think that feeling will last? Use details from the story and your own ideas about life
to support your answers.

2. What do you think Aunt Georgiana would say to a young person who believed love
could overcome all problems in a marriage? Use details from the story to support
your answer.

**E. Linking Literature to Life.** Answer the following question based on your own
experience and knowledge. Write your answer on a separate sheet of paper. (12 points)

The English novelist George Eliot said, "It seems to me we can never give up longing
and wishing while we are thoroughly alive. There are certain things we feel to be
beautiful and good, and we must hunger after them." Think of the "beautiful and good"
things that you "hunger after," and then write a personal response to Eliot's thought.

# The Legend of Gregorio Cortez (page 702)

# Selection Test

**A.** Think about the main message of this legend. Then make a mark in a box next to **one** of the quotations that you think supports the main message. In the box on the right, jot down reasons that support your choice. (20 points)

| | |
|---|---|
| ☐ "The courage we desire and prize is not the courage to die decently, but to live manfully." —Thomas Carlyle | |
| ☐ "Courage ought to be guided by skill, and skill armed by courage." —Sir Philip Sidney | |
| ☐ "Heroism feels and never reasons and therefore is always right." —Ralph Waldo Emerson | |
| ☐ "Heroism . . . is endurance for one moment more." —George Kennan | |
| ☐ "There are stars whose radiance is visible on earth though they have long been extinct. There are people whose brilliance continues to light the world though they are no longer among the living. These lights are particularly bright when the night is dark." —Hannah Senesh | |
| ☐ "Heroes take journeys, confront dragons, and discover the treasure of their own true selves." —Carol Pearson | |

**B.** Write the letter of the best answer. (10 points each)

_____ 1. Cortez is willing to do all of the following **except**
a. kill in self-defense.
b. lead an ordinary life.
c. desert the sorrel mare.
d. lie about breaking the law.

_____ 2. After Cortez kills the first sheriff, his first action is to protect
a. himself.          c. his wife.
b. Román.           d. his people.

_____ 3. Which of the following motivates Cortez to turn himself in to the governor?
a. physical exhaustion
b. emotional exhaustion
c. the desire to set the record straight
d. concern for his family and his people

**C.** Think about Cortez as a cultural hero. What cultural values are revealed through his everyday life before Román is shot? What cultural values are revealed through his words and actions after Román is shot? Jot down some of these values in the boxes below, choosing from those listed or using ideas of your own. (10 points each)

| | | | |
|---|---|---|---|
| courage | skill with animals | determination | honesty |
| modesty | respect for nature | hard work | endurance |
| cleverness | loyalty | courtesy | peaceableness |
| respectfulness | shrewdness | gentleness | lawfulness |

| **1. Cultural values revealed in Cortez's everyday life** | **2. Cultural values revealed through Cortez's crisis** |
|---|---|
| | |

**D.** Answer **one** of the following questions based on your understanding of the legend. Write your answer on a separate sheet of paper. (15 points)

1. How does Cortez compare with American tall tale heroes such as Paul Bunyan and Pecos Bill? Support your ideas with details about the heroes' values, abilities, and deeds.

2. What or who do you think contributes most to Cortez's downfall? Use details from the legend and your own ideas about his downfall to support your answer.

**E. Linking Literature to Life.** Answer the following question based on your own experience and knowledge. Write your answer on a separate sheet of paper. (15 points)

In this legend, men are said to live by the phrase, "I will break before I bend." Do you think that this code is a good one to lead one's life by? Why or why not?

# Unit Four: Conflict and Expansion

# Part Two Open-Book Test

**A.** Write the letter of the best answer to each question. (5 points each)

_____ 1. In "The Indian and the Hundred Cows," what lesson did the priest learn?
   a. Don't count your chickens before they hatch.
   b. A bird in the hand is worth two in the bush.
   c. A rolling stone gathers no moss.
   d. Say what you mean and mean what you say.

_____ 2. In "High Horse's Courting," the father's main purpose is to
   a. make High Horse look like a fool.
   b. determine whether High Horse is worthy of his daughter.
   c. gain as many horses as he can.
   d. let his daughter choose between High Horse and Red Deer.

_____ 3. What was ironic about Mark Twain's experiences in *Life on the Mississippi*?
   a. He expected piloting to be difficult, but it was easy.
   b. As soon as he learned to be a pilot, steamboats became obsolete.
   c. The more he learned about the river, the less he enjoyed it.
   d. He expected to dislike Mr. Bixby, but he came to admire him.

_____ 4. "The Notorious Jumping Frog . . ." is a tall tale because it uses
   a. exaggeration.              c. understatement.
   b. irony.                     d. satire.

**B.** Most of the selections in this part present glimpses of ways of life that have largely ceased to exist. On the line below, write the title of **one** selection from this part that you wish to discuss. In the boxes, write notes describing the custom or way of life that has become a thing of the past and your views on why its passing is or is not a good thing. (20 points)

**Selection:** _____

| Custom or Way of Life | Your Views on Its Passing |
|---|---|
|  |  |
|  |  |
|  |  |
|  |  |

**C.** Answer **two** of the following essay questions based on your understanding of the selections. Write your answers on a separate sheet of paper. (20 points each)

1. Compare and contrast Gregorio Cortez ("The Legend of Gregorio Cortez") as a cultural hero with any other person or character from the selections in this part whom you think might represent the values, experiences, and dreams of a culture.

2. Compare and contrast the young Mark Twain (*The Autobiography of Mark Twain*) and High Horse ("High Horse's Courting") as tricksters. Use details from the selections to support your ideas.

3. Some of the selections in this part present conflicts between groups of people or ways of life that resulted from westward expansion. Choose **one** of the selections and analyze the conflict it presents, the different views of the participants, and how the conflict is resolved.

**D.** Many of these selections convey a strong sense of "before and after." Sometimes the change occurs because of a defining moment or turning point in a person's life, while at other times it is a feeling brought about by the passage of time. Choose **two** of the selections in this part that you wish to discuss. In the boxes below, note the title of each selection. Then write notes describing the "before," what occurs to bring about the change, and the "after." (20 points)

| Selection: | Selection: |
|---|---|
| **Before:** | **Before:** |
| **What Brings About the Change:** | **What Brings About the Change:** |
| **After:** | **After:** |

# Selected Poems by Dickinson (page 750)

# Selection Open-Book Test

**A.** Read the examples of figurative language below. For each example, identify the figure of speech used. Then write notes to answer the question about its meaning. (10 points each)

| Example | Figure of Speech | Meaning |
|---|---|---|
| 1. *From* "'Hope' is the thing with feathers": "'Hope' is the thing with feathers— That perches in the soul— And sings the tune without the words—" <br><br> What does it say about hope? | | |
| 2. *From* "After great pain, a formal feeling comes": "A Quartz contentment, like a stone—" <br><br> What does it say about pain? | | |
| 3. *From* "Because I could not stop for Death": "Because I could not stop for Death— He kindly stopped for me—" <br><br> What does it say about death? | | |

**B.** Write the letter of the best answer. This exercise is continued on the next page. (5 points each)

_____ 1. What is the mood of "My life closed twice before its close"?
   a. sorrowful
   b. curious
   c. joyful
   d. indifferent

_____ 2. Who would the speaker of "Success is counted sweetest" be **most** likely to ask about the importance of winning an Olympic gold medal?
   a. a poet
   b. a competitor who has won a medal
   c. an Olympic judge
   d. a competitor who has failed to win a medal

_____ 3. "Much Madness is divinest Sense" suggests that a person will be considered insane or abnormal if he or she
   a. writes poetry.
   b. chooses to live alone.
   c. disagrees with the majority.
   d. prefers books to people.

_____ 4. Dickinson's main purpose in her letter to Thomas Higginson is to
   a. criticize his views of poetry.
   b. ask for his reactions to her poems.
   c. praise his views as a critic.
   d. ask him for a job.

**C.** Think about Emily Dickinson's style in these poems. For each element of style listed below, write an example from one of the poems. Then write notes describing the effect it achieves in the poem. (5 points each)

| Element of Style | Example | Effect |
|---|---|---|
| 1. Slant rhymes | | |
| 2. Use of dashes | | |
| 3. Unconventional capitalization | | |
| 4. Inverted syntax | | |

**D.** Answer **one** of the following questions based on your understanding of the poems. Write your answer on a separate sheet of paper. (15 points)

1. How do you think the speaker of "This is my letter to the World" feels about nature and about "the World"? Explain your answer.

2. How do you think the speaker of "Because I could not stop for Death" feels about death? Support your answer with details from the poem.

**E. Linking Literature to Life.** Answer the following question based on your own experience and knowledge. Write your answer on a separate sheet of paper. (15 points)

People sometimes refer to "communing with nature," that is, communicating or dealing with nature in close understanding. Does this make sense to you? What kind of message could a person get from nature?

# The Yellow Wallpaper (page 765)

## Selection Test

**A.** Circle the letter next to **one** of the quotations. Then consider two things—what the imagery suggests about the wallpaper and what it suggests about the narrator herself—and make notes in the boxes to reflect your thoughts. (10 points each)

a. "But in the places where it isn't faded and where the sun is just so—I can see a strange, provoking, formless sort of figure, that seems to skulk about behind that silly and conspicuous front design."

b. "But nobody could climb through that pattern—it strangles so; I think that is why it has so many heads.
     They get through, and then the pattern strangles them off and turns them upside down, and makes their eyes white!"

c. "Then I peeled off all the paper I could reach standing on the floor. It sticks horribly and the pattern just enjoys it! All those strangled heads and bulbous eyes and waddling fungus growths just shriek with derision!"

| **1. What does this image suggest about the wallpaper?** |
| --- |
|  |

| **2. What does this image suggest about the narrator?** |
| --- |
|  |

**B.** Write the letter of the best answer. This exercise is continued on the next page. (6 points each)

_____ 1. The narrator disagrees with medical specialists about the benefits or drawbacks of
a. physical exercise.          c. eating certain foods.
b. mental stimulation.        d. spending time with her baby.

_____ 2. John, the narrator's husband, believes that her condition is a result of
a. insanity.          c. pampering.
b. boredom.          d. nervousness.

_____ 3. The narrator believes that the woman behind the wallpaper pattern is
a. happy.          c. in danger.
b. trapped.          d. dangerous.

_____ 4. The narrator believes that John and his sister Jennie are being influenced by
       a. each other.        c. the narrator's mind.
       b. the wallpaper.     d. hatred for the narrator.

_____ 5. The narrator eventually wants to remain in the house in order to
       a. write.          c. study the wallpaper.
       b. spy on the garden.    d. avoid social interactions.

_____ 6. At the end of the story, the narrator believes that she is
       a. the woman in the wallpaper.
       b. the victim of the woman in the wallpaper.
       c. the protector of the woman in the wallpaper.
       d. the one who has trapped the woman in the wallpaper.

**C. Words to Know.** Write the letter of the best answer. (4 points each)

_____ 1. A person with perseverance is **least** likely to be called a
       a. brat.          b. quitter.        c. slow learner.

_____ 2. In which kind of dancing are the movements **most** likely to be described as undulating?
       a. hula dancing    b. break dancing    c. waltzing

_____ 3. A querulous person is someone who is
       a. timid.        b. inefficient.      c. hard to please.

_____ 4. You would laugh with derision at a suggestion that you thought was
       a. very witty.      b. ridiculous.     c. only mildly amusing.

_____ 5. It is impossible for an inanimate object to
       a. be moved.      b. make noise.     c. feel pain.

**D.** Answer **one** of the following questions based on your understanding of the story. Write your answer on a separate sheet of paper. (12 points)

1. Why do you think the narrator imagines what she does about the woman behind the pattern in the wallpaper?

2. To what extent do you think John is responsible for the narrator's mental breakdown? Support your opinion with details from the story.

**E. Linking Literature to Life.** Answer the following question based on your own experience and knowledge. Write your answer on a separate sheet of paper. (12 points)

Which do you think is worse—having too many interests and too many demands on one's time and energy or having too few interests and demands? Explain.

# The Story of an Hour (page 783)

# Selection Test

**A.** Think about the plot of this story. The first and last events are summarized in the chart below. Write a brief summary of each event in between in chronological order. (8 points each)

| Richards hears the news of the railroad disaster and confirms that Brently Mallard has died. |
| --- |
| **1.** |
| **2.** |
| **3.** |
| **4.** |
| **5.** |
| **Mrs. Mallard dies.** |

**B.** Write the letter of the best answer. (8 points each)

_____ 1. Mrs. Mallard's first reaction to the news is
      a. grief.          c. disbelief.
      b. relief.         d. bitterness.

_____ 2. Mrs. Mallard realizes that what is **most** important to her is
      a. love.          c. self-respect.
      b. security.     d. self-determination.

_____ 3. The realization that she has in her room changes Mrs. Mallard's view of
      a. herself.       c. the future.
      b. death.        d. her husband.

**C.** Answer **one** of the following questions based on your understanding of the story. Write your answer on a separate sheet of paper. (20 points)

1. How do you feel about the surprise ending to this story? Why do you suppose the author chose to end the story this way?

2. Why do you think Mrs. Mallard has difficulty, at first, recognizing the realization that she is free, and why does she resist it when she begins to recognize it?

**D. Linking Literature to Life.** Answer the following question based on your own experience and knowledge. Write your answer on a separate sheet of paper. (16 points)

Is marriage today a "better deal" for one gender than for the other? Explain your answer.

# Seventeen Syllables (page 788)

# Selection Test

**A.** Think about the two plot lines in this story and how they help to communicate its theme. Then write notes to describe the conflicts and climax of each plot line and the theme that is communicated through both plot lines. (10 points each)

| Plot Line Involving Mrs. Hayashi and Haiku | | Plot Line Involving Rosie and Jesus |
|---|---|---|
| | **1.**<br>**Conflicts** | |
| | **2.**<br>**Climax** | |
| | **3.**<br>**Theme** | |

**B.** Write the letter of the best answer. This exercise is continued on the next page. (5 points each)

_____ 1. Rosie's father would be **least** likely to describe his wife's sudden interest in haiku as
    a. surprising.        c. amusing.
    b. impractical.     d. harmless.

_____ 2. Which of the following do Rosie's mother and Mrs. Hayano, the woman with four daughters, **most** clearly have in common?
    a. They enjoy intellectual and artistic pursuits.
    b. They seem uncomfortable with people outside their families.
    c. They were significantly changed by the birth of their first child.
    d. Their interactions with their families seem limited to practical matters.

_____ 3. Who seems to find the visit between the Hayashi and Hayano families **least** enjoyable?
    a. the girls
    b. Rosie's father and mother
    c. Rosie's father and Mrs. Hayano
    d. Rosie's mother and Mr. Hayano

_____ 4. When Jesus comes out to the packing shed the day after their meeting, Rosie hides because she
   a. never wants to see him again.
   b. doesn't quite know how to react to him.
   c. is afraid that he will tell everyone about kissing her.
   d. wants to encourage his interest by playing "hard to get."

_____ 5. What is the **most** accurate parallel that can be drawn between the form of poetry that Rosie's mother writes and her career as a poet?
   a. They make people feel sad.
   b. They are difficult to understand.
   c. They are complete and satisfying.
   d. They are very short and condensed.

_____ 6. Rosie feels that her father's response to her mother's winning the poetry contest is
   a. deserved.
   b. frightening.
   c. acceptable.
   d. understandable.

**C. Words to Know.** Write the letter of the best answer. (4 points each)

_____ 1. Which is irrevocable?
   a. a license          b. a murder          c. an accusation

_____ 2. Someone who is adamant is
   a. mistaken.          b. unyielding.          c. overwhelmed.

_____ 3. Which answer to a question shows that a person is dubious?
   a. "No."          b. "Yes."          c. "I'm not sure."

_____ 4. Which person is **most** likely to behave in an unobtrusive way?
   a. a spy          b. a rock star          c. a lion tamer

_____ 5. A vacillating leader is **most** likely to make people feel
   a. inspired.          b. uncertain.          c. overwhelmed.

**D.** Answer **one** of the following questions based on your understanding of the story. Write your answer on a separate sheet of paper. (10 points)

1. Why do you think Mrs. Hayashi asks Rosie to promise that she will never marry? Why do you think Rosie gives her this promise?

2. Do you think that Mr. Hayashi's destruction of the picture is justified? Support your answer with details from the story and your own ideas about the situation and his motivations for destroying the picture.

**E. Linking Literature to Life.** Answer the following question based on your own experience and knowledge. Write your answer on a separate sheet of paper. (10 points)

What signs do you think can help a person to tell whether one's romantic partner would make a good spouse? Explain your ideas.

# Adolescence—III (page 802)

## Selection Open-Book Test

**A.** Circle the letters of **two** images you wish to discuss. Then, in each box on the left, jot down a feeling or idea that each image conveys. In the box on the right, identify the person, place, or thing that that image represents. You may identify the same person, place, or thing twice. (20 points)

a. "The dusky rows of tomatoes.
　As they glowed orange in sunlight
　And rotted in shadow, I too
　Grew orange and softer, swelling out
　Starched cotton slips."

b. "... I see my father coming toward us;
　He carries his tears in a bowl, ..."

c. "I wrapped scarred knees in dresses
　That once went to big-band dances;"

| Feeling or idea suggested | | Person, place, or thing associated with |
|---|---|---|
| | ➡ | |
| | ➡ | |

**B.** Write the letter of the best answer. This exercise is continued on the next page. (5 points each)

_____ 1. As she worked in the garden, the speaker felt that she was
　　a. growing up.　　　　　c. hoping for too much.
　　b. wasting her life.　　 d. losing her mind.

_____ 2. What did the speaker do in her room?
　　a. She cried about her life.
　　b. She vowed to run away.
　　c. She ironed her cotton slips.
　　d. She got dressed up.

_____ 3. The tone and mood of this poem change dramatically when the speaker
　　a. looks at the tomatoes.
　　b. thinks of Dotted Swiss.
　　c. envisions a lover.
　　d. sees her father.

_____ 4. The contrast between the speaker's dream lover and her father is best represented as
        a. love vs. honor.
        b. hope vs. despair.
        c. success vs. failure.
        d. night vs. day.

**C.** Think about how the sensory images help you visualize the real and imaginary worlds described in this poem. In the boxes below, write notes describing the images that appeal to sight, touch, and smell for each of the speaker's worlds. (10 points each)

| Sensory Image | 1. Real World | 2. Imaginary World |
|---|---|---|
| Sight | | |
| Touch | | |
| Smell | | |

**D.** Answer **one** of the following questions based on your understanding of the poem. Write your answer on a separate sheet of paper. (20 points)

1. What would you say is the strongest feeling conveyed in this poem? Why do you think the speaker has that feeling? Use details from the poem and your own ideas about adolescence to support your answer.

2. Write a paragraph or two contrasting the two men described in the final stanza of the poem. Consider their relationship to the speaker, the things she associates with them, what they offer her, their effect on her, and her attitude toward them.

**E. Linking Literature to Life.** Answer the following question based on your own experience and knowledge. Write your answer on a separate sheet of paper. (20 points)

Write a personal response to the following characterization of adolescence by "Miss Manners," the advice columnist Judith Martin.

"Show Miss Manners a grown-up who has happy memories of teenage years, with their endless round of merry-making and dancing the night away, and Miss Manners will show you a person who has either no heart or no memory."

# I Stand Here Ironing (page 806)

# Selection Test

**A.** Was the narrator a "good mother" to Emily? Read the list of five things that parents might be expected to do for their children. Under each one, write an example to show how the narrator did or did not do these things for Emily. In the boxes on the right, write notes explaining how each example influences your judgment of whether or not the narrator was a good mother. (6 points each)

| What Parents Should Do | Your Judgment |
| --- | --- |
| 1. Show affection<br><br>Example: | |
| 2. Make the child feel safe and secure<br><br>Example: | |
| 3. Encourage creativity and independence<br><br>Example: | |
| 4. Teach self-discipline<br><br>Example: | |
| 5. Promote good health<br><br>Example: | |

**B.** Write the letter of the best answer. This exercise is continued on the next page. (5 points each)

_____ 1. As the mother narrates, she is
   a. writing a letter to Emily.
   b. having coffee with a friend.
   c. tending to her physical appearance.
   d. tending to her family responsibilities.

_____ 2. Which of the following does the narrator suggest has had the **least**
influence on Emily's life?
a. world events          c. the narrator herself
b. Emily's father        d. the fact that Emily's father abandoned the family

_____ 3. How does the narrator view her own behavior during Emily's childhood?
a. She thinks her behavior was unforgivable.
b. She thinks she made a few minor mistakes.
c. She thinks she made some serious mistakes.
d. She thinks that no one could have done better.

_____ 4. As a teenager, Emily seems to have found some comfort in
a. performing.
b. her schoolwork.
c. being strikingly beautiful.
d. helping her mother with the other children.

**C. Words to Know.** Write the letter of the best answer. (4 points each)

_____ 1. You can expect articulate people to be good with
a. maps.                b. tools.              c. words.

_____ 2. A ravaged city is **most** likely to be the result of
a. war.                 b. urban planning.     c. population growth.

_____ 3. A denunciation is an expression of
a. regret.              b. blame.              c. suspicion.

_____ 4. In the time of King Arthur's Court, who held a position of prestige?
a. a dragon             b. a knight            c. a peasant

_____ 5. A coherent argument is one that is easy to
a. mock.                b. dismiss.            c. comprehend.

**D.** Answer **one** of the following questions based on your understanding of the story.
Write your answer on a separate sheet of paper. (15 points)

1. Who do you see as a victim in this story—the narrator, Emily, both characters, or
neither of them? Use your own ideas about life and details from the story to
support your opinion.

2. Why can't the narrator account for Emily's success as a comic actress? Why do you think
she says of her daughter, "She has much to her and probably little will come of it"?

**E. Linking Literature to Life.** Answer the following question based on your own
experience and knowledge. Write your answer on a separate sheet of paper. (15 points)

How responsible do you think adults are for the way that the children they raise turn
out? In your answer, explain some things about adults that you think are or are not heavily
influenced by the way that they were raised.

# Unit Five: The Changing Face of America
# Part One Open-Book Test

**A.** Write the answer to each question on the lines. (5 points each)

1. What is the theme of Dickinson's poem "Success is counted sweetest"?

_____

_____

2. Toward the end of "The Story of an Hour," Mrs. Mallard "breathed a quick prayer that life might be long." What is ironic about her prayer?

_____

_____

3. In "Adolescence—III," what does the speaker dream about?

_____

_____

4. What is effective about the use of interior monologue as a narrative technique in "I Stand Here Ironing"?

_____

_____

**B.** Think about how imagery is used in the poems in this part to convey feelings and ideas. (20 points)

- On the line, write the title of **one** poem you wish to discuss.
- In the box on the left, identify an image from that poem.
- In the box on the right, jot down the sense or senses to which that image appeals.
- In the box on the bottom, jot down what the image makes you think about.

**Poem:** _____

| The image of | appeals to the sense or senses of |
|---|---|
| | |
| **and makes me think about** | |
| | |

**C.** Answer **two** of the following essay questions based on your understanding of the selections. Write your answers on a separate sheet of paper. (20 points each)

1. Think about the roles played by the girls or women in these selections. Choose any **three** girls or women and discuss any similarities you see among their lives and roles.

2. Many of the selections in this part concern the idea of loss. Choose **two** selections in which something is lost, given up, or left behind. What is lost in each selection, and how? What are the effects of that loss? Support your answers.

3. Which girl or woman in these selections do you think is most able to determine her own destiny? Which is least able? Use details from the selections and your own ideas about destiny to support your choices.

**D.** Think about the consequences of important actions taken during the lives of the people in these selections. For each group of people, circle the letter of **one** person you wish to discuss. In the box on the left, note an important action that affects or has affected that person's life. In the boxes on the right, note a consequence that action has for that person and for someone else. Remember that consequences can be either good or bad. (20 points)

**Group A**

    a. the narrator's husband in "The Yellow Wallpaper"    c. Mr. Hayashi in "Seventeen Syllables"

    b. Mr. Mallard in "The Story of an Hour"    d. Emily's father in "I Stand Here Ironing"

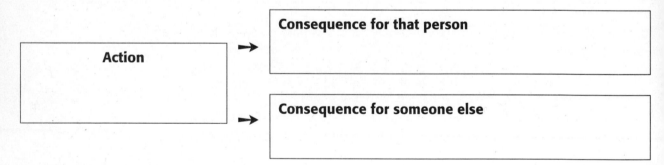

| Action | → | Consequence for that person |
|---|---|---|
|  | → | Consequence for someone else |

**Group B**

    a. the narrator in "The Yellow Wallpaper"    c. Mrs. Hayashi in "Seventeen Syllables"

    b. Mrs. Mallard in "The Story of an Hour"    d. the narrator in "I Stand Here Ironing"

| Action | → | Consequence for that person |
|---|---|---|
|  | → | Consequence for someone else |

# Chicago/Lucinda Matlock (page 824)

# Selection Open-Book Test

**A.** Make a mark in the small box next to the **one** quotation with which you think Lucinda Matlock would agree. Then, in the box at the bottom, write notes supporting your choice. (20 points)

| | |
|---|---|
| | **"In the time of your life, live."—William Saroyan** |
| | **"Life, be it happy or unhappy, fortunate or unfortunate, is the only good man possesses, and he who does not love life is unworthy of life."—Casanova** |
| | |

**B.** Write the letter of the best answer. (10 points each)

_____ 1. The speaker of "Chicago" admits that the city is all of the following **except**
        a. cruel.           b. weary.           c. corrupt.

_____ 2. The attitude of the speaker of "Chicago" toward the city could **best** be described as
        a. proud.           b. apologetic.        c. pessimistic.

_____ 3. Lucinda Matlock views her own death with
        a. regret.           b. acceptance.       c. mixed emotions.

_____ 4. For which of the following does Lucinda Matlock show contempt?
        a. her life           b. life in general       c. human weakness

**C.** Answer **one** of the following questions based on your understanding of the poems. Write your answer on a separate sheet of paper. (20 points)

1. The people of Chicago sometimes call that city by the epithet "City of the Big Shoulders" (line 5). What is there about this poem, and about that epithet in particular, that would encourage Chicagoans to claim it as a description of their city?

2. Explain Lucinda Matlock's meaning in the line, "It takes life to love Life." Do you think that this is a lesson she learned in life or after death? Explain.

**D. Linking Literature to Life.** Answer the following question based on your own experience and knowledge. Write your answer on a separate sheet of paper. (20 points)

Identify a person or place that you think of as being truly alive. What is it about that person or place that gives you this impression? Why do you think that quality isn't more common than it is?

Name _____    Date _____

# Selected Poems by Robinson (page 830)

# Selection Open-Book Test

**A.** Think about the methods of characterization that Robinson used to portray Richard Cory and Miniver Cheevy. For each method of characterization listed below, write notes describing what information is revealed about the main character of each poem. (10 points each)

| Method of Characterization | "Richard Cory" | "Miniver Cheevy" |
|---|---|---|
| 1. Physical description | | |
| 2. Character's own actions | | |
| 3. Other characters' thoughts and feelings or those of the speaker | | |

**B.** Write the letter of the best answer. This exercise is continued on the next page. (6 points each)

_____ 1. In "Richard Cory," the townspeople seem to equate wealth and an attractive appearance with

a. innocence.                    c. snobbishness.
b. happiness.                    d. corruption.

_____ 2. At the end of the poem, the townspeople's envy of Richard Cory is revealed to be

a. misplaced.                    c. petty.
b. insincere.                    d. accurate.

_____ 3. Which sentence **best** states the theme of "Richard Cory"?
　　　　　a. Death comes to those who least expect it.
　　　　　b. Beauty is only skin deep.
　　　　　c. Appearances can be deceiving.
　　　　　d. Stop to smell the roses.

_____ 4. The speaker's tone in "Miniver Cheevy" can **best** be described as
　　　　　a. oppressive.
　　　　　b. lively.
　　　　　c. angry.
　　　　　d. sarcastic.

_____ 5. At the end of the poem, what happens to Miniver Cheevy?
　　　　　a. He realizes that regrets are futile.
　　　　　b. He decides to live only for the future.
　　　　　c. He vows to live in the present.
　　　　　d. He is filled with regret and continues to drink.

**C.** Answer **one** of the following questions based on your understanding of "Richard Cory" and "Miniver Cheevy." Write your answer on a separate sheet of paper. (20 points)

1. In about 1900, a Kentucky mountain woman said, "It's a lot worse to be soul-hungry than to be body-hungry." How does this statement apply to each of these two poems? Use details from the poems to support your ideas.

2. What philosophy of life does each of these poems suggest to you? What advice would you give to the townspeople in "Richard Cory" and to Miniver Cheevy to reflect that philosophy of life?

**D. Linking Literature to Life.** Answer the following question based on your own experience and knowledge. Write your answer on a separate sheet of paper. (20 points)

　Both poems deal with feelings of material and personal failure. At some point in life, everyone experiences these emotions. What advice would you give to someone who feels as if he or she has not "measured up" or has failed to be successful in some way?

## Selected Poems by Dunbar (page 835)

# Selection Open-Book Test

**A.** Think about the use of symbolism in "We Wear the Mask" and "Sympathy." Look at the list of symbols from the poems. In the boxes, write notes describing what each symbol represents and what the speaker is suggesting by using that particular symbol. (15 points each)

### 1. "We Wear the Mask"

| Symbol | What It Represents | What It Suggests |
|---|---|---|
| Line 1: mask | | |
| Line 4: hearts | | |
| Line 10: clay | | |

### 2. "Sympathy"

| Symbol | What It Represents | What It Suggests |
|---|---|---|
| Line 1: caged bird | | |
| Line 4: cruel bars | | |
| Line 10: heart's deep core | | |

**B.** Write the letter of the best answer. This exercise is continued on the next page. (5 points each)

_____ 1. The speaker of "We Wear the Mask" would **most** likely describe the world as a place of great
   a. variety.
   b. hostility.
   c. promise.
   d. compassion.

Name _____     Date _____

2. If you were to ask the people who wear the mask what is troubling them, what response would you be **most** likely to get?
   a. "None of your business!"
   b. "Nothing, I'm fine, thank you."
   c. "I'm so glad you asked."
   d. "I'd like to tell you, but I can't explain it clearly."

3. The people who wear the mask can be relied on almost always to
   a. tell the truth.
   b. appear to be strong.
   c. believe whatever they hear.
   d. stand up for the rights of others.

4. The tone of the speaker in "Sympathy" can **best** be described as
   a. frustrated.          c. lighthearted.
   b. satisfied.           d. apathetic.

5. The caged bird's song is **best** described as one of
   a. joy.                 c. pleading.
   b. glee.                d. sadness.

6. You can infer that because the bird is caged, it
   a. is afraid to live independently.
   b. wants and needs confinement.
   c. is not able to live freely or express itself.
   d. cannot cope with self-expression.

**C.** Answer **one** of the following questions based on your understanding of "We Wear the Mask" and "Sympathy." Write your answer on a separate sheet of paper. (20 points)

1. What do you think the speaker of "We Wear the Mask" means by the question, "Why should the world be otherwise, / In counting all our tears and sighs?" Do you agree with the speaker? Support your answers with reference to the poem and your own life experiences.

2. Some of Dunbar's most popular and influential poems attempt to teach white America about the struggle that African Americans face. What do you think Dunbar is trying to explain to white America about the plight of African Americans in the poems "Sympathy" and "We Wear the Mask"? Use examples from the poems to support your answers.

**D. Linking Literature to Life.** Answer the following question based on your own experience and knowledge. Write your answer on a separate sheet of paper. (20 points)

In both poems, the speaker feels that he must hide his inner feelings and cannot express himself freely. What are some feelings that you think people of your age and situation in life tend to keep hidden? Why do you think they tend to hide those particular feelings?

# Winter Dreams (page 840)

# Selection Test

**A.** What judgments did you make about Judy Jones and Dexter Green at different points in this story? Did you like them as people? Do you think they made the right decisions for themselves and for others? Read the list of events in the boxes on the left and think about what happened at the time. In the boxes on the right, write notes explaining the judgments you made about both characters after each event. (6 points each)

| Event | Judgments About the Characters |
|---|---|
| 1. Judy Jones hits T. A. Hedrick with a golf ball and plays through Dexter's group. | |
| 2. Dexter goes to Judy's house for dinner and kisses her afterward. | |
| 3. Dexter asks Judy to marry him, but she doesn't really respond. | |
| 4. Dexter, now engaged to Irene, sees Judy at a dance and goes home with her. | |
| 5. Judy and Dexter are engaged, but Judy breaks the engagement after one month. | |

**B.** Write the letter of the best answer. This exercise is continued on the next page. (5 points each)

_____ 1. Which of the following **best** describes Dexter's family at the time that he first meets Judy?
 a. penniless       b. lower class       c. middle class       d. upper class

_____ 2. Which of the following **best** describes Judy the first time that Dexter sees her?

      a. shy          b. dull          c. happy          d. spoiled

_____ 3. Judy's feelings for the men she dates tend to be all of the following **except**

      a. shallow.          b. wavering.          c. concealed.          d. passionate.

_____ 4. Which aspect of Irene, the woman to whom Dexter becomes engaged, is **most** similar to that of Judy?

      a. her class          c. her appearance

      b. her behavior          d. her feelings for Dexter

_____ 5. Which of the following **best** describes Judy as Mrs. Lud Simms at the end of the story?

      a. happy          b. settled          c. alluring          d. suicidal

**C. Words to Know.** Write the letter of the best answer. (4 points each)

_____ 1. A surfeit of food would make a person feel

      a. hungry.          b. contented.          c. uncomfortable.

_____ 2. People are **most** likely to behave in a malicious way in order to get

      a. even.          b. hired.          c. a date.

_____ 3. Who is **most** likely to want to sully a candidate's image?

      a. a comedian          b. an opponent          c. the candidate

_____ 4. A person's face is **most** likely to show a grimace if he or she is

      a. hurt.          b. bored.          c. happy.

_____ 5. People who dislike being in a precarious position want to be sure they are

      a. safe.          b. famous.          c. respected.

**D.** Answer **one** of the following questions based on your understanding of the story. Write your answer on a separate sheet of paper. (10 points)

1. What does Dexter lose besides Judy, and why is this more painful than the loss of Judy? What theme or themes are related through this loss?

2. What do you think Judy wants from Dexter? Does she get what she wants from him? Explain your answers.

**E. Linking Literature to Life.** Answer the following question based on your own experience and knowledge. Write your answer on a separate sheet of paper. (15 points)

Do you think that it is possible to be happy without also being content? Is it possible to be content without also being happy? Explain your answers.

# America and I (page 863)

# Selection Test

**A.** Think about the analogy drawn in this story between the Pilgrims' and the narrator's experiences in America. Then write notes to answer the questions in the boxes below. (5 points each)

| 1. What did they leave behind in their old countries? | 2. What did they expect life in America to be like? | 3. How did they respond to hardship in America? |
|---|---|---|
| **The Pilgrims** | **The Pilgrims** | **The Pilgrims** |
| **The narrator** | **The narrator** | **The narrator** |

▼                           ▼                           ▼

| 4. What does this analogy help the narrator to understand about her life as an American? |
|---|
|  |

**B.** Write the letter of the best answer. This exercise is continued on the next page. (6 points each)

_____ 1. The one thing the narrator wants **most** from her work is the ability to
   a. enjoy herself.
   b. support herself.
   c. express herself.
   d. challenge herself.

_____ 2. Why did the narrator prefer her second job to her first job?
   a. She wasn't taken advantage of at her second job.
   b. The second job increased her standard of living.
   c. The second job allowed her more time to herself.
   d. The second job was more like the work she did in Russia.

_____ 3. From her second job in America, the narrator learned
        a. skills she needed to get a better job.
        b. not to protest her employers' policies.
        c. how to earn the respect of her employers.
        d. that the way to get ahead was to work hard.

_____ 4. The narrator's third job helps her to do all of the following **except**
        a. achieve peace of mind.     c. become fluent in English.
        b. appear more American.     d. increase her standard of living.

_____ 5. From reading American history, the narrator comes to see America as being
        a. savage.               c. capable of change.
        b. doomed.             d. too stuck in its ways.

**C. Words to Know.** Write the letter of the best answer. (4 points each)

_____ 1. To <u>delve</u> into a subject suggests that one's interest in it is
        a. intense.          b. shallow.         c. secretive.

_____ 2. People are **most** likely to <u>simper</u> when they feel
        a. sick.            b. uneasy.         c. panicky.

_____ 3. People tend to be <u>avid</u> eaters if they are
        a. full.            b. picky.          c. very hungry.

_____ 4. A person with an <u>indomitable</u> spirit is
        a. kindly.          b. unbeatable.         c. wishy-washy.

_____ 5. A victim of <u>pestilence</u> would be **most** likely to need the services of a
        a. doctor.          b. lawyer.         c. banker.

**D.** Answer **one** of the following questions based on your understanding of the story. Write your answer on a separate sheet of paper. (15 points)

1. What are some of the reasons that the narrator found working as a servant for an American family unsatisfactory? Do you find her reaction, considering her situation at the time, to be reasonable? Explain.

2. The narrator expresses her desire "to give something, to do something, to be something." By the end of the story, does she seem to have fulfilled this desire? Support your answer with details from the story and your own ideas.

**E. Linking Literature to Life.** Answer the following question based on your own experience and knowledge. Write your answer on a separate sheet of paper. (15 points)

The narrator of this story says, "The Americans of to-morrow, the America that is every day nearer coming to be, will be too wise, too open-hearted, too friendly-handed, to let the least last-comer at their gates knock in vain with his gifts unwanted." Do you think this is true of America today? Does it seem as if it might be true of America in the near future? Explain your opinions.

# In the American Society (page 877)

# Selection Test

**A.** Think about what Mr. and Mrs. Chang's ambitions reveal about the kind of people they are and what is important to them. Then, in each box at the top, identify one ambition of the character. In each box at the bottom, note something that the ambition reveals about him or her. (8 points each)

| 1. Mr. Chang | 2. Mrs. Chang |
|---|---|
| His ambition | Her ambition |
| What the ambition reveals | What the ambition reveals |

**B.** Write the letter of the best answer. (5 points each)

_____ 1. Mrs. Chang characterizes her husband's attitude toward his employees as
      a. criminal.             c. tyrannical.
      b. Chinese.             d. distinctly American.

_____ 2. Mr. Chang believes that his good fortune obligates him to
      a. put up with abuse.
      b. help the less fortunate.
      c. uphold Americans laws.
      d. carry himself with an air of superiority.

_____ 3. How does Mr. Chang respond to the disappearance of Booker and Cedric?
      a. He is angry.          c. He is disappointed.
      b. He is relieved.       d. He doesn't really care.

_____ 4. Mr. Chang's wife and daughters respond to his behavior at the party with
      a. anger.               c. silent gloom.
      b. approval.            d. embarrassment.

**C.** Think about the structure of the story. Then, in the boxes at the top, note what each section focuses on. In the box at the bottom, write notes to answer the question. (8 points each)

| 1. Section One: "His Own Society" | 2. Section Two: "In the American Society" |
|---|---|
|  |  |

| 3. How might the effect of the story be different if the two parts were reversed? |
|---|
|  |

**D. Words to Know.** Write the letter of the best answer. (4 points each)

_____ 1. Someone's <u>forte</u> would be considered one of his or her
   a. peculiarities.      b. strong points.      c. shortcomings.

_____ 2. If you were trying to <u>cajole</u> someone, you would use
   a. threats.      b. reason.      c. compliments.

_____ 3. A fictional character known for his <u>largesse</u> is
   a. Daffy Duck.      b. Santa Claus.      c. Paul Bunyan.

_____ 4. To <u>intercede</u> is to make an effort to
   a. aid someone.      b. avoid someone.      c. annoy someone.

_____ 5. A person's <u>panache</u> would be **most** apparent in his or her choice of
   a. books.      b. friends.      c. clothes.

**E.** Answer **one** of the following questions based on your understanding of the story. Write your answer on a separate sheet of paper. (10 points)

1. At the end of the story, Mr. Chang says, "You girls are good swimmers . . . Not like me." How does this statement relate to the theme of the story?

2. What role does Mr. Chang play in the rise and fall of the restaurant's business? Support your answer with details from the story.

**F. Linking Literature to Life.** Answer the following question based on your own experience and knowledge. Write your answer on a separate sheet of paper. (10 points)

Identify **two** qualities or characteristics that strike you as being particularly American. Explain your choices.

Name _____     Date _____

# Defining the Grateful Gesture/Refugee Ship (page 894)

# Selection Open-Book Test

**A.** Think about how ideas in a poem help to reinforce or support the theme. In the boxes below, write notes describing the theme of each poem. Under each theme, write three ideas or examples from the poem that support the theme. (15 points each)

## 1. "Defining the Grateful Gesture"

| Theme: | | |
|---|---|---|
| **Ideas That Support the Theme** | | |
| a. | b. | c. |

## 2. "Refugee Ship"

| Theme: | | |
|---|---|---|
| **Ideas That Support the Theme** | | |
| a. | b. | c. |

**B.** Write the letter of the best answer. This exercise is continued on the next page. (6 points each)

_____ 1. In "Defining the Grateful Gesture," the main function of meals in the mother's childhood home seems to have been to
   a. provide pleasure.
   b. provide nourishment.
   c. promote family intimacy.
   d. discuss events of the day.

_____ 2. In "Defining the Grateful Gesture," the last stanza of the poem strongly suggests that the mother's efforts had
   a. little effect on her children.
   b. the desired effect on her children.
   c. an effect different from the one desired.
   d. no effect at all on her children.

_____  3. In "Defining the Grateful Gesture," which of the following best describes
the speaker's feeling toward her mother?
a. affection                    c. appreciation
b. devotion                    d. resentment

_____  4. In "Refugee Ship," the speaker suggests that she
a. does not communicate with her grandmother.
b. wishes she and her mother would move.
c. longs to travel to Mexico.
d. does not want to know about her heritage.

_____  5. "Like wet cornstarch, I slide past my grandmother's eyes" is an example of
a. irony.                       c. simile.
b. personification.            d. alliteration.

**C.** Answer **one** of the following questions based on your understanding of "Defining the
Grateful Gesture" and "Refugee Ship." Write your answer on a separate sheet of paper.
(20 points)

1. In "Defining the Grateful Gesture," explain what the speaker's mother expects of
her children and why. Do you think that her expectations are reasonable? Why or
why not?

2. How would you describe the mood of "Refugee Ship"? How does the poet create
that mood?

**D. Linking Literature to Life.** Answer the following question based on your own
experience and knowledge. Write your answer on a separate sheet of paper. (20 points)

What are some important distinctions between feeling grateful for what one has and
feeling guilty about what one has? Explain your opinions.

# Unit Five: The Changing Face of America

# Part Two Open-Book Test

**A.** Write the letter of the best answer to each question. (5 points each)

_____ 1. Both "Richard Cory" and "Miniver Cheevy" emphasize themes of
a. failure and alienation.    c. money and the good life.
b. self-esteem and success.    d. attitude and accomplishment.

_____ 2. Both "We Wear the Mask" and "Sympathy" use symbolism to express ideas about the
a. difficulty of writing about the truth.
b. poet's desire for more education.
c. struggles faced by African Americans.
d. joys of everyday life.

_____ 3. In "Winter Dreams," what does Dexter lose at the end of the story?
a. his money    c. a chain of laundries
b. Judy Jones    d. his youthful dreams

_____ 4. "In the American Society" and "Refugee Ship" both concern the difficulties of
a. trying to speak English.
b. becoming successful in America.
c. living in two different cultures.
d. meeting new friends.

**B.** Choose **two** selections from this part that emphasize an aspect of American culture—one positive and one negative. In the boxes below, write the title of each selection you choose and the aspect of American culture that is emphasized. Then explain how the people in the selection are affected by that aspect of the culture and whether the effect is positive or negative. (20 points)

| **Title:** | **Title:** |
|---|---|
| **Aspect of American Culture:** | **Aspect of American Culture:** |
| **How People Are Affected:** | **How People Are Affected:** |

**C.** Answer **two** of the following essay questions based on your understanding of the selections. Write your answers on a separate sheet of paper. (20 points each)

1. Choose a person or group of people from this part for whom the American Dream appears to be an illusion and a person or group for whom that dream seems to be a reality. Support your choices with reference to the selection or selections and your own ideas about the American Dream.

2. Which person from this part do you think best represents what it means to be an American? Which person do you think least represents this concept? Support your answers with reference to the selection or selections and your own ideas about what it means to be an American.

3. Choose **two** people from different selections and explain what you think matters most in life to them. How does the thing that matters most to each of them affect their lives and their dreams?

**D.** Think about the people in this part as "insiders" and "outsiders." (20 points)

- On the line at the top of each set of boxes, write the name of an "insider" or "outsider" from this part.
- In each box at the top, note the group or culture into which the person is welcomed or accepted or from which the person is excluded or rejected.
- In each box at the bottom, write notes explaining why the person is considered an insider or an outsider by that group or culture.

**Insider:** _____    **Outsider:** _____

| **Group into which this person is welcomed:** | **Group from which this person is excluded:** |
|---|---|
| | |
| **Why is this person welcomed or accepted?** | **Why is this person excluded or rejected?** |
| | |

# Selected Poems by Hughes (page 924)

# Selection Open-Book Test

**A.** Think about how the theme and the speaker's tone contribute to the mood in each of these poems. In the boxes below, write notes describing the theme and the tone for each poem. Then explain how those two elements help establish the mood, which is the feeling you have as you read the poem. (15 points each)

| Poem | Theme | Tone | Mood |
|---|---|---|---|
| 1. "I, Too" | | | |
| 2. "Harlem" | | | |
| 3. "The Weary Blues" | | | |

**B.** Write the letter of the best answer. This exercise is continued on the next page. (5 points each)

_____ 1. In lines 3 and 16 of "I, Too," the word *they* most likely refers to
   a. white Americans.
   b. the lower class.
   c. other poets.
   d. African Americans.

_____ 2. For the musician in "The Weary Blues," playing the blues all night seems to be
   a. inspiring.
   b. boring.
   c. draining.
   d. refreshing.

_____ 3. In "Harlem," the "dream deferred" **most** likely refers to the
a. hopes and aspirations of people who have been oppressed.
b. poet's vision of equality among peoples of all nations.
c. city's plan to rebuild and revitalize Harlem.
d. state of peacefulness that prevails in Harlem.

**C.** Answer **one** of the following questions based on your understanding of these three poems by Langston Hughes. Write your answer on a separate sheet of paper. (20 points)

1. Reread the similes used in the poem "Harlem." What do all the similes have in common? How is the last line of the poem different from the other lines? How does the last line change the mood of the poem?

2. How does the mood of the blues verses in "The Weary Blues" compare with the overall mood of the poem? Do you think the moods are similar or different? Explain your answer.

**D. Linking Literature to Life.** Answer the following question based on your own experience and knowledge. Write your answer on a separate sheet of paper. (20 points)

Jazz, a distinct art form with a strong African heritage, has influenced musicians and writers from many cultures. What kind of music influences you? What kind of effect does music have on your life and on the lives of your friends, and why?

# When the Negro Was in Vogue (page 932)

# Selection Test

**A.** Think about Langston Hughes's tone in this essay. Read the excerpts below. Then write notes explaining how the use of different words and phrases in each excerpt reveals his attitude toward the events he is writing about. (20 points each)

| Excerpt 1 |
|---|
| Nor did ordinary Negroes like the growing influx of whites toward Harlem after sundown, flooding the little cabarets and bars where formerly only colored people laughed and sang, and where now the strangers were given the best ringside tables to sit and stare at the Negro customers—like amusing animals in a zoo.<br><br>   The Negroes said: "We can't go downtown and sit and stare at you in your clubs. You won't even let us in your clubs." But they didn't say it out loud—for Negroes are practically never rude to white people. |

| How Words and Phrases Reveal the Writer's Tone |
|---|
|  |

| Excerpt 2 |
|---|
| Some of the small clubs, however, had people like Gladys Bentley, who was something worth discovering in those days, before she got famous, acquired an accompanist, specially written material, and conscious vulgarity. But for two or three amazing years, Miss Bentley sat, and played a big piano all night long, literally all night, without stopping—singing songs like "The St. James Infirmary," from ten in the evening until dawn . . . sliding from one song to another, with a powerful and continuous underbeat of jungle rhythm. |

| How Words and Phrases Reveal the Writer's Tone |
|---|
|  |

**B.** Write the letter of the best answer. (5 points each)

_____ 1. Hughes felt that the music played in Harlem was
   a. boring.
   b. exciting.
   c. disappointing.
   d. repetitive.

_____ 2. You can conclude that Hughes felt the house-rent parties were
   a. commercialized and exploitative.
   b. too exclusive for most people in Harlem.
   c. rowdy and destructive.
   d. more fun than going to the clubs.

_____ 3. According to Hughes, how did most "Negroes" of the time feel about whites coming to Harlem?
   a. resentful
   b. proud
   c. pleased
   d. depressed

_____ 4. What does Hughes imply that he knew about the "period when the Negro was in vogue"?
   a. Its main purpose was to make as much money as possible.
   b. It would change Harlem forever.
   c. It would not last long.
   d. Its main purpose was to encourage integration.

**C.** Answer **one** of the following questions based on your understanding of "When the Negro Was in Vogue." Write your answer on a separate sheet of paper. (20 points)

1. What is the mood of "When the Negro Was in Vogue"? In other words, as you read the essay, how did you feel about Harlem and the "period when the Negro was in vogue"? Support your answer with reference to the essay.

2. A major element of the tone in this essay is Hughes's choice of words. Compare Hughes's word choice in the first paragraph to his word choice in the last paragraph. Which paragraph is more serious and formal? Why, do you think, does his choice of words differ from the beginning to the end? Use examples to support your answer.

**D. Linking Literature to Life.** Answer the following question based on your own experience and knowledge. Write your answer on a separate sheet of paper. (20 points)

Why, do you think, does Hughes seem sarcastic throughout most of this essay? Toward what or whom does he direct his sarcasm? Do you think his feelings are justified? Explain.

# My City/Any Human to Another (page 940)

## Selection Open-Book Test

**A.** In the box on the left, jot down the question that is raised in the octave of "My City."
In the box on the right, jot down the answer given in the sestet. (8 points each)

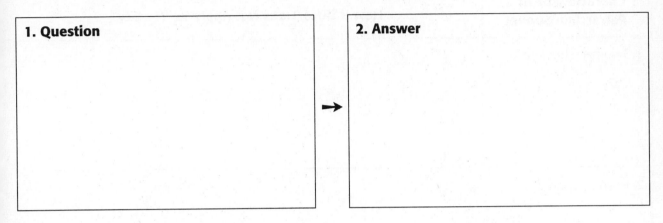

**1. Question**

→

**2. Answer**

**B.** Write the letter of the best answer. (5 points each)

_____ 1. Which **least** helps to identify "My City" as a Petrarchan sonnet?
　　　　　a. the rhyme scheme of the octave
　　　　　b. the division of the poem into two parts
　　　　　c. the question that is raised in the octave
　　　　　d. the existence of an octave and a sestet

_____ 2. "Any Human to Another" implies that sorrow is all of the following **except**
　　　　　a. diverse.　　　　　c. unavoidable.
　　　　　b. universal.　　　　d. impossible to share.

_____ 3. "Any Human to Another" compares sorrow to all of the following **except**
　　　　　a. an arrow.　　　　　c. a sharp blade.
　　　　　b. a "little tent."　　　d. the mixing of "sea and river."

_____ 4. With which of the following quotations would the speaker of "Any Human
　　　　　to Another" be **least** likely to agree?
　　　　　a. "Every man for himself."—John Heywood
　　　　　b. "I am a man, and whatever concerns humanity is of interest to me."
　　　　　　　—Terence
　　　　　c. "True freedom is to share / All the chains our brothers wear."
　　　　　　　—James Russell Lowell
　　　　　d. "No man is an island, entire of itself; every man is a piece of the continent,
　　　　　　　a part of the main."—John Donne

**C.** Does "My City" fit the form of a Petrarchan sonnet? Read the characteristics of a Petrarchan sonnet listed below. In the boxes on the right, write notes describing how "My City" fits or does not fit each characteristic. (8 points each)

| Characteristic of a Petrarchan Sonnet | How It Does/Does Not Apply to "My City" |
|---|---|
| 1. Two-part structure | |
| 2. Rhyme scheme | |
| 3. Meter | |

**D.** Answer **one** of the following questions based on your understanding of the poems. Write your answer on a separate sheet of paper. (20 points)

1. What are some reasons that Manhattan appeals to the speaker of "My City"? Support your ideas with details from the poem.

2. The title of "Any Human to Another" is a clue to its meaning. What is Cullen's statement on the topic of human brotherhood? What do the lines "My sorrow must be laid / On your head like a crown" add to this idea?

**E. Linking Literature to Life.** Answer the following question based on your own experience and knowledge. Write your answer on a separate sheet of paper. (20 points)

Do you think that the various peoples of the world are more alike than they are different? Defend your opinion.

# If We Must Die/A Black Man Talks of Reaping (page 945)

## Selection Open-Book Test

**A.** In the boxes below, jot down the main point that is made in each quatrain and in the couplet of the sonnet "If We Must Die." (10 points each)

| 1. First quatrain | 2. Second quatrain |
|---|---|
| | |
| **3. Third quatrain** | **4. Couplet** |
| | |

**B.** Write the letter of the best answer. (8 points each)

_____ 1. The speaker of "If We Must Die" assumes that the foe will
  a. lose the fight.                     c. fight to the death.
  b. listen to reason.                  d. back down if opposed.

_____ 2. In "If We Must Die," the foe is associated with all of the following **except**
  a. animals.                           c. defenders.
  b. monsters.                          d. murderers.

_____ 3. In "A Black Man Talks of Reaping," who does the speaker hold responsible for the fact that his children "glean in fields"?
  a. himself                            c. all African Americans
  b. white people                       d. only the children themselves

_____ 4. In "A Black Man Talks of Reaping," all of the following threaten to spoil the speaker's efforts **except** for
  a. the wind.                          c. grain-eating fowl.
  b. his own children.                  d. "my brother's sons."

**C.** Answer **one** of the following questions based on your understanding of the poems. Write your answer on a separate sheet of paper. (14 points)

1. Which of these poems do you feel is more relevant to racial issues in America today? Support your opinion with reference to the poems.

2. Relate the ideas that Bontemps uses agricultural imagery and language to convey in each stanza of "A Black Man Talks of Reaping."

**D. Linking Literature to Life.** Answer the following question based on your own experience and knowledge. Write your answer on a separate sheet of paper. (14 points)

Do you believe that there is anything unique about the African-American experience that can truly be understood only by African Americans? Explain.

# How It Feels to Be Colored Me (page 950)

# Selection Test

**A.** In this essay, Hurston reveals much about herself through contrasts between objective descriptions and subjective expressions of feelings. Read each objective description from the essay. In the boxes on the right, write notes describing the contrasting subjective comments she makes about each subject and what her comments reveal about her. (5 points each)

| Objective Description | Subjective Comments/What They Reveal |
|---|---|
| 1. "But the Northerners were something else again. They were peered at cautiously from behind curtains by the timid." | |
| 2. "Someone is always at my elbow reminding me that I am the granddaughter of slaves." | |
| 3. "The position of my white neighbor is much more difficult." | |
| 4. "I . . . find the white friend sitting motionless in his seat, smoking calmly." | |

**B.** Write the letter of the best answer. This exercise is continued on the next page. (10 points each)

_____ 1. According to Hurston, she "became" colored when she
   a. was born.
   b. heard jazz music for the first time.
   c. watched the white tourists go through her hometown.
   d. moved to a place where African Americans were not in the majority.

_____ 2. When Hurston says that she is "busy sharpening [her] oyster knife," she means that she
   a. always expects trouble.
   b. is prepared to defend herself.
   c. is looking for the best life has to offer.
   d. is preparing for a time when she can gain vengeance.

_____ 3. Which of the following does Hurston imply is the single **most** important ingredient in making her who she is?
   a. her soul
   b. her identity as a woman
   c. her identity as an American
   d. her identity as an African American

_____ 4. According to Hurston, when she is discriminated against, she feels all of the following **except**
   a. confused.          c. an awareness of her skin color.
   b. surprised.          d. angry with the person who discriminates against her.

**C. Words to Know.** Write the letter of the best answer. (4 points each)

_____ 1. If you say that a man has a <u>veneer</u> of sympathy, you mean that his pity is
   a. shallow.          b. undeserved.          c. praiseworthy.

_____ 2. One would <u>rend</u> a magazine by
   a. skimming it.          b. ripping it up.          c. subscribing to it.

_____ 3. A <u>specter</u> is something you see that is
   a. beautiful.          b. expensive.          c. supernatural.

_____ 4. If you <u>deplore</u> something, you give it your
   a. okay.          b. attention.          c. condemnation.

_____ 5. Which would be an <u>extenuating</u> reason for turning homework in late?
   a. being sick          b. being lazy          c. forgetting to do it

**D.** Answer **one** of the following questions based on your understanding of the selection. Write your answer on a separate sheet of paper. (10 points)

1. What do you think Hurston means when she says you could empty the different-colored bags into one pile and then refill them without significantly changing the nature of their contents? Do you agree with her? Explain.

2. Describe Hurston's attitude toward slavery and explain why you think she has been criticized for it. What do you think of her attitude, and why?

**E. Linking Literature to Life.** Answer the following question based on your own experience and knowledge. Write your answer on a separate sheet of paper. (10 points)

Do you think that it is possible for people to refuse to be harmed by discrimination? Explain.

# My Dungeon Shook: Letter to My Nephew on the One Hundredth Anniversary of the Emancipation (page 959)

## Selection Test

**A.** To emphasize the points that Baldwin is making in this letter, he sometimes refers to people, literature, events, and circumstances from the past. Below are quotations in which Baldwin does this. On the line at the top of each box, write the letter of **one** quotation you wish to discuss. In the box, jot down one or more points that Baldwin is making or emphasizing. (30 points)

a. "Now, my dear namesake, these innocent and well-meaning people, your countrymen, have caused you to be born under conditions not very far removed from those described for us by Charles Dickens in the London of more than a hundred years ago."

c. "You come from a long line of great poets, some of the greatest poets since Homer. One of them said, The very time I thought I was lost, My dungeon shook and my chains fell off."

b. "It will be hard, James, but you come from sturdy, peasant stock, men who picked cotton and dammed rivers and built railroads, and, in the teeth of the most terrifying odds, achieved an unassailable and monumental dignity."

d. "You know, and I know, that the country is celebrating one hundred years of freedom one hundred years too soon."

**Quotation** _____

**Quotation** _____

**B.** Write the letter of the best answer. This exercise is continued on the next page. (5 points each)

_____ 1. Baldwin feels that white Americans need to
  a. forget about the ways they have treated blacks.
  b. forgive themselves for the ways they have treated blacks.
  c. take responsibility and change their behavior toward blacks.

_____ 2. Baldwin feels that black Americans need to
  a. accept whites for what they are and learn to love them.
  b. forget about the ways they have been treated by whites.
  c. take responsibility for the ways that whites have treated them.

_____ 3. Baldwin believes that racism is proof of the
               a. inferiority of whites.
               b. superiority of whites.
               c. fear and inhumanity of whites.

_____ 4. Baldwin argues that the falsehood of blacks' inferiority to whites
               is an essential part of the identity of
               a. all people.
               b. all Americans.
               c. white Americans.

**C. Words to Know.** Write the letter of the best answer. (4 points each)

_____ 1. If you put two <u>truculent</u> people together in a room, you can expect
               a. conflict.                b. laughter.                c. productivity.

_____ 2. Which is **most** likely to result in <u>devastation</u>?
               a. an apology            b. an earthquake          c. a practical joke

_____ 3. A <u>vulnerable</u> person is easily
               a. hurt.                 b. amused.               c. angered.

_____ 4. Which of the following <u>constitutes</u> water?
               a. rain                 b. a dryer               c. hydrogen

_____ 5. On a scale from 1 (worst) to 10 (best), a <u>mediocrity</u> would be rated
               a. 1.                 b. 5.                 c. 10.

**D.** Answer **one** of the following questions based on your understanding of the letter. Write your answer on a separate sheet of paper. (15 points)

1. Baldwin wrote this letter to his nephew with the intention of publishing it. What are some reasons that Baldwin might have chosen to formally address this open letter to his nephew instead of simply to the American public?

2. If Baldwin's nephew were to fall into one of the traps of inner-city life that threaten Harlem's African-American youth—drugs, gangs, crime—who or what do you think Baldwin would hold most responsible? Support your opinion with reference to the letter.

**E. Linking Literature to Life.** Answer the following question based on your own experience and knowledge. Write your answer on a separate sheet of paper. (15 points)

Describe **one** thing you have learned from personal experience that you don't think you could have learned or understood as well without having had that experience. Why do you think that is so?

# Selected Poems by Brooks (page 967)

# Selection Open-Book Test

**A.** Noted in each box on the left is an example of style from one of Brooks's poems. In each box on the right, note a main idea in the poem that the element of style helps to stress, emphasize, or draw attention to. (5 points each)

## "Life for My Child Is Simple"

| Example of Style | Main Idea(s) Emphasized |
|---|---|
| 1. Anaphora: the word *or* in lines 5–8 | |
| 2. Punctuation: "No. There is more to it than that." | |
| 3. Alliteration: "His lesions are legion." | |

## "Primer for Blacks"

| Example of Style | Main Idea(s) Emphasized |
|---|---|
| 4. Personification: "Blackness marches on." | |
| 5. Anaphora: the word *the* in lines 32–37 | |
| 6. Capitalization: lines 50–63 | |

**B.** Write the letter of the best answer. This exercise is continued on the next page. (6 points each)

_____ 1. In "Life for My Child Is Simple," the "undeep and unabiding things" (line 4) are
    a. the simple pleasures of life.
    b. the things that one never reaches for.
    c. the mysteries that one can never know.
    d. all of those things that one reaches for.

_____ 2. In "Life for My Child Is Simple," the speaker interprets the child's actions as a sign of
   a. boredom.                 c. angry defiance.
   b. fearlessness.            d. conflicting emotions.

_____ 3. In "Life for My Child Is Simple," reaching has
   a. discouraged the child.
   b. begun to bore the child.
   c. hurt the child uncountable times.
   d. taught the child to accept limitations.

_____ 4. In "Life for My Child Is Simple," the speaker believes that reaching
   a. is learned.              c. leads to sure success.
   b. can be dangerous.        d. makes people unafraid.

_____ 5. In the second stanza of "Primer for Blacks," the speaker implies that the strength of blacks is being used
   a. efficiently.             c. against them.
   b. too carefully.           d. as well as can be expected.

_____ 6. The third stanza of "Primer for Blacks" most emphasizes the power of bloodlines to
   a. bind.        b. forget.        c. shame.        d. restrict.

_____ 7. What does the speaker of "Primer for Blacks" request of "self-shriveled Blacks" in lines 48–50?
   a. an apology
   b. an agreement to respectfully disagree
   c. the explanation of a basic truth about life
   d. the acknowledgment of a personal connection

**C.** Answer **one** of the following questions based on your understanding of the poems. Write your answer on a separate sheet of paper. (14 points)

1. In "Life for My Child Is Simple," what difference do you see between the speaker's approach to life and the child's approach to life? How do you think the speaker feels about this difference? Support your answers with details from the poem.

2. The word _primer_ has several meanings. Among them are the following: (a) "Any book of basic or fundamental principles," (b) "That which prepares or supplies for action."

   Do you think that Brooks intended the title of "Primer for Blacks" to suggest one, both, or neither of these meanings? Support your opinion with reference to the poem.

**D. Linking Literature to Life.** Answer the following question based on your own experience and knowledge. Write your answer on a separate sheet of paper. (14 points)

   What are some ways in which one can tell whether his or her fears are reasonable? Explain your ideas.

# Thoughts on the African-American Novel (page 973)

# Selection Test

**A.** Think about what Morrison believes led to the creation of the novel and the African-American novel as art forms. Then, in each box on the left, write notes describing something that she believes led to the creation of these art forms. (30 points)

**B.** Write the letter of the best answer. (15 points each)

_____ 1. Why, according to Morrison, does she incorporate elements of the oral tradition in her novels?
   a. to create humor             c. to add an element of suspense
   b. to complicate the plot      d. to engage and involve the reader

_____ 2. Which of the following is both a common element of Morrison's novels and something that she believes is characteristic of black art?
   a. a menacing tone             c. impersonal narration
   b. slang and dialect           d. the presence of a chorus

**C.** Answer **one** of the following questions based on your understanding of the selection. Write your answer on a separate sheet of paper. (20 points)

1. Based on this selection, what do you think Morrison would say is the role of the African-American writer in American society? Does she seem to think that her role is different from that of a white writer? Support your answers with reference to the selection.

2. Have you been affected by novels in the way that Morrison feels that readers should be affected? Support your answer with details from the selection.

**D. Linking Literature to Life.** Answer the following question based on your own experience and knowledge. Write your answer on a separate sheet of paper. (20 points)

   What, to you, are the **three** most important things a novel must have or do in order to be worth reading? Explain.

# Unit Six: The Modern Age

# Part One Open-Book Test

**A.** Write the letter of the best answer to each question. (5 points each)

_____ 1. What theme or idea is expressed in both "I, Too" and "Harlem"?
   a. African Americans are oppressed, but things will change.
   b. There will soon be a violent revolt in America.
   c. African Americans oppose the principles of integration.
   d. Dreams dry up like grapes left in the sun.

_____ 2. Which poem emphasizes the major idea that people of all colors and races are connected in the brotherhood of humanity?
   a. "Life for My Child Is Simple"      c. "If We Must Die"
   b. "Any Human to Another"      d. "A Black Man Talks of Reaping"

_____ 3. In "How It Feels to Be Colored Me," the author's main purpose is to
   a. criticize whites for having practiced slavery.
   b. honor the memory of her grandmother, who was a slave.
   c. encourage people of all colors to enjoy life.
   d. explain how good she feels about herself, regardless of her color.

_____ 4. In "Thoughts on the African-American Novel," Morrison says that one function of the novel as a form is to
   a. increase the size of the middle class.
   b. exclude people from specific social groups.
   c. teach people things they do not know.
   d. classify people into different social classes.

**B.** Think about the strong feelings expressed in the poems in this part. From each group of poems, circle the letter of **one** poem you wish to discuss. In the top box, identify the strongest feeling expressed by the speaker. In the bottom box, write notes explaining why the speaker has that emotion. This exercise is continued on the next page. (20 points)

**Group One**
   a. "I, Too"                          c. "My City"
   b. "The Weary Blues"                 d. "Any Human to Another"

| **Strong Feeling** |
| --- |
| **Reason(s) for the Feeling** |
|  |

**Group Two**
  a. "If We Must Die"                          c. "Life for My Child Is Simple"
  b. "A Black Man Talks of Reaping"            d. "Primer for Blacks"

| **Strong Feeling** |
| --- |
| **Reason(s) for the Feeling** |

**C.** Answer **two** of the following essay questions based on your understanding of the selections. Write your answers on a separate sheet of paper. (20 points each)

1. The writer Carl Van Doren once stated that "What American literature decidedly needs at the moment is color, music, gusto, the free expression of gay or desperate moods." Which **two** poems from this part do you think come closest to providing for these needs? Support your answer with details from the poems.

2. Which poem from this part do you think comes closest to expressing the ideas, concerns, and feelings expressed by Zora Neale Hurston in "How It Feels to Be Colored Me"? Support your answer with reference to the poem and the essay.

3. Which poem from this part do you think comes closest to expressing the concerns, feelings, and ideas expressed by James Baldwin in "My Dungeon Shook: Letter to My Nephew . . ."? Support your answer with reference to the poem and the letter.

4. Think about what concerns Morrison in her essay, "Thoughts on the African-American Novel." Then choose **two** writers from this part whose works you think reflect concerns similar to those of Morrison. Support your choices with reference to Morrison's essay as well as the chosen selections.

**D.** Think about the new cultural identity that crystallized during the Harlem Renaissance and has carried over into more recent times. In the boxes below, write the title of **one** selection from this part that emphasizes important elements of the new cultural identity. Then, write notes explaining what element of cultural identity is emphasized and how the selection reflects this element. (20 points)

| **Selection** | **Element of Cultural Identity** | **How the Selection Reflects This Element** |
| --- | --- | --- |
|  |  |  |

# Selected Poems by Frost (page 1000)

# Selection Open-Book Test

**A.** Think about Frost's use of symbolism in these poems. Then, for each poem, make a mark in the small box next to **one** person or thing you wish to discuss. In each box on the right, tell what you think that person or thing represents in the poem and write notes to support your answer. (14 points each)

---

### 1. "Acquainted with the Night"

☐ night

☐ the watchman

**What do you think this person or thing represents? Explain.**

---

### 2. "Mending Wall"

☐ the wall being mended

☐ the saying, "Good fences make good neighbors"

**What do you think this person or thing represents? Explain.**

---

### 3. " 'Out, Out—' "

☐ the boy

☐ the buzz saw

**What do you think this person or thing represents? Explain.**

---

**B.** Write the letter of the best answer. This exercise is continued on the next page. (4 points each)

_____ 1. Which of the poems has a first-person speaker?
   a. none of the poems
   b. all three of the poems
   c. "Acquainted with the Night" and "Mending Wall" only

_____ 2. In "Acquainted with the Night," the mood
      a. abruptly changes at line 3.
      b. abruptly changes at line 13.
      c. remains constant from beginning to end.

_____ 3. If someone who was not a poet wanted to say what Frost expresses in
      "Mending Wall," he or she would **most** probably say,
      a. "Walls may not be necessary, but they can't hurt."
      b. "People should never build walls."
      c. "People ought to think carefully before they build walls."

_____ 4. Which of the following sets of lines contributes **most** to the playful quality
      of "Mending Wall"?
      a. lines 18, 19, 25, and 26
      b. lines 30 and 31
      c. lines 32–34

_____ 5. In "Mending Wall," the speaker and the neighbor are mending this
      particular wall
      a. because they always have.
      b. to keep hunters off their property.
      c. to keep animals out of the orchard.

_____ 6. In " 'Out, Out—,' " lines 15 and 16 suggest that the buzz saw is
      a. alive.
      b. exhausted.
      c. unemotional.

_____ 7. In lines 15–18 of " 'Out, Out—,' " the speaker suggests that he or she
      a. isn't certain what happened.
      b. could have prevented what happened to the boy.
      c. knows what happened was deliberate, not an accident.

**C.** Answer **one** of the following questions based on your understanding of the poems. Write your answer on a separate sheet of paper. (15 points)

1. In "Mending Wall," what do you think is the darkness that the speaker says the neighbor moves in? Explain your answer.

2. What do you think " 'Out, Out—' " suggests about the nature of accidents? What do you think the poem has to say about the value of life? Support your answers with reference to the poem.

**D. Linking Literature to Life.** Answer the following question based on your own experience and knowledge. Write your answer on a separate sheet of paper. (15 points)

Do you think that intimacy is necessary to happiness? Explain your answer.

# The Death of the Hired Man (page 1006)

# Selection Open-Book Test

**A.** Think about what you have learned about Mary's character through her words and actions in this poem. Perhaps more than anything else, she seems to be sympathetic, kind, and persuasive. For each of these character traits, note examples or details from the poem that help to illustrate the trait. (8 points each)

| Character Trait | Details from the Poem That Illustrate the Trait |
| --- | --- |
| 1. Sympathetic | |
| 2. Kind | |
| 3. Persuasive | |

**B.** Write the letter of the best answer. (5 points each)

_____ 1. How can you tell that this poem is written in blank verse?
   a. It has numerous line breaks.
   b. It is written in stanzas of equal length.
   c. The rhyme scheme is *aabbcc.*
   d. It uses unrhymed iambic pentameter.

_____ 2. Silas was particularly talented at
   a. plowing
   b. pruning
   c. haying
   d. singing

_____ 3. What does Silas seem to believe about the young man, Harold?
   a. He will make an excellent farmer.
   b. He will be a success in life.
   c. He should be admired for his education.
   d. He has not learned anything useful in life.

_____ 4. Which word **best** describes what Silas felt towards Harold?
   a. irritation
   b. admiration
   c. hatred
   d. love

**C. Words to Know.** Write the letter of the best answer. (4 points each)

_____ 1. If you <u>harbor</u> a lost animal, you
   a. call the police.       b. provide shelter.       c. send it away.

_____ 2. You would most likely be <u>beholden</u> to a person who
   a. asked for help.       b. argued with you.       c. did you a favor.

_____ 3. People who act with <u>assurance</u> are
   a. uncertain.       b. self-confident.       c. frightened.

_____ 4. Your muscles become <u>taut</u> when you
   a. exercise.       b. relax.       c. sleep.

_____ 5. If you cannot <u>abide</u> someone else's rules, you cannot
   a. tolerate them.       b. break them.       c. change them.

**D.** Answer **one** of the following questions based on your understanding of "The Death of the Hired Man." Write your answer on a separate sheet of paper. (20 points)

1. Throughout the poem, you never meet Silas or directly hear him speak, yet you learn a great deal about him. Describe what you know about Silas's character. Use details from the poem to support your ideas.

2. "The Death of the Hired Man" has been successfully performed as a one-act play. Visualize this poem performed as a play. What elements of the poem do you think might make it easy to transform it into a play?

**E. Linking Literature to Life.** Answer the following question based on your own experience and knowledge. Write your answer on a separate sheet of paper. (16 points)

According to Frost's famous line, "Home is the place where, when you have to go there, / They have to take you in." Do you agree with this definition of "home"? How would you define "home"? Explain your views.

# The End of Something (page 1018)

# Selection Test

**A.** Think about the title of this story, and why Hemingway might have chosen to use the word *something* instead of a more descriptive or decisive word. Then, in each box on the left, jot down a word or phrase that you think would be an appropriate replacement for the word *something* in the title. In each box on the right, write notes explaining why that word or phrase would be appropriate. (20 points each)

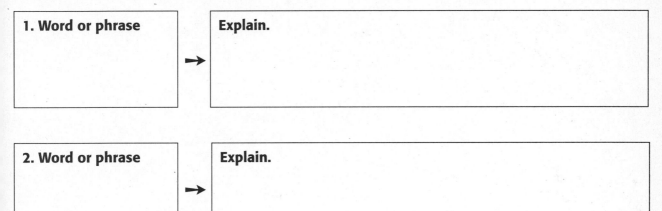

| **1. Word or phrase** | ➡ | **Explain.** |

| **2. Word or phrase** | ➡ | **Explain.** |

**B.** Write the letter of the best answer. (10 points each)

_____ 1. Marjorie's fishing skills and knowledge seem to be
    a. those of a beginner.
    b. equal to those of Nick.
    c. superior to those of Nick.

_____ 2. Which of the following does Nick seem to want most?
    a. Marjorie's happiness
    b. a life apart from Marjorie
    c. a chance to make things right with Marjorie

**C.** Answer **one** of the following questions based on your understanding of the story. Write your answer on a separate sheet of paper. (20 points)

1. The third-person limited point of view in this story is much more limited than is usually the case. What are some of the things that Hemingway's choice of style does not reveal directly to the reader? Do you like Hemingway's style in this story? Explain.

2. Think about how you felt about the main characters while reading this story. Do you feel that Hemingway wrote the story in such a way to distance you from one or both of the main characters, or to encourage you to sympathize with one or both of them? Explain your answer with reference to the story.

Name _____ Date _____

**D. Linking Literature to Life.** Answer the following question based on your own experience and knowledge. Write your answer on a separate sheet of paper. (20 points)

What are some forces in modern American society that encourage long-term romantic relationships, and what are some forces that discourage them? Explain.

# The Love Song of J. Alfred Prufrock (page 1025)

## Selection Open-Book Test

**A.** Think about the images that reveal Prufrock's personality and his opinion of himself. In the boxes below, note what you think the image or images in each quotation suggest about Prufrock. (6 points each)

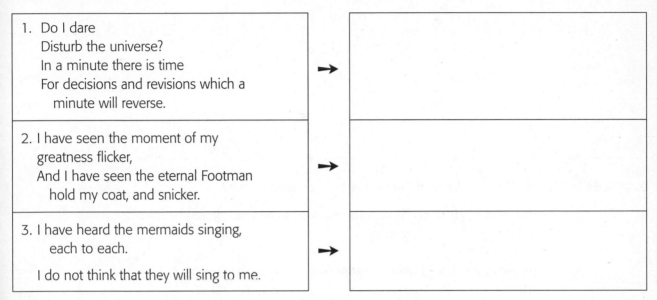

1. Do I dare
   Disturb the universe?
   In a minute there is time
   For decisions and revisions which a
      minute will reverse.

2. I have seen the moment of my
      greatness flicker,
   And I have seen the eternal Footman
      hold my coat, and snicker.

3. I have heard the mermaids singing,
      each to each.

   I do not think that they will sing to me.

**B.** Write the letter of the best answer. (4 points each)

_____ 1. What does Prufrock think the people at the party will notice about him?
   a. his clothes
   b. his thinning hair
   c. his indecisiveness
   d. his "prepared" face

_____ 2. Line 51 suggests that Prufrock views his life as all of the following **except**
   a. trivial.
   b. cautious.
   c. full and rich.
   d. detail-oriented.

_____ 3. Prufrock's courage ultimately fails him in the stanza beginning with
   a. line 49.
   b. line 70.
   c. line 75.
   d. line 120.

_____ 4. In the final stanza, "we" could refer to any of the following **except**
   a. all human beings.
   b. Prufrock and a companion.
   c. Prufrock and the woman he loves.
   d. two sides of Prufrock's personality.

**C.** Through stream of consciousness, Eliot uses several contrasting images to characterize Prufrock. In the boxes below, jot down what Eliot is saying about how Prufrock is like, or unlike, each person. (6 points each)

| 1. John the Baptist (line 83) | 2. Lazarus (line 94) | 3. Prince Hamlet (line 111) |
| --- | --- | --- |
|  |  |  |

**D. Words to Know**. Write the letter of the best answer. (4 points each)

_____ 1. A person who tends to presume is **most** likely to be considered
        a. curious.         b. gracious.         c. interfering.

_____ 2. A person who tends to digress is **most** likely to be considered
        a. unstable.         b. unfocused.         c. uneducated.

_____ 3. A person who tends to malinger is **most** likely to be considered
        a. cautious.         b. deceitful.         c. slow-moving.

_____ 4. A person who tends to be meticulous is **most** likely to be considered
        a. optimistic.         b. agreeable.         c. painstaking.

_____ 5. A person who tends to be obtuse is **most** likely to be considered
        a. bored.         b. dim-witted.         c. short-tempered.

**E.** Answer **one** of the following questions based on your understanding of the poem. Write your answer on a separate sheet of paper. (14 points)

1. What do you think Prufrock finally realizes about himself, and what future does he see for himself? Support your answer with reference to the poem.

2. Do you think Eliot presents Prufrock as a unique individual, as a representative of modern life, or as both? Explain your answer.

**F. Linking Literature to Life.** Answer the following question based on your own experience and knowledge. Write your answer on a separate sheet of paper. (14 points)

Near the middle of his life, Eliot came to view religious faith as "the only hopeful course for the world." Do you agree with that view? Why or why not?

# The Jilting of Granny Weatherall (page 1034)

# Selection Test

**A.** Think about how the use of stream of consciousness in this story reveals what is going on inside and outside Granny's mind. In the boxes below, write notes describing the main points of what Granny remembers and thinks about and notes describing what is going on around her. (10 points each)

| 1. What is happening inside Granny's mind? | 2. What is happening outside Granny's mind? |
|---|---|
|  |  |
|  |  |

**B.** Write the letter of the best answer. (5 points each)

_____ 1. Granny Weatherall has never gotten over
   a. being jilted by George on their wedding day.
   b. her husband's death.
   c. feeling angry that Doctor Harry was called.
   d. having to work so hard all her life.

_____ 2. Granny resents Cornelia mainly for the way she
   a. cleans the house.
   b. speaks to Doctor Harry.
   c. treats her grandchildren.
   d. treats her like a child.

_____ 3. Granny's death is symbolized by
   a. her desire to see Hapsy again.
   b. wanting to see her children.
   c. blowing out the light.
   d. the arrival of the doctor.

_____ 4. In her last moments, Granny concludes that
   a. Hapsy's death is what ruined her.
   b. she will never forgive George.
   c. John is the best man she has ever known.
   d. Cornelia will carry on just fine without her.

**C. Words to Know.** Write the letter of the best answer. (4 points each)

_____ 1. People who are <u>tactful</u> can best be described as
        a. considerate.        b. abrupt.        c. rude.

_____ 2. If you <u>rummage</u> through a drawer, you are
        a. cutting a hole through it.
        b. looking for something.
        c. organizing its contents.

_____ 3. If people <u>plague</u> you with questions, you probably feel
        a. interested.        b. curious.        c. annoyed.

_____ 4. A person who stares <u>intently</u> is most likely
        a. depressed.        b. delirious.        c. concentrating.

_____ 5. A <u>marvel</u> is most likely to cause a sense of
        a. wonder.        b. pain.        c. grief.

**D.** Answer **one** of the following questions based on your understanding of "The Jilting of Granny Weatherall." Write your answer on a separate sheet of paper. (20 points)

1. A critic might say that this story is filled with psychological insights and symbolic elements. What examples in the story support this statement?

2. What do you think Granny means when she says, "It was good to be strong enough for everything, even if all you made melted and changed and slipped under your hands, so that by the time you finished you almost forgot what you were working for"? How might this statement relate to her experience with George?

**E. Linking Literature to Life.** Answer the following question based on your own experience and knowledge. Write your answer on a separate sheet of paper. (20 points)

You may be familiar with the term "closure," which refers to dealing with a problem directly and thereby putting an end to any emotional pain it has caused. Do you think Granny would have had more peace of mind as she was dying if she had confronted George? If you were Granny, what would you have said to George?

# The Man Who Was Almost a Man (page 1045)

# Selection Test

**A.** At the end of the story, Dave travels "away, away to somewhere, somewhere where he could be a man. . . . " In the box at the top, write notes to answer the question. Then, fill in the bar graph to show how important you think the role of each factor is in preventing Dave from being a man in his own community. In the boxes at the bottom, write notes to explain why you rated each factor as you did. (6 points each)

| 1. What does Dave think it means to be a man? |
| --- |
| |

What do you think prevents Dave from being a man in his own community?

| | Not Important | Very Important |
| --- | --- | --- |
| Dave's Level of Maturity | | |
| Dave's Mother and Father | | |
| Dave's Economic Situation | | |
| Racism and the Sharecropping System | | |

| 2. Dave's level of maturity | 3. Dave's mother and father | 4. Dave's economic situation | 5. Racism and sharecropping |
| --- | --- | --- | --- |
| | | | |

**B.** Write the letter of the best answer. This exercise is continued on the next page. (5 points each)

_____ 1. Dave's mother finally agrees to give him the money to buy the gun because she
  a. trusts his judgment.
  b. wants her husband to have the gun.
  c. believes he should be allowed to spend his wages as he likes.

_____ 2. Dave wants the gun **mainly** for
      a. hunting.        b. social status.        c. family security.

_____ 3. When Dave shoots the mule, he does so
      a. by accident.
      b. to prove he is a man.
      c. to take revenge on Hawkins, his employer.

_____ 4. What is the **main** reason that Dave's parents themselves don't pay Hawkins for the mule?
      a. They don't have the money.
      b. They are too angry with Dave.
      c. They want to teach Dave a lesson.

**C.** Think about the consequences of the action Dave takes at the end of the story. Then, in the boxes below, note some of the consequences that you think will result for each party from Dave's action. (10 points each)

| 1. Dave | 2. Dave's mother and father | 3. Hawkins |
|---|---|---|
|  |  |  |

**D.** Answer **one** of the following questions based on your understanding of the story. Write your answer on a separate sheet of paper. (10 points)

1. Identify **two** ideas that you think Wright intended to convey through the title of this story. Explain how his use of verbal irony conveys these ideas.

2. Do you believe that the punishment for Dave's crime outweighs the crime itself? Explain your opinion.

**E. Linking Literature to Life.** Answer the following question based on your own experience and knowledge. Write your answer on a separate sheet of paper. (10 points)

Do you think that being an African-American male today is any more difficult than being a white American male? Explain your opinion.

# Mirror/Self in 1958 (page 1057)

# Selection Open-Book Test

**A.** In each box on the top, jot down an image or an example of figurative language that strongly affects you. On each line on the right, jot down a word or phrase that describes the tone that the image or figurative language helps to create. Then, in each box on the bottom, write notes telling how you are affected by that image or example of figurative language. (15 points each)

### 1. "Mirror"

**Tone**

| Image or Example of Figurative Language |
|---|
|  |
| ➡ |

_____

_____

| **Effect on You** |
|---|
|  |

### 2. "Self in 1958"

**Tone**

| Image or Example of Figurative Language |
|---|
|  |
| ➡ |

_____

_____

| **Effect on You** |
|---|
|  |

**B.** Write the letter of the best answer. This exercise is continued on the next page. (4 points each)

_____ 1. In the first four lines of "Mirror," the speaker suggests that it (the mirror) is
     a. ironic.
     b. objective.
     c. deceptive.
     d. sympathetic.

_____ 2. The woman in "Mirror" reacts to her reflection with
        a. grief.               c. gratitude.
        b. defiance.           d. objectivity.

_____ 3. By comparing herself to a doll, the speaker of "Self in 1958" conveys the idea that she feels
        a. alienated.           c. bigger-than-life.
        b. appreciated.      d. magical or imaginative.

_____ 4. What characteristic of the doll is emphasized in lines 21–26 of "Self in 1958"?
        a. her sorrow          c. her deceptiveness
        b. her attractiveness    d. her submissiveness

_____ 5. In lines 31–35 of "Self in 1958," the speaker suggests that the doll **should** be all of the following **except**
        a. honest.            c. confident.
        b. flexible.         d. dissatisfied.

**C.** Think about the mirror's reflections of the woman in "Mirror" and what can be inferred about her from those reflections. Then, in the box on the left, list specific things that the mirror reflects. In the box on the right, write notes about what can be inferred about the woman's feelings and concerns, based on the mirror's reflections of her. (10 points each)

| 1. **What the mirror reflects** | 2. **What can be inferred about the woman from those reflections** |
| --- | --- |
| | |

**D.** Answer **one** of the following questions based on your understanding of the poems. Write your answer on a separate sheet of paper. (15 points)

1. Do you think the woman in "Mirror" can find in the mirror "what she really is"? Does the mirror seem to think she can? Explain your answers.

2. Describe what you believe is the main conflict facing the speaker in "Self in 1958." With whom or what is she in conflict, and why? Support your ideas with reference to the poem.

**E. Linking Literature to Life.** Answer the following question based on your own experience and knowledge. Write your answer on a separate sheet of paper. (15 points)

Do you think that, in this day and age, it is more difficult for women to obtain and maintain a positive self-image than it is for men? Support your opinion.

# Unit Six: The Modern Age

# Part Two Open-Book Test

**A.** Write the answer to each question on the lines. (5 points each)

1. In "The Death of the Hired Man," how does Warren feel about having Silas back?

_____

_____

2. In "The End of Something," what does the word *something* refer to?

_____

_____

3. In "The Love Song of J. Alfred Prufrock," what do you think is the "overwhelming question" that Prufrock wants to ask, and why does he decide not to?

_____

_____

4. In "The Jilting of Granny Weatherall," what does Granny realize in the final moments before her death?

_____

_____

**B.** Think about how imagery and symbolism are used in the poems in this part. Choose **two** poems that you wish to discuss. In the boxes below, write the title of each poem you choose. For the first poem, jot down an image from the poem and describe the ideas and feelings it conveys. For the second poem, identify a symbol from the poem and describe what it symbolizes and what feelings or meaning it suggests. (20 points)

| **Title:** | **Title:** |
|---|---|
| **Image:** | **Symbol:** |
| **Ideas and Feelings Conveyed:** | **What It Symbolizes and Suggests:** |

**C.** Answer **two** of the following essay questions based on your understanding of the selections. Write your answers on a separate sheet of paper. (20 points each)

1. Many of the poems in this part concern the idea of loss. Choose **two** poems in which something or someone is lost, given up, or left behind. What is lost in each poem, and how? What are the effects of each loss?

2. Think about the dilemmas addressed in these selections. Then choose **two** selections, describe the dilemmas with which they are concerned, and explain what makes these dilemmas difficult. Do the selections offer solutions to these dilemmas? If so, what are they? If not, offer the best solutions you can think of.

3. Which of the poems from this part most appeals to your heart, and which most appeals to your intellect? Give at least **two** reasons for each of your choices.

**D.** Think about the characteristics that have come to be identified with modernism that are evident in the selections in this part. (20 points)

• Above each pair of boxes is a characteristic identified with modernism.

• In each box on the left, write the title of a selection in which that characteristic is revealed or demonstrated.

• In each box on the right, write notes describing that characteristic as it appears or is reflected in that selection. **Do not discuss the same selection more than once.**

1. Characteristic: the belief that individuals are becoming increasingly threatened by and isolated amid the mass society of modern life

| Selection | |
|---|---|
| | Describe this characteristic as it appears or is reflected in the selection. |

2. Characteristic: the lack of a narrative voice to provide the reader with guidance, explanations, or details

| Selection | |
|---|---|
| | Describe this characteristic as it appears or is reflected in the selection. |

# Armistice (page 1076)

# Selection Test

**A.** Think about how the title of this story relates to its theme. Then, in the boxes below, makes notes to answer the questions about the armistice between France and Germany and the one between Morris and Gus. (5 points each)

| | Armistice Between France and Germany | Armistice Between Morris and Gus |
|---|---|---|
| 1. How and why does it come about? | | |
| 2. How does Morris, the grocer, feel about it, and why? | | |
| 3. How does Gus, the delivery driver, feel about it, and why? | | |
| 4. In what ways are the two armistices similar? | | |
| 5. In what ways are the two armistices different? | | |
| 6. What is the theme of the story? | | |

**B.** Write the letter of the best answer. This exercise is continued on the next page. (5 points each)

_____ 1. It is **most** important to Morris that France defeat Germany so that
        a. Gus will be humiliated.
        b. the Nazis will be humiliated.
        c. French democracy will be saved.
        d. the Jews in France will be safeguarded.

_____ 2. The way that Gus reacts to Leonard, Morris's son, shows feelings of
      a. hostility.              c. confusion.
      b. inferiority.           d. mild concern.

_____ 3. In this story, the one thing that Leonard seems to desire **most** from his
      father is
      a. respect.             c. harmony.
      b. freedom.            d. truth and honesty.

_____ 4. As Gus drives away from Morris's shop at the end of the story, Gus
      imagines himself as a
      a. boy.      b. Jew.          c. victim.        d. conqueror.

**C. Words to Know.** Write the letter of the best answer. (4 points each)

_____ 1. Teachers usually tell <u>overwrought</u> students to
      a. speak up.         b. calm down.        c. study harder.

_____ 2. Which is intended to <u>inflict</u> wounds?
      a. stitches          b. weapons        c. bandages

_____ 3. When you <u>derive</u> something, you
      a. seek it.           b. avoid it.         c. acquire it.

_____ 4. A <u>pretense</u> of friendship is an act or gesture that is
      a. insincere.         b. intimate.        c. thoughtful.

_____ 5. When people respond <u>contemptuously</u> to your idea, it is a sign that they
      a. reject it.         b. appreciate it.        c. understand it.

**D.** Answer **one** of the following questions based on your understanding of the story. Write your answer on a separate sheet of paper. (15 points)

1. Is there just cause in this story for sympathizing with Gus? Give at least **three** reasons for your answer.

2. Think about how Leonard, Morris's son, interacts with Morris and Gus. How does Leonard complicate the relationship between Morris and Gus? What do Leonard's interactions with the two men add to your understanding of them as individuals?

**E. Linking Literature to Life.** Answer the following question based on your own experience and knowledge. Write your answer on a separate sheet of paper. (15 points)

Write a paragraph or two in which you give a personal response to this quotation by the writer Ayn Rand:

> "The moral [rule] should be: if and when, in any dispute, one side *initiates* the use of physical force, *that side is wrong*—and no consideration or discussion of the issues is necessary or appropriate."

Name _____    Date _____

# The Death of the Ball Turret Gunner/
# Why Soldiers Won't Talk (page 1088)

# Selection Test

**A.** Think about how imagery and tone are used in the last line of "The Death of the Ball Turret Gunner" to convey ideas about war, the speaker's death, and the government's attitude toward his death. Then write notes as directed in the boxes below. (10 points each)

| "When I died they washed me out of the turret with a hose." | | |
|---|---|---|
| 1. Note adjectives that describe the image in this line. | 2. Describe the tone of this line. | 3. Note ideas that are conveyed through the expression of this event in this manner. |

**B.** Write the letter of the best answer. (10 points each)

_____ 1. In the poem, the image of "black flak and the nightmare fighters" is one of
   a. chaos, darkness, and fear.
   b. innocence and vulnerability.
   c. heroism, courage, and victory.

_____ 2. According to "Why Soldiers Won't Talk," the worse a battle is,
   a. the less likely a soldier is to remember it.
   b. the more likely a soldier is to remember it.
   c. the more likely a soldier is to want to discuss it.

_____ 3. In "Why Soldiers Won't Talk," Steinbeck argues that, under extreme stress, the body's natural reaction is to
   a. prepare to die.      b. dull its senses.      c. sharpen its senses.

**C.** Answer **one** of the following questions based on your understanding of the selections. Write your answer on a separate sheet of paper. (20 points)

1. Identify **two** words or phrases you would use to describe the death of the speaker of "The Death of the Ball Turret Gunner." Explain your choices.

2. Do you agree or disagree with the central assumption or hypothesis of "Why Soldiers Won't Talk"? Give at least **two** reasons for your opinion.

**D. Linking Literature to Life.** Answer the following question based on your own experience and knowledge. Write your answer on a separate sheet of paper. (20 points)

November 11, Veterans Day, is set aside to honor all American veterans. What did your community do last Veterans Day to honor American veterans? Did you participate in the commemorations? Why or why not?

# Letter from Paradise, 21° 19' N., 157° 52' W./
# In Response to Executive Order 9066 (page 1095)

## Selection Test

**A.** Think about how the mood of "Letter from Paradise . . ." changes as the essay progresses. Then, in each box on the right, jot down words or phrases that describe the mood of each section of the essay. (10 points each)

| | |
|---|---|
| 1. Didion watches the other passengers and the coin divers as the tour boat leaves for Pearl Harbor. | |
| 2. Didion recalls old war movies and notes that "It is hard to remember what we came to remember." | |
| 3. The boat passes the harbor sites where the *Utah* and the *Arizona* lie. | |
| 4. Didion watches a couple placing leis on a grave at the National Memorial Cemetery of the Pacific. | |

**B.** Write the letter of the best answer. (10 points each)

_____ 1. In "Letter from Paradise . . . ," what reason is suggested for the Navy's considering the *Arizona* to be "still in commission"?
   a. The *Arizona* is a historical site of military importance.
   b. The Navy hopes to return the *Arizona* to full active duty.
   c. The *Arizona* continues to protect and defend Pearl Harbor.
   d. The *Arizona* is fully "manned" by the corpses of its entire crew.

_____ 2. In "In Response to Executive Order 9066," it is suggested that the attack on Pearl Harbor causes Denise, the speaker's best friend, to
   a. pity the speaker.          c. forgive the speaker.
   b. miss the speaker.          d. suspect the speaker.

**C.** Answer **one** of the following questions based on your understanding of the selections. Write your answer on a separate sheet of paper. (20 points)

1. In "Letter from Paradise . . . ," how would you describe Didion's attitude toward the sailors who died at Pearl Harbor? Support your answer with reference to the essay.

2. Think about what the tomato seeds in "In Response to Executive Order 9066" might represent. Then explain the significance of each of the following:
   • The father says that, where the family is going, the seeds won't grow.
   • The speaker notes that Denise calls tomatoes "love apples."
   • The speaker gives Denise a packet of tomato seeds "and asked her to plant them for me, told her / when the first tomato ripened / she'd miss me."

**D. Linking Literature to Life.** Answer the following question based on your own experience and knowledge. Write your answer on a separate sheet of paper. (20 points)

Imagine that you are telling an alien from outer space what war is all about. What would you say about the causes, purposes, and effects of war? Explain.

# Ambush (page 1105)

# Selection Test

**A.** The narrator of this story faces two difficult moments—one involving his daughter and another involving war. In the boxes below, write notes to answer the questions about these difficult moments. (15 points each)

**Difficult Moments**

|  | The narrator's daughter asks him if he has ever killed anyone. | A young Vietnamese soldier walks by as the narrator keeps watch. |
|---|---|---|
| 1. Why is the moment so difficult for the narrator? |  |  |
| 2. How does the narrator respond to this difficulty? |  |  |
| 3. Why does the narrator respond in that way? |  |  |

**B.** Write the letter of the best answer. This exercise is continued on the next page. (5 points each)

_____  1. The first internal conflict described by the narrator in this selection came about as a result of
a. the fact that he survived the war.
b. his daughter's question.
c. the lies he had told during the war.
d. his decision to write war stories.

_____  2. Kiowa did not see any conflict in the death of the Vietnamese soldier because he felt that the
a. narrator did what a soldier is supposed to do.
b. Vietnamese soldier was about to shoot.
c. narrator was not responsible for the soldier's death.
d. Vietnamese soldier should not have been on that trail.

_____ 3. The act of killing the young soldier is something that the narrator clearly
hopes he will one day be able to
  a. forget.
  b. take pride in.
  c. explain to his daughter.
  d. apologize for.

**C.** Answer **one** of the following questions based on your understanding of the story. Write your answer on a separate sheet of paper. (20 points)

1. In your opinion, in the difficult situation with his daughter, does the narrator do the right thing? Give at least two reasons for your answer.

2. Identify **three** words or phrases you would use to describe the action that the narrator takes in the difficult situation with the young Vietnamese soldier. Explain each of your choices.

**D. Linking Literature to Life.** Answer the following question based on your own experience and knowledge. Write your answer on a separate sheet of paper. (20 points)

Do you think that soldiers in the midst of war should be held to the same moral standards as everyone else? Explain why you feel that way.

# Camouflaging the Chimera/Deciding (page 1111)

# Selection Open-Book Test

**A.** Think about the different perspectives on the Vietnam War offered by these poems. Then, in the boxes below, write notes to answer the questions. (6 points each)

|  | **"Camouflaging the Chimera"** | **"Deciding"** |
|---|---|---|
| 1. Who are the "we" in the poem? |  |  |
| 2. What state of mind are "we" in? |  |  |
| 3. Why are "we" in this state of mind? |  |  |
| 4. How does nature seem to affect the speaker? |  |  |
| 5. How does the war seem to affect the speaker? |  |  |
| 6. With which speaker do you sympathize more? Why? |  |  |

**B.** Write the letter of the best answer. This exercise is continued on the next page. (6 points each)

_____ 1. In what sense are the soldiers in "Camouflaging the Chimera" "not there" (line 26)?
    a. They have blended into the scenery.
    b. They have sneaked away from the VC.
    c. They aren't on the hillside with the VC.
    d. They are dreaming about faraway places.

_____ 2. The rhythm of lines 10–17 of "Deciding" helps to create a feeling of

        a. relief.               c. nostalgia.

        b. urgency.           d. steadfastness.

**C.** Think about how imagery is used in these poems to convey ideas, feelings, and actions, and to create moods. Then, in each box in the middle, jot down some ideas, feelings, and actions conveyed by the image. In each box on the right, describe the mood that you think the image helps to create. (6 points each)

|  | **Ideas, Feelings, and Actions Conveyed** | **Mood Created** |
|---|---|---|
| 1. "We wove / ourselves into the terrain, / content to be a hummingbird's target." |  |  |
| 2. "But we waited / till the moon touched metal, / till something almost broke / inside us." |  |  |
| 3. ". . . the small bridge / where we'd sit hour after hour / letting our hands dip into the water / trying to catch the silver-brown fish." |  |  |
| 4. "The family hiding together in our house in Cholon / sunlight coming through the bullet holes." |  |  |

**D.** Answer **one** of the following questions based on your understanding of the poems. Write your answer on a separate sheet of paper. (14 points)

1. What meaning do you think the poet intended to convey through the title "Camouflaging the Chimera"? In your answer, consider who or what in the poem might be the "Chimera," and why and what that chimera might be "camouflaging" or "camouflaged."

2. What course of action does the speaker of "Deciding" seem to have decided upon? What in the poem suggests that this is the course of action she has decided upon?

**E. Linking Literature to Life.** Answer the following question based on your own experience and knowledge. Write your answer on a separate sheet of paper. (14 points)

Identify an aspect of your character or personality that you like or are proud of. How do you think that quality would affect you as a civilian caught up in a war? How would it affect you as a soldier engaged in combat?

# At the Justice Department, November 15, 1969 (page 1118)

# Selection Open-Book Test

**A.** Think about the use of imagery in this poem and how each word or phrase evokes an idea, a feeling, or a scene. Read the excerpt from the poem below. Then write notes describing which of your senses are affected by the imagery and what you visualize as you read it. (15 points each)

| Excerpt | 1. Senses Affected | 2. What You Visualize |
|---|---|---|
| Up that bank where gas curled in the ivy, dragging each other up, strangers, brothers and sisters. Nothing will do but to taste the bitter taste. No life other, apart from. | | |

**B.** Write the letter of the best answer. (10 points each)

_____ 1. In this poem, being tear-gassed gives the speaker a sense of
   a. determination.
   b. fear.
   c. depression.
   d. hopelessness.

_____ 2. How do the protesters seem to feel about one another?
   a. resentful
   b. uneasy
   c. united
   d. cordial

_____ 3. The speaker feels an urgent need to
   a. leave the protest.
   b. stay with the other protesters.
   c. rethink her reasons for protesting.
   d. think only of her personal welfare.

**C.** Answer **one** of the following questions based on your understanding of "At the Justice Department, November 15, 1969." Write your answer on a separate sheet of paper. (20 points)

1. Think about the repetition of the word *wanting* in the poem. What purpose does the repetition of this word serve? Support your ideas with references to the poem.

2. How does Levertov's style—word choice, imagery, sentence length, rhythm—help you to understand and appreciate the event described in this poem? Support your ideas with references to the poem.

**D. Linking Literature to Life.** Answer the following question based on your own experience and knowledge. Write your answer on a separate sheet of paper. (20 points)

What aspect of life in America would you like to see radically changed and why? How might this change come about?

# Unit Seven: War Abroad and Conflict at Home

# Part One Open-Book Test

**A.** Write the answer to each question on the lines. (5 points each)

1. At the end of the story "Armistice," why did Morris and Gus agree to a kind of peace between them?

   _____

   _____

2. What is the mood at the beginning of "Letter from Paradise . . . ," and why does it change?

   _____

   _____

3. In "Ambush," why does the narrator "keep writing war stories"?

   _____

   _____

4. The speaker in "At the Justice Department . . ." is saying that what she is experiencing is "trivial." Why, do you think, does she feel this way?

   _____

   _____

**B.** Think about the effect of the imagery in the poems in this part. (20 points)

- Circle the letter of **one** poem you wish to discuss.
- In the box on the left, identify an image from that poem.
- In the box on the right, jot down the sense or senses to which that image appeals.
- In the box at the bottom, note some things that the image makes you think about.

   a. "The Death of the Ball Turret Gunner"""
   b. "In Response to Executive Order 9066"
   c. "Camouflaging the Chimera"

   d. "Deciding"
   e. "At the Justice Department,
      November 15, 1969"

| The image of | appeals to the sense or senses of |
|---|---|
|  |  |
| **and makes me think about** | |
|  |  |

Name _____     Date _____

..................................................................................................................................

**C.** Answer **two** of the following essay questions based on your understanding of the selections. Write your answers on a separate sheet of paper. (20 points each)

1. Compare and contrast the wartime experiences or the effects of war on any two civilians **or** any two soldiers from different selections in this part.

2. From the selections in this part, choose **two** people or groups of people—one that you admire and one that you don't admire. Support your choices with details from the selections and your own ideas about life.

3. Many of these selections deal with the subject of personal responsibility. Compare and contrast **two** people from different selections in terms of responsibility. Which of the two do you think acts more responsibly? Support your ideas with details from the selections.

**D.** Think about how people in this part are affected by other individuals and groups of people. (20 points)

- For each set of boxes, circle the letter of **one** person you wish to discuss. **Do not choose a person from a selection that you discussed in Part B.**
- In each set of boxes, write notes to answer the questions.

a. Morris in "Armistice"
b. the speaker of "The Death of the Ball Turret Gunner"

c. the writer of "Letter from Paradise . . ."
d. the speaker of "In Response to Executive Order 9066"

| Who strongly affects this person? | |
|---|---|
| **How is the person you chose affected?** | **Why is the person you chose affected in this way?** |
| | |

a. the speaker of "At the Justice Department . . ."
b. the speaker in "Deciding"

c. the narrator in "Ambush"

| Who strongly affects this person? | |
|---|---|
| **How is the person you chose affected?** | **Why is the person you chose affected in this way?** |
| | |

# Letter from Birmingham Jail (page 1136)

# Selection Test

**A.** In this letter, King uses allusions in two ways: he appeals to reason to change the way a reader *thinks* about an issue, and he appeals to emotion to try to influence the way a reader *feels* about an issue. Read each of the quotations in the chart below. For each quotation, write notes explaining what the allusion refers to, whether it is intended to appeal to reason or emotions, and how effective it is in King's argument. (10 points each)

| Quotation | What It Alludes To | What It Appeals To | Its Effectiveness |
|---|---|---|---|
| 1. "Like Paul, I must constantly respond to the Macedonian call for aid." | | | |
| 2. "We should never forget that everything Adolf Hitler did in Germany was 'legal'. . . ." | | | |
| 3. "And Abraham Lincoln: 'This nation cannot survive half slave and half free.'" | | | |

**B.** Write the letter of the best answer. This exercise is continued on the next page. (5 points each)

_____ 1. What was King arrested for?
    a. entering a white neighborhood
    b. leading a violent protest
    c. causing a riot
    d. parading without a permit

_____ 2. King's main purpose in this letter was to
    a. threaten the state of Alabama.
    b. explain his motives and actions to a large audience.
    c. demand support from the religious community.
    d. issue a warning to city officials.

_____ 3. From this letter, you can conclude that King
      a. wanted to be granted a pardon.
      b. preferred a more violent form of protest.
      c. accepted that his actions would be punished.
      d. felt that the city had attacked his religious beliefs.

**C. Words to Know.** Write the letter of the best answer. (4 points each)

_____ 1. The person most likely to be <u>cognizant</u> of legal matters is a
      a. lawyer.         b. carpenter.        c. cashier.

_____ 2. An <u>appraisal</u> always involves
      a. an approval.     b. a criticism.      c. an evaluation.

_____ 3. People who work <u>diligently</u> toward their goals are likely to
      a. fail.           b. succeed.        c. recover.

_____ 4. In the United States, a <u>statute</u> is enacted by a
      a. parent.        b. teacher.       c. legislature.

_____ 5. A husband and wife who experience an <u>estrangement</u> are
      a. separated.      b. supportive.     c. happily married.

**D.** Answer **one** of the following questions based on your understanding of "Letter from Birmingham Jail." Write your answer on a separate sheet of paper. (20 points)

1. What criticisms did the clergymen make against King and his actions? Briefly explain King's arguments in response to each of these criticisms.

2. In "Letter from Birmingham Jail," King states that the "white moderate" is more of an obstruction to the civil rights movement than are white racists. Do you agree with his assessment of the situation? Why or why not? Explain, using details from the selection to support your opinion.

**E. Linking Literature to Life.** Answer the following question based on your own experience and knowledge. Write your answer on a separate sheet of paper. (15 points)

In this letter, King argues for the proposition that one has a moral responsibility to disobey unjust laws. Do you agree with this statement? Explain your opinions.

# Wandering (page 1150)

## Selection Test

**A.** In each box on the right, jot down what the dialogue reveals about the character. (20 points each)

| | |
|---|---|
| **Him.** I don't believe in war.<br>**He.** There's no danger of war. . . .<br>**Him.** But armies, see, I don't believe in it.<br>**He.** Do you love your country?<br>**Him.** No more than any other, the ones I've seen.<br>**He.** That's treason. | **1. Him** |
| **Him.** I'm sorry.<br>**He.** Quite all right; we'll take you.<br>**Him.** I won't go. . . . It's my right.<br>**He.** You'll learn.<br>**Him.** I don't believe in killing people. . . .<br>**He.** We'll teach you. | **2. He** |

**B.** Write the letter of the best answer. (5 points each)

_____ 1. Everyone in Him's life seems to have tried to
  a. change Him.          c. destroy Him.
  b. make Him happy.       d. make Him miserable.

_____ 2. The tone of this play is best described as
  a. amused.              c. angry.
  b. curious.             d. cynical.

**C. Words to Know.** Write the letter of the best answer. (4 points each)

_____ 1. The <u>aggressor</u> in a war is the side that
  a. wins.          b. starts it.          c. is in the right.

_____ 2. Which is <u>compulsory</u> for American teenagers?
  a. dating          b. attending school          c. playing video games

_____ 3. Who are **most** likely to be going through a period of <u>indoctrination</u>?
  a. recruits          b. veterans          c. generals

_____ 4. Where is one **most** likely to take part in <u>regimentation</u>?
  a. on campus          b. at boot camp          c. around a campfire

_____ 5. A <u>specimen</u> is generally expected to be
  a. unique.          b. defective.          c. representative.

**D.** Answer **one** of the following questions based on your understanding of the play. Write your answer on a separate sheet of paper. (15 points)

1. Write a paragraph or two comparing and contrasting the roles played in Him's life by his mother and wife.

2. Contrast what "wandering" represents to Him with what it represents to He and She. How do you account for these opposing views on "wandering"?

**E. Linking Literature to Life.** Answer the following question based on your own experience and knowledge. Write your answer on a separate sheet of paper. (15 points)

What is the difference between being selfish and being true to oneself? Explain.

# The Writer in the Family (page 1157)

# Selection Test

**A.** Think about the plot of "The Writer in the Family." What is the main conflict in the story, how is it introduced, and how is it resolved? In the story map below, write notes describing what happens in each stage of the plot. (5 points each)

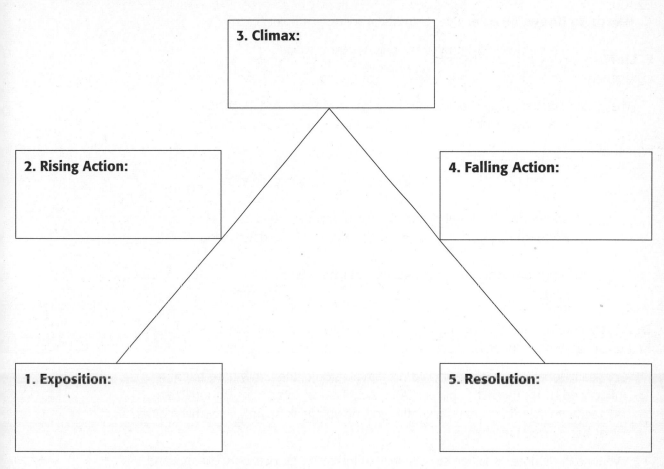

**3. Climax:**

**2. Rising Action:**

**4. Falling Action:**

**1. Exposition:**

**5. Resolution:**

**B.** Write the letter of the best answer. This exercise is continued on the next page. (6 points each)

_____ 1. The conflict in this story arises mainly from
   a. Jack's desire to be a sailor.
   b. family resentments.
   c. Harold's desire to go to college.
   d. Ruth's need to find a job.

_____ 2. What can you conclude about Jonathan's father?
   a. He never fulfilled his dream.
   b. He was quite satisfied with life.
   c. He was considered a hero by his sons.
   d. He disliked his family.

_____ 3. Jonathan can best be described as
   a. mean and thoughtless.
   b. depressed and sad.
   c. sarcastic and inconsiderate.
   d. thoughtful and reflective.

**C. Words to Know.** Write the letter of the best answer. (4 points each)

_____ 1. A person with a terminal condition is expected to
   a. recover.          b. improve.          c. die.

_____ 2. Which of these would most likely be considered indestructible?
   a. a crystal glass      b. a jigsaw puzzle      c. an army tank

_____ 3. A robust person is
   a. hearty.          b. sickly.          c. depressed.

_____ 4. Someone who is debilitated by fear is best described as
   a. weakened.          b. strengthened.          c. determined.

_____ 5. A person implicated in a crime is thought to be
   a. faultless.          b. involved.          c. innocent.

**D.** Answer **one** of the following questions based on your understanding of "The Writer in the Family." Write your answer on a separate sheet of paper. (20 points)

1. For years, Jonathan's feelings toward his father's side of the family have been influenced by his mother's opinions. After Aunt Frances has a talk with Jonathan, he seems to see his mother differently. How do you think he now views his mother? What has caused this change?

2. What conflicts does Jonathan struggle with in this story? Discuss both external and internal conflicts that he may be experiencing. Use details from the story to support your ideas.

**E. Linking Literature to Life.** Answer the following question based on your own experience and knowledge. Write your answer on a separate sheet of paper. (17 points)

It is often difficult for children to see their parents as individuals who once may have had very different lives. How do you see your parent(s), and what do you know about the dreams and aspirations they may have had—or still have?

# Teenage Wasteland (page 1168)

# Selection Test

**A.** Decide who you think is the protagonist and who are the antagonists in this story. Then, for each character, make a mark in a small box next to the description that best fits him or her. In the boxes on the right, write notes or cite details from the story that support your views. You might find it best to begin with the character that you think is the protagonist instead of working in numerical order. (10 points each)

| | |
|---|---|
| **1. Donny**<br><br>☐ protagonist<br><br>☐ antagonist<br><br>☐ neither | |
| **2. Daisy**<br><br>☐ protagonist<br><br>☐ antagonist<br><br>☐ neither | |
| **3. Cal**<br><br>☐ protagonist<br><br>☐ antagonist<br><br>☐ neither | |

**B.** Write the letter of the best answer. (5 points each)

_____ 1. When Donny gets into trouble, **both** he and Cal tend to
   a. take personal responsibility.
   b. blame the authority figures in Donny's life.
   c. say they're sorry without really meaning it.
   d. make a big joke out of it so that people won't be mad.

_____ 2. Why do Daisy and Matt stop calling the parents of Donny's friends about the parties his friends are throwing?
   a. Donny stops going to parties.
   b. They've begun to trust Donny.
   c. They think it might make Donny more trusting.
   d. They think it might give Donny greater confidence.

**C.** How do you think Daisy and Cal would fare if they were subjected to the grading process that Donny is subjected to? For each "report card" category below, make a mark in a small box to indicate which character you think deserves the better grade in that skill area. In each box on the right, write notes supporting your opinions. (5 points each)

| Skill Area | Best Grade | Support |
|---|---|---|
| 1. Ability to communicate well with others | ☐ Daisy ☐ Cal | |
| 2. Willingness to communicate with others | ☐ Daisy ☐ Cal | |
| 3. Possession of feelings of self-worth and self-respect | ☐ Daisy ☐ Cal | |
| 4. Ability to tolerate others' individual needs and desires | ☐ Daisy ☐ Cal | |

**D. Words to Know.** Write the letter of the best answer. (4 points each)

_____ 1. People who behave amiably are showing their
   a. scorn.         b. friendliness.         c. bad manners.

_____ 2. Which is **most** likely to be considered a morass?
   a. sports         b. politics         c. charities

_____ 3. The appearance of a looming figure is **most** likely to make a person feel
   a. worried.         b. amused.         c. sympathetic.

_____ 4. If you temporize, you are trying to
   a. stall.         b. be brief.         c. explain something.

_____ 5. A forlorn dog is **most** likely to
   a. snap.         b. whimper.         c. wag its tail.

**E.** Answer **one** of the following questions based on your understanding of the story. Write your answer on a separate sheet of paper. (10 points)

  1. Who do you think is the better influence on Donny—Daisy or Cal? Explain.

  2. With whom do you sympathize more—Daisy or Donny? Why?

**F. Linking Literature to Life.** Answer the following question based on your own experience and knowledge. Write your answer on a separate sheet of paper. (10 points)

   What can teenagers do to gain the trust of adults? What can adults do to encourage teenagers to be trustworthy? Explain your answers.

# Separating (page 1180)

# Selection Test

**A.** Think about what Joan's plan for informing the children of the separation reveals about her and what Richard's plan reveals about him. Then write notes to answer the questions in the boxes below. (10 points each)

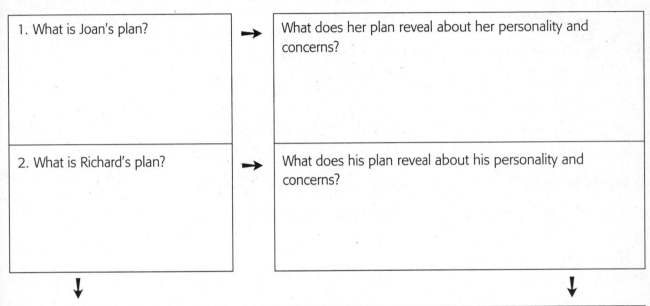

| 1. What is Joan's plan? | → | What does her plan reveal about her personality and concerns? |
| 2. What is Richard's plan? | → | What does his plan reveal about his personality and concerns? |

| 3. Although Richard agrees to Joan's plan, it is Richard's plan that, for the most part, ends up being followed. | |
| How and why does this occur? | What specific aspects of Joan's and Richard's characters are revealed by this incident? |

**B.** Write the letter of the best answer. This exercise is continued on the next page.
(5 points each)

_____ 1. Richard and Joan are separating because they
  a. argue constantly.
  b. never loved each other.
  c. don't make each other happy.
  d. are too proud to forgive each other.

_____ 2. Richard's replacing the lock on the door is symbolic of his desire to
     a. remarry.              c. protect his family.
     b. hurt Joan.            d. get on with his life.

_____ 3. Judith, the oldest daughter, reacts to the news of the separation
     a. sadly.               c. happily.
     b. calmly.             d. with disgust.

_____ 4. Which of the following **best** explains why Richard's telling Dickie, his oldest son, about the separation is an example of dramatic irony?
     a. The other children already know about the separation.
     b. The reader knows about the separation, but Dickie doesn't.
     c. Dickie has been away and doesn't suspect that anything is wrong.
     d. Dickie should have sensed that his parents were unhappy, but didn't.

**C. Words to Know.** Write the letter of the best answer. (4 points each)

_____ 1. Which is **most** likely to be described as being opulent?
     a. a cottage          b. a palace          c. an office building

_____ 2. It would be considered congruous behavior to sing in
     a. a choir.           b. a library.          c. your sleep.

_____ 3. Which is **most** likely to be described as succulent?
     a. a pine cone        b. a stone          c. an orange

_____ 4. Which group of people is **most** likely to show tumultuous behavior?
     a. rioters           b. chess players       c. choir members

_____ 5. People who talk stiltedly speak too
     a. long.             b. formally.          c. briefly.

**D.** Answer **one** of the following questions based on your understanding of the story. Write your answer on a separate sheet of paper. (15 points)

1. In your opinion, does this story have any heroes or villains? Support your answer with details from the story and your own ideas.

2. Which do you believe concerns Richard more—his happiness or that of his children? Use details from the story and your own ideas to support your answer.

**E. Linking Literature to Life.** Answer the following question based on your own experience and knowledge. Write your answer on a separate sheet of paper. (15 points)

Divorces are more socially acceptable and easier to get than they once were. Do you think that this is mainly a good thing or a bad thing?

# Mexicans Begin Jogging/Legal Alien (page 1194)

# Selection Test

**A.** Think about how the titles of these poems relate to the themes. Then, in each box on the left, jot down the main theme of the poem. In each box on the right, write notes explaining how the title relates to or reflects the theme. (20 points each)

|  | **Theme of the Poem** | **How the Title Relates to or Reflects the Theme** |
|---|---|---|
| 1. "Mexicans Begin Jogging" |  |  |
| 2. "Legal Alien" |  |  |

**B.** Write the letter of the best answer. (10 points each)

_____ 1. In "Mexicans Begin Jogging," Soto's boss views Soto as
        a. a legal alien.           c. an American.
        b. a Mexican American.    d. an illegal alien.

_____ 2. The speaker of "Legal Alien" suggests that **both** Americans and Mexicans tend to view her with
        a. pity.               c. fascination.
        b. suspicion.        d. embarrassment.

**C.** Answer **one** of the following questions based on your understanding of the poems. Write your answer on a separate sheet of paper. (20 points)

1. How would you describe the tone of "Mexicans Begin Jogging"? Identify at least **two** words, phrases, images, or other elements of the poem and explain how they help to convey that tone.

2. Contrast the "grin" in line 21 of "Mexicans Begin Jogging" with the "smile" referred to in line 19 of "Legal Alien."

**D. Linking Literature to Life.** Answer the following question based on your own experience and knowledge. Write your answer on a separate sheet of paper. (20 points)

Write a personal response to this quotation by Deborah Tannen: "We all know we are unique individuals, but we tend to see others as representatives of groups."

# Hostage (page 1200)

## Selection Test

**A.** Think about whether Bruno qualifies as a tragic hero. An element of the definition of a tragic hero is noted in each box on the left. In each box on the right, write notes telling how Bruno conforms to or differs from that element. (12 points each)

| | |
|---|---|
| 1. A tragic hero is a character whose basic goodness and superiority are marred by a tragic flaw—a fatal error in judgment that leads to the hero's downfall. | |
| 2. Before tragic heroes meet their downfall, they perceive how they have contributed to their own destruction. | |

**B.** Write the letter of the best answer. (4 points each)

_____ 1. Before the incident with the madman, the narrator wants Bruno to
a. love her.
b. notice her.
c. ignore her.
d. defend her.

_____ 2. Before the incident with the madman, which of the following do Bruno and the narrator have **most** in common?
a. leadership skills
b. thirst for knowledge
c. experience with violence
d. curiosity about each other

_____ 3. Among the people in the neighborhood, the death of Bruno's father is considered
a. just.
b. routine.
c. terribly sad.
d. newsworthy.

.......................................................................................................................................

**C.** Think about how Bruno is changed by the incident with the madman. Then, in the box on the left, write notes describing what he is like and how he is perceived by others before the incident. In the box on the right, write notes describing what he is like and how he is perceived by others after the incident. (6 points each)

| **1. Before** | ➤ | **2. After** |
| --- | --- | --- |
| | | |

**D. Words to Know.** Write the letter of the best answer. (4 points each)

_____ 1. An <u>obscure</u> object is one that you cannot easily
   a. destroy.             b. replace.             c. make out.

_____ 2. An <u>affronted</u> person is **most** likely to react by
   a. glaring.             b. grinning.             c. grieving.

_____ 3. If you feel <u>antagonistic</u> toward a person, you **most** probably consider that person your
   a. enemy.             b. role model.             c. close friend.

_____ 4. An action that is often done in a <u>subtle</u> way is a
   a. scream.             b. nudge.             c. salute.

_____ 5. An example of something that is physically <u>abrasive</u> is
   a. ice.             b. down.             c. sandpaper.

**E.** Answer **one** of the following questions based on your understanding of the story. Write your answer on a separate sheet of paper. (16 points)

1. Compare and contrast the reactions of the narrator and Bruno to the madman and the reasons each may have for reacting as she or he does.

2. Identify what you feel is the main reason that various people have for suspecting that Bruno's actions are not truly heroic. How do you judge Bruno's reaction to the madman, and why?

**F. Linking Literature to Life.** Answer the following question based on your own experience and knowledge. Write your answer on a separate sheet of paper. (16 points)

What in American society seems to you to encourage violence? Identify at least **two** elements in, or forces of, American society and explain how they encourage violence.

# Mother Tongue (page 1215)

# Selection Test

**A.** Think about how Tan felt toward her mother as she was growing up and then how she feels toward her as an adult. In the boxes below, write notes describing Tan's feelings and the examples she uses in this essay to illustrate those feelings. (10 points each)

| Amy Tan's Attitude Toward Her Mother | |
|---|---|
| **1. Growing Up** | **2. As an Adult** |
| | |

**B.** Write the letter of the best answer. (6 points each)

_____ 1. What is Tan's main point about her mother's English?
   a. It expresses who she is.
   b. It is unintelligible to others.
   c. It is very difficult for Tan to understand.
   d. It is as good as her Chinese.

_____ 2. Which word **best** describes Tan's attitude toward her mother?
   a. disappointed          c. charmed
   b. resentful             d. respectful

_____ 3. One thing that embarrassed Tan as she grew up was pretending to
   a. be her mother and making her phone calls.
   b. understand what her mother was saying.
   c. be better at math than at history.
   d. act as if she did not understand Chinese.

_____ 4. One reason Tan became an English major was because she
   a. always wanted to be an editor.
   b. did poorly in math courses.
   c. felt squeamish in premed classes.
   d. wanted to disprove assumptions about her abilities.

**C. Words to Know.** Write the letter of the best answer. (4 points each)

_____  1. A speech that has been <u>transcribed</u> was
            a. recited from memory.  b. censored.          c. copied in writing.

_____  2. An <u>impeccable</u> solution to a problem has
            a. many errors.          b. no mistakes.       c. faulty premises.

_____  3. Which person would be most likely to make a <u>diagnosis</u>?
            a. an artist             b. a lawyer           c. a physician

_____  4. A <u>disobedient</u> child is most likely to be
            a. punished.             b. rewarded.          c. cooperative.

_____  5. A <u>quandary</u> is most like a
            a. mixture.              b. dilemma.           c. foreword.

**D.** Answer **one** of the following questions based on your understanding of "Mother Tongue." Write your answer on a separate sheet of paper. (20 points)

1. Why does Tan include her mother's story about the political gangster in Shanghai? How does this story help you better understand the point Tan is making in her essay?

2. Do you think that Tan and her mother have a close relationship? Why or why not? Give at least three details from the essay to support your opinion.

**E. Linking Literature to Life.** Answer the following question based on your own experience and knowledge. Write your answer on a separate sheet of paper. (16 points)

Do you agree or disagree with Amy Tan's conclusions about standardized tests? Do you feel that people's abilities can be judged fairly by these kinds of tests? Explain.

# The Latin Deli: An Ars Poetica (page 1223)

# Selection Open-Book Test

**A.** Think about the imagery and figurative language used in this poem to create vivid word pictures. For each example below, write notes in the boxes to identify the correct figure of speech (simile, metaphor, or hyperbole) and explain its meaning. (10 points each)

| Example | Figure of Speech | Meaning |
|---|---|---|
| 1. "... the green plantains / hanging in stalks like votive offerings" | | |
| 2. "a woman ... who spends her days selling canned memories" | | |
| 3. "... it would be cheaper to fly to San Juan / than to buy a pound of Bustelo coffee here" | | |

**B.** Write the letter of the best answer. (10 points each)

_____ 1. Which image from the poem appeals to the sense of smell?
      a. "plastic Mother and Child magnetized"
      b. "... the open bins / of dried codfish"
      c. "... the family portrait / of her plain wide face"
      d. "... plain ham and cheese"

_____ 2. You can infer that the speaker of this poem understands
      a. that people need reminders of home.
      b. how terrifying it is to be an immigrant.
      c. why immigrants do not learn to speak English.
      d. why people choose to leave their homelands.

_____ 3. The mood of this poem suggests a sense of
      a. bitterness.
      b. distrust.
      c. rebellion.
      d. nostalgia.

**C.** Answer **one** of the following questions based on your understanding of "The Latin Deli." Write your answer on a separate sheet of paper. (20 points)

1. Poets are conscious of each word's denotation, or dictionary meaning, as well as each word's connotation—the emotion that the word evokes or suggests. For example, the word *house* means a place where you live, but the word *home* suggests a cozy, comfortable feeling. Reread the poem and pay close attention to the following words: *presiding, heady, gaze, hunger, divine,* and *conjuring.* Then explain the connotation, as opposed to the denotation, of each word.

2. Think about the word choices and the use of imagery in this poem. How do you think the speaker feels about the deli? How does the speaker feel about the owner and the customers? Use references from the poem to support your answer.

**D. Linking Literature to Life.** Answer the following question based on your own experience and knowledge. Write your answer on a separate sheet of paper. (20 points)

Suppose that you moved to another country. After living there for some time, what do you think you might become homesick for? What do you think you might see, hear, or smell in another country that would remind you of something at home?

# Straw into Gold (page 1227)

## Selection Test

**A.** Think about how the author's voice is heard in this essay through the sentence structure, diction, and tone. Read the excerpt in the chart below. Then write notes explaining its sentence structure, diction, and tone, and how these elements contribute to the author's voice. (10 points each)

| Excerpt | "I like to think that somehow my family, my Mexicanness, my poverty, all had something to do with shaping me into a writer. I like to think my parents were preparing me all along for my life as an artist even though they didn't know it. From my father I inherited a love of wandering. . . . From him I inherited a sappy heart." |
|---|---|
| **1. Sentence Structure** | |
| **2. Diction** | |
| **3. Tone** | |

**B.** Write the letter of the best answer. (5 points each)

_____ 1. Why did Cisneros's fellow artists in France expect her to make tortillas?
   a. They knew that she was a very good cook.
   b. Everyone had to make a contribution to meals.
   c. They assumed that because she was Mexican she would know how.
   d. They wanted her to learn how to cook.

_____ 2. Which statement best reflects the main theme of this essay?
   a. Cisneros inherited her father's love of travel and his sappy heart.
   b. Her mother flourished in her own home.
   c. She managed to make tortillas, which were burnt.
   d. She has done a lot of things in her life that she didn't think she could do.

_____ 3. Cisneros broke a "terrible taboo" by
   a. becoming a writer.
   b. leaving home before her brothers.
   c. disobeying her parents.
   d. not doing well in the fifth grade.

Name _____     Date _____

## C. Words to Know. Write the letter of the best answer. (4 points each)

_____ 1. An artist who works <u>intuitively</u> depends most on
        a. feelings.        b. reason.        c. live models.

_____ 2. Which of these is <u>edible</u>?
        a. a book        b. a glass        c. an apple

_____ 3. If you were going to <u>document</u> an event, you would make a
        a. record of it.        b. file folder.        c. poster.

_____ 4. A person who <u>ventured</u> into the wilderness would probably be
        a. going fishing.        b. camping out.        c. taking risks.

_____ 5. An <u>avalanche</u> of paperwork is
        a. a snowstorm.        b. a huge amount.        c. an organized list.

**D.** Answer **one** of the following questions based on your understanding of "Straw into Gold." Write your answer on a separate sheet of paper. (20 points)

1. How does the concept of turning "straw into gold" apply to the author's life and her work? Use details from the essay to support your ideas.

2. What is the central idea in this essay, and what details does the author provide to support this idea?

**E. Linking Literature to Life.** Answer the following question based on your own experience and knowledge. Write your answer on a separate sheet of paper. (15 points)

In this essay, Cisneros writes, "I didn't like school because all they saw was the outside me. School was lots of rules and sitting with your hands folded and being very afraid all the time." How did you react to this statement? Have you ever felt this way? Explain.

# Unit Seven: War Abroad and Conflict at Home

# Part Two Open-Book Test

**A.** Write the letter of the best answer to each question. (5 points each)

_____ 1. In "Letter from Birmingham Jail," King alludes to Hitler's Germany in order to
   a. give an example of a segregated society that failed.
   b. explain that unjust laws should be disobeyed.
   c. emphasize its similarities to the United States.
   d. warn what will happen if nonviolent protests are not allowed.

_____ 2. Both *Wandering* and "The Writer in the Family" convey ideas about the theme of
   a. living up to other people's expectations.
   b. hiding family secrets from outsiders.
   c. the aimlessness of people who have no ambitions.
   d. the positive influences of family relationships.

_____ 3. Both "Mother Tongue" and "Legal Alien" focus on
   a. problems in education in the United States.
   b. the difficulties of understanding one's parents.
   c. the shame of being an illegal immigrant.
   d. perceptions of people who speak different languages.

_____ 4. In "Straw into Gold," Cisneros explains how she
   a. survived a tragic childhood to become successful.
   b. made the decision to leave Mexico.
   c. turned her own experiences into subjects for stories.
   d. rebelled against authority when she was a child.

**B.** Many of these selections draw contrasts between two different or opposing things or ideas. Write the title of **one** selection you wish to discuss. Then write notes explaining what things or ideas are contrasted and what ideas or feelings this contrast helps communicate to the reader. (20 points)

| **Title of Selection:** |
| --- |
| **Things or Ideas Contrasted:** |
| **Ideas or Feelings Communicated to the Reader:** |

**C.** Answer **two** of the following essay questions based on your understanding of the selections. Write your answers on a separate sheet of paper. (20 points each)

1. Think about the political and personal causes that are advanced by the people in this part. Which person from this part do you think does the best job of advancing his or her cause? Which do you think does the worst job? Support your opinions with reference to the selections.

2. Which issue raised in these selections seems to you to be primarily one of individual responsibility about which there is little, if anything, that governmental action can or could do? Support your answer with reference to the selection and your own ideas about responsibility.

3. Several selections in this part express ideas and feelings about biculturalism. Which selection seems to suggest the most positive feelings about a bicultural American experience, and which suggests the most negative feelings? Support your opinions with reference to the selections.

4. Think about the conflicts addressed in these selections. Then choose **two** selections, describe the central conflicts of each, and explain what makes these conflicts difficult to resolve. Are the conflicts resolved? If so, explain how. If not, offer the best solutions you can think of.

**D.** Think about the strong emotions that are expressed in these selections. Choose a person from **one** of the selections that you wish to discuss. Write the title of the selection and the name of the person. Then write notes to identify the strong emotion expressed by that person and your opinion about why the person feels that emotion. (20 points)

| Selection: | Person: |
|---|---|
| **Strong Emotion:** | **Reasons for That Emotion:** |
| | |

# The Language of Literature: American Literature

# End-of-Year Test

**Directions:** Read the selection below. Then answer the questions that follow.

### The Murderer
*Ray Bradbury*

Music moved with him in the white halls. He passed an office door: "The Merry Widow Waltz." Another door: *Afternoon of a Faun.* A Third: "Kiss Me Again." He turned into a cross-corridor: "The Sword Dance" buried him in cymbals, drums, pots, pans, knives, forks, thunder, and tin lightning. All washed away as he hurried through an anteroom where a secretary sat nicely stunned by Beethoven's Fifth. He moved himself before her eyes like a hand; she didn't see him.

His wrist radio buzzed.

"Yes?"

"This is Lee, Dad. Don't forget about my allowance."

"Yes, Son, yes. I'm busy."

"Just didn't want you to forget, Dad," said the wrist radio. Tchaikovsky's *Romeo and Juliet* swarmed about the voice and flushed into the long halls.

The psychiatrist moved in the beehive of offices, in the cross-pollination of themes, Stravinsky mating with Bach, Haydn unsuccessfully repulsing Rachmaninoff, Schubert slain by Duke Ellington. He nodded to the humming secretaries and the whistling doctors fresh to their morning work. At his office he checked a few papers with his stenographer, who sang under her breath, then phoned the police captain upstairs. A few minutes later a red light blinked, a voice said from the ceiling:

"Prisoner delivered to Interview Chamber Nine."

He unlocked the chamber door, stepped in, heard the door lock behind him.

"Go away," said the prisoner, smiling.

The psychiatrist was shocked by that smile.

A very sunny, pleasant warm thing, a thing that shed bright light upon the room. Dawn among the dark hills. High noon at midnight, that smile. The blue eyes sparkled serenely above that display of self-assured dentistry.

"I'm here to help you," said the psychiatrist, frowning. Something was wrong with the room. He had hesitated the moment he entered. He glanced around. The prisoner laughed. "If you're wondering why it's so quiet in here, I just kicked the radio to death."

Violent, thought the doctor.

The prisoner read this thought, smiled, put out a gentle hand. "No, only to machines that yak-yak-yak."

Bits of the wall radio's tubes and wires lay on the gray carpeting. Ignoring these, feeling that smile upon him like a heat lamp, the psychiatrist sat across from his patient in the unusual silence which was like the gathering of a storm.

"You're Mr. Albert Brock, who calls himself The Murderer?"

Brock nodded pleasantly. "Before we start . . ." He moved quietly and quickly to detach the wrist radio from the doctor's arm. He tucked it in his teeth like a walnut, gritted, heard it crack, handed it back to the appalled psychiatrist as if he had done them both a favor. "That's better."

The psychiatrist stared at the ruined machine. "You're running up quite a damage bill."

"I don't care," smiled the patient. "As the old song goes: 'Don't Care What Happens to Me!' " He hummed it.

The psychiatrist said: "Shall we start?"

"Fine. The first victim, or one of the first, was my telephone. Murder most foul. I shoved it in the kitchen Insinkerator! Stopped the disposal unit in mid-swallow. Poor thing strangled to death. After that I shot the television set!"

The psychiatrist said, "Mmm."

"Fired six shots right through the cathode.[1] Made a beautiful tinkling crash, like a dropped chandelier."

"Nice imagery."

"Thanks, I always dreamt of being a writer."

"Suppose you tell me when you first began to hate the telephone."

"It frightened me as a child. Uncle of mine called it the Ghost Machine. Voices without bodies. Scared the living hell out of me. Later in life I was never comfortable. Seemed to me a phone was an impersonal instrument. If it *felt* like it, it let your personality go through its wires. If it didn't *want* to, it just drained your personality away until what slipped through at the other end was some cold fish of a voice, all steel, copper, plastic, no warmth, no reality. It's easy to say the wrong thing on telephones; the telephone changes your meaning on you. First thing you know, you've made an enemy. Then, of course, the telephone's such a *convenient* thing; it just sits there and *demands* you call someone who doesn't want to be called. Friends were always calling, calling, calling me. Hell, I hadn't any time of my own. When it wasn't the telephone it was the television, the radio, the phonograph. When it wasn't the television or radio or the phonograph it was motion pictures at the corner theater, motion pictures projected, with commercials on low-lying cumulus clouds. It doesn't rain rain any more, it rains soapsuds. When it wasn't High-Fly Cloud advertisements, it was music by Mozzek[2] in every restaurant; music and commercials on the busses I rode to work. When it wasn't

---

[1] a cathode-ray tube, used in television picture tubes

[2] a company that made musical recordings for use as background music in such places as elevators and restaurants

music, it was interoffice communications, and my horror chamber of a radio wristwatch on which my friends and my wife phoned every five minutes. What is there about such 'conveniences' that makes them so *temptingly* convenient? The average man thinks, Here I am, time on my hands, and there on my wrist is a wrist telephone, so why not just buzz old Joe up, eh? 'Hello, *hello!*' I love my friends, my wife, humanity, very much, but when one minute my wife calls to say, 'Where are you *now,* dear?' and a friend calls and says, 'Got the best off-color joke to tell you. Seems there was a guy—' And a stranger calls and cries out, 'This is the Find-Fax Poll. What gum are you chewing at this very *instant?*' Well!"

"How did you feel during the week?"

"The fuse lit. On the edge of the cliff. That same afternoon I did what I did at the office."

"Which was?"

"I poured a paper cup of water into the intercommunications system."

The psychiatrist wrote on his pad.

"And the system shorted?"

"Beautifully! The Fourth of July on wheels! My God, stenographers ran around looking *lost!* What an uproar!"

"Felt better temporarily, eh?"

"Fine! Then I got the idea at noon of stomping my wrist radio on the sidewalk. A shrill voice was just yelling out of it at me, 'This is People's Poll Number Nine. What did you eat for lunch?' when I kicked the wrist radio!"

"Felt even *better,* eh?"

"It *grew* on me!" Brock rubbed his hands together. "Why didn't I start a solitary revolution, deliver man from certain 'conveniences'? 'Convenient for who?' I cried. Convenient for friends: 'Hey, Al, thought I'd call you from the locker room out here at Green Hills. Just made a sockdolager[3] hole in one! A hole in one, Al! A *beautiful* day. Having a shot of whiskey now. Thought you'd want to know, Al!' Convenient for my office, so when I'm in the field with my radio car there's no moment when I'm not in touch. *In touch! There's* a slimy phrase. Touch, hell. *Gripped!* Pawed, rather. Mauled and massaged and pounded by FM voices. You can't leave your car without checking in: 'Have stopped to visit gas-station men's room.' 'Okay, Brock, step on it!' 'Brock, what *took* you so long?' 'Sorry, sir.' 'Watch it next time, Brock.' '*Yes,* sir!' So, do you know what I did, Doctor? I bought a quart of French chocolate ice cream and spooned it into the car radio transmitter."

"Was there any *special* reason for selecting French chocolate ice cream to spoon into the broadcasting unit?"

---

[3]*something outstanding*

Brock thought about it and smiled. "It's my favorite flavor."

"Oh," said the doctor.

"I figured, hell, what's good enough for me is good enough for the radio transmitter."

"What made you think of spooning *ice cream* into the radio?"

"It was a hot day."

The doctor paused.

"And what happened next?"

"Silence happened next. God, it was *beautiful*. That car radio cackling all day, 'Brock go here, Brock go there, Brock check in, Brock check out, okay Brock, hour lunch, Brock, lunch over, Brock, Brock, Brock.' Well, that silence was like putting ice cream in my ears."

"You seem to like ice cream a lot."

"I just rode around feeling of the silence. It's a big bolt of the nicest, softest flannel ever made. Silence. A whole hour of it. I just sat in my car, smiling, feeling of that flannel with my ears. I felt *drunk* with Freedom!"

"Go on."

"Then I got the idea of the portable diathermy machine.[4] I rented one, took it on the bus going home that night. There sat all the tired commuters with their wrist radios, talking to their wives, saying, 'Now I'm at Forty-third, now I'm at Forty-fourth, here I am at Forty-ninth, now turning at Sixty-first.' One husband cursing, 'Well, get *out* of that bar, damn it, and get home and get dinner started, I'm at Seventieth!' And the transit-system radio playing 'Tales from the Vienna Woods,' a canary singing words about a first-rate wheat cereal. Then—I switched on my diathermy! Static! Interference! All wives cut off from husbands grousing about a hard day at the office. All husbands cut off from wives who had just seen their children break a window! The 'Vienna Woods' chopped down, the canary mangled. *Silence!* A terrible, unexpected silence. The bus inhabitants faced with having to converse with each other. Panic! Sheer, animal panic!"

"The police seized you?"

"The bus *had* to stop. After all, the music was being scrambled, husbands and wives *were* out of touch with reality. Pandemonium, riot, and chaos. Squirrels chattering in cages! A trouble unit arrived, triangulated on me[5] instantly, had me reprimanded, fined, and home, minus my diathermy machine, in jig time."

"Mr. Brock, may I suggest that so far your whole pattern here is not very— practical? If you didn't like transit radios or office radios or car business radios, why

---

[4]*a machine that is used for medical purposes and that produces a high-frequency electric current*

[5]*a reference to triangulation, the process of locating something by means of taking measurements from two fixed points, as can be done with radio signals*

didn't you join a fraternity of radio haters, start petitions, get legal and constitutional rulings? After all, this *is* a democracy."

"And I," said Brock, "am that thing best called a minority. I *did* join fraternities, picket, pass petitions, take it to court. Year after year I protested. Everyone laughed. Everyone else *loved* bus radios and commercials. *I* was out of step."

"Then you should have taken it like a good soldier, don't you think? The majority rules."

"But they went too far. If a little music and 'keeping in touch' was charming, they figured a lot would be ten times as charming. I went *wild!* I got home to find my wife hysterical. *Why?* Because she had been completely out of touch with me for half a day. Remember, I did a dance on my wrist radio? Well, that night I laid plans to murder my house."

"Are you *sure* that's how you want me to write it down?"

"That's semantically[6] accurate. Kill it dead. It's one of those talking, singing, humming, weather-reporting, poetry-reading, novel-reciting, jingle-jangling, rockaby-crooning-when-you-go-to-bed houses. A house that screams opera to you in the shower and teaches you Spanish in your sleep. One of those blathering caves where all kinds of electronic Oracles make you feel a trifle larger than a thimble, with stoves that say, 'I'm apricot pie, and I'm *done,*' or 'I'm prime roast beef, so *baste* me!' and other nursery gibberish like that. With beds that rock you to sleep and *shake* you awake. A house that *barely* tolerates humans, I tell you. A front door that barks: 'You've mud on your feet, sir!' And an electronic vacuum hound that snuffles around after you from room to room, inhaling every fingernail or ash you drop. . . ."

"Quietly," suggested the psychiatrist.

"Remember that Gilbert and Sullivan song—'I've Got It on My List, It Never Will Be Missed'? All night I listed grievances. Next morning early I bought a pistol. I *purposely* muddied my feet. I stood at our front door. The front door shrilled, 'Dirty feet, muddy feet! Wipe your feet! Please be *neat!*' I shot the damn thing in its keyhole! I ran to the kitchen, where the stove was just whining, 'Turn me *over!*' In the middle of a mechanical omelet I did the stove to death. Oh, how it sizzled and screamed, 'I'm *shorted!*' Then the telephone rang like a spoiled brat. I shoved it down the Insinkerator. I must state here and now I have *nothing* whatever against the Insinkerator; it was an innocent bystander. I feel sorry for it now, a practical device indeed, which never said a word, purred like a sleepy lion most of the time, and digested our leftovers. I'll have it restored. Then I went in and shot the televisor, that insidious beast, that Medusa,[7] which freezes a billion people to

[6]*in a manner that has to do with the meaning of words*

[7]*in Greek mythology, a beautiful woman who was punished for loving a god by having her hair turned into snakes; after that, anyone who looked at her turned to stone*

stone every night, staring fixedly, that Siren which called and sang and promised so much and gave, after all, so little, but myself always going back, going back, hoping and waiting until—bang! Like a headless turkey, gobbling, my wife whooped out the front door. The police came. Here I *am!*"

He sat back happily and lit a cigarette.

"And did you realize, in committing these crimes, that the wrist radio, the broadcasting transmitter, the phone, the bus radio, the office intercoms, all were rented or were someone else's property?"

"I would do it all over again, so help me God."

The psychiatrist sat there in the sunshine of that beatific[8] smile.

"You don't want any further help from the Office of Mental Health? You're ready to take the consequences?"

"This is only the beginning," said Mr. Brock. "I'm the vanguard[9] of the small public which is tired of noise and being taken advantage of and pushed around and yelled at, every moment music, every moment in touch with some voice somewhere, do this, do that, quick, quick, now here, now there. You'll *see.* The revolt begins. My name will go down in history!"

"Mmm." The psychiatrist seemed to be thinking.

"It'll take time, of course. It was all so enchanting at first. The very *idea* of these things, the practical uses, was wonderful. They were almost toys, to be played with, but the people got too involved, went too far, and got wrapped up in a pattern of social behavior and couldn't get out, couldn't admit they were *in,* even. So they rationalized their nerves as something else. 'Our modern age,' they said. 'Conditions,' they said. 'High-strung,' they said. But mark my words, the seed has been sown. I got world-wide coverage on TV, radio, films; *there's* an irony for you. That was five days ago. A billion people know about me. Check your financial columns. Any day now. Maybe today. Watch for a sudden spurt, a rise in sales for French chocolate ice cream!"

"I see," said the psychiatrist.

"Can I go back to my nice private cell now, where I can be alone and quiet for six months?"

"Yes," said the psychiatrist quietly.

"Don't worry about me," said Mr. Brock, rising. "I'm just going to sit around for a long time stuffing that nice soft bolt of quiet material in both ears."

"Mmm," said the psychiatrist, going to the door.

"Cheers," said Mr. Brock.

"Yes," said the psychiatrist.

[8]*angelic*
[9]*the leader of thought, taste, or opinion in a field*

He pressed a code signal on a hidden button, the door opened, he stepped out, the door shut and locked. Alone, he moved in the offices and corridors. The first twenty yards of his walk were accompanied by "Tambourine Chinois." Then it was "Tzigane," Bach's Passacaglia and Fugue in something Minor, "Tiger Rag," "Love Is Like a Cigarette." He took his broken wrist radio from his pocket like a dead praying mantis. He turned in at his office. A bell sounded; a voice came out of the ceiling, "Doctor?"

"Just finished with Brock," said the psychiatrist.

"Diagnosis?"

"Seems completely disoriented, but convivial.[10] Refuses to accept the simplest realities of his environment and work *with* them."

"Prognosis?"[11]

"Indefinite. Left him enjoying a piece of invisible material."

Three phones rang. A duplicate wrist radio in his desk drawer buzzed like a wounded grasshopper. The intercom flashed a pink light and click-clicked. Three phones rang. The drawer buzzed. Music blew in through the open door. The psychiatrist, humming quietly, fitted the new wrist radio to his wrist, flipped the intercom, talked a moment, picked up one telephone, talked, picked up another telephone, talked, picked up the third telephone, talked, touched the wrist-radio button, talked calmly and quietly, his face cool and serene, in the middle of the music and the lights flashing, the phones ringing again, and his hands moving, and his wrist radio buzzing, and the intercoms talking, and voices speaking from the ceiling. And he went on quietly this way through the remainder of a cool, air-conditioned, and long afternoon; telephone, wrist radio, intercom, telephone, wrist radio, intercom, telephone, wrist radio, intercom, telephone, wrist radio, intercom, telephone, wrist radio, intercom, telephone, wrist radio . . .

[10]*merry*

[11]*a forecast of the probable course of a disease*

Name _____  Date _____

..............................................................................................................................................

**A.** The following items test your understanding of the selection. Circle the letter of the response that best completes the sentence or answers the question.

1. In this story, Mr. Brock is being interviewed by a
   a. policeman.
   b. wrist radio.
   c. musician.
   d. psychiatrist.

2. Mr. Brock has been arrested for
   a. neglecting his wife.
   b. destroying technology.
   c. inciting a riot.
   d. stopping a bus.

3. You can tell from this story that a *stenographer* is
   a. an office worker.
   b. a prison official.
   c. a medical assistant.
   d. a detective.

4. From Mr. Brock's point of view, the main conflict in this story is between him and
   a. his wife.
   b. the interviewer.
   c. his telephone.
   d. society.

5. What did Mr. Brock do first when the psychiatrist entered Chamber Nine?
   a. He asked for some French chocolate ice cream.
   b. He put flannel in his ears.
   c. He broke the psychiatrist's wrist radio.
   d. He sang the song "Don't Care What Happens to Me!"

6. Mr. Brock seems to think that he will become famous for
   a. starting a revolt.
   b. selling ice cream.
   c. praising his Insinkerator.
   d. talking back to a robot.

**B.** The following items check your understanding of the way in which the selection is written. Circle the letter of the response that best completes the sentence or answers the question.

7. Calling the passengers on the bus "Squirrels chattering in cages" is an example of
   a. simile.
   b. hyperbole.
   c. metaphor.
   d. personification.

8. Which sentence best helps you visualize what Chamber Nine looks like?
   a. "Bits of the wall radio's tubes and wires lay on the gray carpeting."
   b. "High noon at midnight, that smile."
   c. "A very sunny, pleasant warm thing, a thing that shed bright light upon the room."
   d. "Something was wrong with the room."

9. Mr. Brock uses an allusion to Medusa to
   a. explain why he likes ice cream.
   b. describe his uncle who hated telephones.
   c. explain why he does not get along with his wife.
   d. describe the effect of the televisor on people who watch it.

10. Mr. Brock can best be described as
    a. peaceful.
    b. nonconformist.
    c. tolerant.
    d. vain.

**C.** The following items check your understanding of the way in which the selection is written. Write your response after each item.

11. Write a brief summary of the plot of this story.

_____

_____

_____

12. Describe the kinds of imagery and figurative language Mr. Brock uses to describe his house. How does his use of imagery and figurative language make the description more effective?

_____

_____

_____

13. How does the narrator's point of view in this story influence how the reader feels about Mr. Brock's actions?

_____

_____

_____

**D.** The following items check your ability to analyze and evaluate the selection. Circle the letter of the response that best completes the sentence or answers the question.

14. You can tell that this story takes place in the future because
    a. people listen to music.
    b. every office has telephones.
    c. people have wrist radios.
    d. kitchens include garbage disposals.

15. Why did the psychiatrist feel uncomfortable when he first entered Chamber Nine?
    a. The room was quiet.
    b. Mr. Brock threatened him.
    c. He was thinking about his son's reminder.
    d. He did not like the music that was playing.

16. Which statement best expresses Mr. Brock's view of democracy?
    a. Everyone in a democracy should follow the rules like a "good soldier."
    b. It ignores the needs and desires of people in the minority.
    c. It is no better than slavery.
    d. It is the best possible system of government.

17. Unlike Mr. Brock, the psychiatrist thinks that
    a. Mr. Brock's actions will lead to a worldwide revolt.
    b. ice cream is the key to Mr. Brock's recovery.
    c. people should accept reality and learn to live with it.
    d. anyone who appreciates technology is insane.

**E.** The following items check your ability to analyze and evaluate the selection. Write your response after each item.

18. What is the theme of this story?

_____

_____

_____

19. Think about the main characters in this story as representing two opposing views in a larger conflict. What views do the psychiatrist and Mr. Brock represent?

_____

_____

_____

20. Whom did you sympathize or agree with most in this story—the psychiatrist or Mr. Brock? Explain your views.

_____

_____

_____

Name _____ Date _____

........................................................................................................................................................

**Writing Exercise** The following activity is designed to assess your writing ability. The prompt asks you to explain something. Think of your audience as being any reader other than yourself.

When scorers evaluate your writing, they will look for evidence that you can:

- respond directly to the prompt;

- make your writing thoughtful and interesting;

- organize your ideas so that they are clear and easy to follow;

- develop your ideas thoroughly by using appropriate details and precise language;

- stay focused on your purpose for writing by making sure that each sentence you write contributes to your composition as a whole; and

- communicate effectively by using correct spelling, capitalization, punctuation, grammar, usage, and sentence structures.

Prompt: At one point in this story, Mr. Brock says, "And I . . . am that thing best called a minority. . . . I was out of step." Mr. Brock did not feel that he fit in with the rest of the people in the world, and he decided to resist the pressure to conform. Many of the selections you have read also focus on individuals who cannot or do not accept the reality of change in the world around them.

Choose one of the characters or persons you have read about in the selections, such as Emily Dickinson, Black Elk in "High Horse's Courting," Langston Hughes in "When the Negro Was in Vogue," the speaker in "The Love Song of J. Alfred Prufrock," Joan Didion in "Letter from Paradise . . . ," or Martin Luther King, Jr., in "Letter from Birmingham Jail." Or think about a person you know who seems to hear "the beat of a different drum" and resists conforming to the behaviors and ideals of the majority. Write a short essay explaining how the character or person you choose is different from the majority and how he or she resists conforming to the rest of the world. Do you think the character or person does the right thing by following his or her own views? Use the bottom of the page to organize your ideas. Then write your essay on a separate sheet of paper.

_____

_____

_____

_____

_____

_____

_____

_____

**Revising/Editing** The purpose of the following exercise is to check your ability to proofread and revise a piece of writing in order to improve its readability and presentation of ideas. Read the following paragraph. Then, for each underlined section, circle the letter of the revision below that most improves the writing. Or, if the section is best left as it is, circle letter *d*.

In the 1960s and 1970s, many young people in America rebelled

against what was known as "the Establishment." African Americans <u>holding</u>
                                                                        1.
<u>protests</u> and demonstrations to fight for equal rights. Women struggled for

equality. Student protesters chanting "Make Love Not War" helped bring an

end to the conflict in <u>Vietnam and president Nixon</u> was forced to resign.
                        2.
In the 1980s, the era of protest and change <u>spread to</u> other parts of
                                              3.
the world. <u>The Cold War ended the Berlin Wall fell.</u> The Soviet Union
            4.
broke up, and South Africa abolished apartheid.

Today, society is very different <u>from itself</u> 40 years ago. <u>Because</u> we
                                   5.                              6.
begin the 21st century, we can only speculate on the shape of the future.

1.  a. have held protests
    b. was holding protests
    c. held protests
    d. Correct as is

2.  a. Vietnam, and President Nixon
    b. Vietnam and President Nixon
    c. Vietnam; and president Nixon
    d. Correct as is

3.  a. spreaded to
    b. spreading to
    c. spreads to
    d. Correct as is

4.  a. The Cold War ended, the Berlin Wall fell.
    b. The Cold War ended, and the Berlin Wall fell.
    c. The Cold War ended, but the Berlin Wall fell.
    d. Correct as is

5.  a. from themselves
    b. from what they were
    c. from what it was
    d. Correct as is

6.  a. As
    b. Although
    c. Since
    d. Correct as is

# Additional Test Generator Questions

## Contents

## To the Teacher

The following pages contain additional selection questions, which you may wish to use to construct tests that are customized to better meet the needs of your students. Correct responses to questions on these pages are marked with an asterisk. Read the questions and determine if any of them are appropriate for your students. Then use the Test Generator software to call up the questions and add them to your customized tests. Directions for using the Test Generator software are included in the *Test Generator User's Guide,* which accompanies the software.

# UNIT ONE

## *Part One*
## The World on the Turtle's Back
## Test Generator

1. According to this myth, what element of the earth did not exist in the beginning?
   a. sky
   *b. land
   c. water
   d. animals

2. According to this myth, in the beginning, the gods lived
   *a. in the sky.
   b. in the water.
   c. on the earth.
   d. underneath the earth.

3. In the beginning, the gods viewed the Great Tree that stood at the center of the universe with
   *a. awe.
   b. terror.
   c. scorn.
   d. jealousy.

4. When the birds see the pregnant woman falling, their initial response is one of
   a. fear.
   b. envy.
   c. ridicule.
   *d. sympathy.

5. In the short period after her fall, the pregnant woman is most in need of
   *a. food.
   b. water.
   c. courage.
   d. medical attention.

6. According to the myth, which of the following is least involved in the creation of earth?
   *a. the gods
   b. the animals
   c. the pregnant woman
   d. the pregnant woman's daughter

7. Why does the daughter faint when she sees the man?
   a. She has fallen in love with him.
   *b. She has never seen a man before.
   c. She believes that he is her father.
   d. He threatens to kill her with the two arrows.

8. At what point do the twins begin arguing with each other?
   *a. before they are born
   b. when they are born
   c. when their mother dies
   d. when their grandmother begins to favor one over the other

9. The dead body of the mother of the twins gives birth to
   a. only things that are bad for people.
   *b. only things that are good for people.
   c. both good and bad things.
   d. things that are neither good nor bad for people.

10. The right-handed twin reacts to his grandmother's favoring his brother with
    a. grief and despair.
    *b. jealousy and anger.
    c. complete indifference.
    d. acceptance and understanding.

11. What motivates the twins to create new life forms?
    a. sorrow
    b. gratitude
    c. loneliness
    *d. sibling rivalry

12. Which of the following is most responsible for the right-handed twin's victory over his brother?
    a. luck
    b. innocence
    *c. deception
    d. physical strength

## Song of the Sky Loom
## Hunting Song/Dinni-e Sin
## Test Generator Open-Book Test

1. The overall feeling of "Song of the Sky Loom" could best be described as
   a. fearful.
   b. amused.
   c. impatient.
   *d. respectful.

2. Where is the deer when the hunter in "Hunting Song" begins singing?

  *a. on a mountaintop
  b. at the foot of a mountain
  c. in a flowery meadow
  d. in a heavily wooded forest

3. The deer believes that the hunter is

  a. a god.
  *b. a bird.
  c. a person.
  d. another deer.

4. The main purpose of the hunter's song is to

  a. entertain the hunter.
  b. apologize to the deer.
  c. praise the hunter's skills.
  *d. ensure that the hunt will be successful.

5. The hunter's song does not

  a. trick the deer.
  *b. warn the deer.
  c. guide the deer.
  d. please the deer.

# Coyote and the Buffalo
# Fox and Coyote and Whale
# Test Generator

1. In "Coyote and the Buffalo," which of the following is not part of Bull Buffalo's feelings for Coyote?

  a. mercy
  b. anger
  *c. jealousy
  d. gratitude

2. Bull Buffalo's new horns gain him the power to

  *a. kill his rival.
  b. rise from the dead.
  c. raise others from the dead.
  d. influence Coyote's spirit helper.

3. Which of the following brings about the death of Coyote's cow?

  a. anger
  *b. greed
  c. revenge
  d. desperation

4. Why does the old woman offer to cook the cow's bones for Coyote?

  a. to honor Coyote
  b. to fulfill her duty to Coyote
  *c. to put Coyote off his guard
  d. to gain Coyote's protection

5. Which of the following is the result of magic or the supernatural?

  a. Bull Buffalo's death
  *b. Bull Buffalo's new horns
  c. the death of Coyote's cow
  d. the escape of the old woman

6. Who refuses to give Coyote a second chance?

  a. Bull Buffalo
  b. Coyote himself
  *c. Coyote's cow
  d. Coyote's spirit helper

7. In "Fox and Coyote and Whale," when Fox discovers that his wife is in love with Whale, Fox begins to treat her more

  a. shyly.
  b. meanly.
  c. trustingly.
  *d. considerately.

8. Who does Fox hold most responsible for his wife's betrayal?

  *a. Whale
  b. Coyote
  c. his wife
  d. Fox, himself

9. What is Fox's attitude toward the task of stealing back his wife?

  a. fearful
  b. cheerful
  c. indifferent
  *d. determined

10. What motivates Mouse to lie to the Water People about what she said about Coyote?

  a. fear
  b. honor
  *c. greed
  d. compassion

11. What most enables Fox and Coyote to sneak up on Whale and Fox's wife?
    a. love
    b. magic
    *c. trickery
    d. goodness

12. Fox kills Whale
    a. by accident.
    *b. to get revenge.
    c. in a panic.
    d. in self defense.

13. In "Fox and Coyote and Whale," Coyote is presented as
    a. lazy and stupid.
    *b. insightful and helpful.
    c. violent and dangerous.
    d. cowardly and untrustworthy.

## The Man to Send Rain Clouds
## Test Generator

1. Teofilo died as a result of
    a. suicide.
    b. murder.
    c. accident.
    *d. natural causes.

2. Teofilo died while he was
    a. hunting.
    *b. watching sheep.
    c. exploring the area.
    d. walking back to town.

3. Leon is the type of person who
    a. offers detailed explanations.
    *b. carefully measures every word.
    c. loves to use colorful expressions.
    d. always says whatever pops into his head.

4. At the funeral and burial, Teofilo's body is treated with
    *a. respect.
    b. suspicion.
    c. disregard.
    d. indifference.

5. Which of the following is not a clue that the story has a contemporary setting?
    a. Teofilo's clothes
    *b. the face painting
    c. the priest driving a car
    d. Leon's green army jacket

## *from* The Way to Rainy Mountain
## Test Generator

1. The "way" to Rainy Mountain represents
    a. a philosophical journey for the author's grandmother.
    b. a history of the Crows.
    c. directions on the highway.
    *d. the migration history of the Kiowa tribe.

2. The Rainy Mountain area can best be described as
    a. idyllic.
    b. lush.
    *c. harsh.
    d. fertile.

3. You can conclude that Momaday's attitude toward nature is one of
    *a. respect and wonder.
    b. indifference.
    c. awe and fear.
    d. scorn.

4. According to Momaday, the Kiowa eventually found the mountains to be
    a. frightening.
    b. breathtaking.
    c. exhilarating.
    *d. confining.

5. Why did the Kiowa back away from the ceremonial medicine tree forever?
    a. They converted to Christianity.
    *b. Soldiers dispersed the tribe.
    c. They felt betrayed by Tai-me.
    d. There were no longer enough members for the ceremony.

6. Which of the following is an example of a simile?
    a. ". . . the prairie is an anvil's edge."
    b. "the grass . . . cracks beneath your feet."
    *c. "grasshoppers . . . popping up like corn. . . ."
    d. "The sun is at home on the plains."

7. What did the author visit that was "there, where it ought to be, at the end of a long and legendary way"?
 *a. his grandmother's grave
 b. Fort Sill
 c. the medicine tree
 d. his grandfather's grave

8. The Kiowa were originally a tribe of
 a. agriculturists.
 *b. hunters and warriors.
 c. fishers.
 d. horse breeders.

## Part Two
### from La Relación
### Test Generator

1. When Cabeza de Vaca realizes that all of his men are going to die on the barge, he
 a. becomes frightened and panics.
 *b. becomes depressed but doesn't give up.
 c. does all he can to make dying easier for the men.
 d. accepts the situation as God's will and leaves it in His hands.

2. Which of the following is not a reason that the Spanish are frightened of the Karankawas when they first meet them?
 a. The Karankawas carry weapons.
 b. The Karankawas outnumber them.
 *c. The Karankawas make threats and demands.
 d. The Spanish aren't prepared to defend themselves.

3. What is the most likely reason that the Karankawas grieve for the three drowned Spanish men?
 a. They feel responsible for the deaths.
 b. They were especially fond of the men.
 *c. They believe that death is a sad event.
 d. They believe that it will bring the men back to life.

4. What is Cabeza de Vaca's main motivation for asking the Karankawas to take his men into their homes?
 a. grief
 b. pride
 *c. survival
 d. curiosity

5. The Karankawas withdraw food from the Spanish in order to
 a. kill them.
 b. test their loyalty.
 c. encourage them to leave.
 *d. encourage them to cooperate.

6. The Karankawas respond to the efforts of the Spanish to cure the sick with
 a. fear.
 b. anger.
 c. hostility.
 *d. gratitude.

### from Of Plymouth Plantation
### Test Generator

1. According to Bradford, upon reaching the harbor at Cape Cod, the Pilgrims were filled with
 a. fear and worry.
 *b. gratitude and joy.
 c. pride and goodwill.
 d. regret and misgivings.

2. In his descriptions of the new land, Bradford reveals that his attitude toward nature is mainly one of
 a. awe.
 b. respect.
 *c. hostility.
 d. fondness.

3. At first, the Pilgrims assume that the Native Americans will want to
 *a. harm them.
 b. avoid them.
 c. worship them.
 d. welcome them.

4. Which of the following does Bradford credit for the Pilgrims' surviving their first violent encounter with the Native Americans?
 *a. God's will
 b. the Pilgrims' common sense
 c. the Pilgrims' superior weaponry
 d. the Pilgrims' respect for human life

5. Bradford does not characterize "the starving time" as a period in which the Pilgrims
   a. suffered.
   b. cooperated.
   *c. questioned their faith.
   d. were looked after by God.

6. The terms of the peace treaty imply that the Pilgrims were not willing to
   a. recognize the equality of men and women.
   b. recognize the right of individuals to own property.
   c. hold another people responsible for their actions.
   *d. subject their actions to the judgment of another people.

7. The tone of the section on the first Thanksgiving could best be described as
   a. smug.
   *b. hopeful.
   c. anxious.
   d. humorous.

## from The Interesting Narrative of the Life of Olaudah Equiano
## Test Generator

1. As Equiano is loaded on the ship, his greatest worry is that he will
   a. drown.
   b. lose his temper.
   *c. be killed by the crew.
   d. never again see his family.

2. It is clear from Equiano's reactions to his experiences that he has come from a country that is
   *a. inland.
   b. uncivilized.
   c. near the sea.
   d. chiefly agricultural.

3. The crew reacts to Equiano's refusal to eat by
   *a. beating him.
   b. confining him below deck.
   c. throwing his food overboard.
   d. having another slave feed him.

4. Equiano is allowed to spend time on the deck because he is
   a. weary.
   *b. sickly.
   c. desperately unhappy.
   d. respected for his social standing.

5. Equiano's greatest objection to slavery is that it is
   a. racist.
   b. irrational.
   *c. inhumane.
   d. uneconomical.

## from Blue Highways
## Test Generator

1. Both Fritz and Heat-Moon could be described as
   a. significantly bitter.
   b. suspicious and skeptical.
   *c. tolerant and open-minded.

2. Fritz believes that being a Hopi in the modern world is
   *a. difficult.
   b. impossible.
   c. relatively easy.

3. By saying that "the Big Vision made the Indian, but the white man invented him," Fritz's grandfather was making a point about the white man's
   a. religion.
   b. inferiority.
   *c. arrogance.

4. Fritz plans to return to Tuba City to practice medicine because
   a. he feels pressured by his family to do so.
   *b. he feels a responsibility to serve the Hopi community.
   c. he does not feel comfortable outside the Hopi community.

5. Fritz would not describe life as a
   a. series of journeys.
   b. circle that is never broken.
   *c. straight line with beginning and ending points.

6. According to the Hopi Way, children are born
   a. ignorant.
   *b. open-minded.
   c. self-centered.

7. To Fritz, the Hopi Way is basically a
   a. myth.
   b. religion.
   *c. way of life.

8. Of the following things discussed in the selection, which appears to have the least symbolic value to the Hopi?
   a. blue corn
   *b. the myth of the noble savage
   c. the image of the four worlds

6. The acceptance that Angelou finds in Dunkwa most affects her identity as
   a. a writer.
   b. a woman.
   *c. an African.
   d. an American.

## My Sojourn in the Lands of My Ancestors
## Test Generator

1. Angelou's reaction to rejection by black Africans is one of
   *a. sorrow.
   b. indifference.
   c. amusement.
   d. understanding.

2. What is the main thing that motivates Angelou to pull off the road and watch the "troupe of tragic players enter and exit the stage"?
   a. pride
   b. curiosity
   c. weariness
   *d. a sense of responsibility or duty

3. Watching the "troupe of tragic players" leaves Angelou feeling
   a. foolish.
   b. angered.
   c. hopeless.
   *d. calm and subdued.

4. Angelou's reaction to being accepted by the people of Dunkwa is one of
   a. horror.
   *b. pleasure.
   c. intense guilt.
   d. astonishment.

5. What does Angelou reveal about the customs in Arkansas and Dunkwa?
   *a. They are similar.
   b. They place unfair burdens on the poor.
   c. They have little purpose in the modern world.
   d. Their origins can be traced to the system of slavery.

# UNIT TWO

## Part One
### Selected Poems by Bradstreet
### Test Generator Open-Book Test

1. In which set of lines does the speaker of "To My Dear and Loving Husband" establish her unity with her husband?
   *a. lines 1–4
   b. lines 5 and 6
   c. lines 7 and 8
   d. lines 9–12

2. In lines 5–8 of "To My Dear and Loving Husband," the speaker develops the idea that the love in her marriage is
   a. moral.
   *b. strong.
   c. eternal.
   d. spiritual.

3. The speaker of "To My Dear and Loving Husband" feels that her husband's love for her is
   a. far weaker than her love for him.
   b. slightly weaker than her love for him.
   *c. as powerful as her love for him.
   d. far stronger than her love for him.

4. What is the meter of "Upon the Burning of Our House"?
   a. iambic trimeter
   *b. iambic tetrameter
   c. iambic pentameter
   d. trochaic pentameter

5. In "Upon the Burning of Our House," the speaker's initial feeling when she realizes that the house is on fire is one of
   *a. panic.
   b. gratitude.
   c. mild disbelief.
   d. calm acceptance.

6. In line 36 of "Upon the Burning of Our House," the word *all's* applies to
   a. all future matters.
   b. all moral matters.
   *c. all worldly matters.
   d. all spiritual matters.

7. In which three stanzas does the speaker mourn the loss of her house?
   a. stanzas 2–4
   *b. stanzas 4–6
   c. stanzas 6–8
   d. stanzas 7–9

8. In "Upon the Burning of Our House," the speaker most closely associates the afterlife with
   a. a burning house.
   b. a humble dwelling place.
   *c. a richly furnished, fireproof house.
   d. the ruins of her house.

9. The destruction of her house makes heaven seem more
   a. unreal to the speaker.
   *b. appealing to the speaker.
   c. frightening to the speaker.
   d. distant and remote to the speaker.

10. The speaker of "Upon the Burning of Our House" would describe God as all of the following except
   a. just.
   *b. distant.
   c. merciful.
   d. reasonable.

11. Which of the following is a source of comfort to the speakers of both poems?
   *a. faith
   b. nature
   c. reason
   d. misfortune

## The Examination of Sarah Good
### Test Generator

1. What does Good admit to muttering when leaving people's homes?
   a. curses
   b. threats
   c. complaints
   *d. verses from the Christian Bible

2. The prosecutor gets Good to accuse Sarah Osborne of witchcraft by
   a. threatening her.
   b. fooling or lying to her.
   c. sympathizing with her.
   *d. badgering or pressuring her.

3. Good's husband believes that his wife is
   a. definitely guilty.
   b. definitely innocent.
   *c. possibly guilty.
   d. possibly insane.

4. Which of the following was not true of courtroom practices during this time?
   a. Children were permitted to testify against adults.
   b. Spouses were permitted to testify against one another.
   c. The accused could be assumed guilty until proven innocent.
   *d. The accused were forbidden knowledge of their accusers' identities.

## *from* Sinners in the Hands of an Angry God
## Test Generator

1. According to Edwards, God's attitude toward sinners is
   a. loving.
   *b. ruthless.
   c. sorrowful.
   d. indifferent.

2. According to Edwards, what is God's attitude toward a person's living a good life?
   a. proud
   b. loving
   c. merciful
   *d. indifferent

3. Which of the following human traits does Edwards associate with God in this sermon?
   a. cunning
   b. generosity
   c. compassion
   *d. sense of justice

4. Which emotion of God does Edwards most emphasize in this sermon?
   a. joy
   *b. anger
   c. relief
   d. disappointment

## The Crucible: Act One
## Test Generator

1. Most of the villagers view Rebecca Nurse as a
   a. harmless gossip.
   *b. kind and respectable woman.
   c. spiteful woman.
   d. merciless judge of others.

2. Reverend Parris is most concerned with
   *a. his reputation.
   b. Betty's health.
   c. Abigail's soul.
   d. the spiritual needs of the people.

3. Abigail went into the forest because she wanted to
   *a. get rid of Goody Proctor.
   b. threaten Tituba.
   c. watch the other girls dance.
   d. persuade the girls to return home.

4. You can infer that the citizens of Salem thought dancing was
   a. only for children.
   b. good exercise.
   *c. evil and sinful.
   d. a delightful entertainment.

5. Which statement made by Abigail shows that she is not as harmless as she appears?
   a. "Uncle, you've prayed since midnight."
   *b. "I can make you wish you had never seen the sun go down!"
   c. "My name is good in the village!"
   d. "She is blackening my name in the village!"

6. Tituba most likely confessed to meeting with the devil because she
   a. wanted the villagers to fear her.
   b. wanted to please Parris.
   c. did not want Abigail to get into trouble.
   *d. thought it might save her life.

7. Which sentence best describes John Proctor?
   a. He respects Reverend Hale's opinions.
   b. He believes in witchcraft.
   c. He will do whatever he can to destroy Thomas Putnam.
   *d. He rebels against authority by speaking his mind.

8. Rebecca advised Parris to sent Reverend Hale away because she
   a. thought the villagers might resent the help of an outsider.
   b. feared she would be exposed as a witch.
   *c. knew his presence would only cause more hysteria in Salem.
   d. felt that Parris could handle the situation better than Hale.

## The Crucible: Act Two
### Test Generator

1. Sarah Good is accused of witchcraft because she
   a. was named by Elizabeth Proctor in court.
   b. put a curse on Goody Putnam.
   *c. could not recite the Ten Commandments.
   d. slept in a ditch.

2. At first, Mary Warren enjoys her role in court because she
   a. thinks she has been chosen by God.
   *b. likes the power and status she has in the village.
   c. knows she can destroy Elizabeth Proctor.
   d. plans to accuse Abigail of witchcraft.

3. Why is there tension between Elizabeth Proctor and her husband?
   a. Elizabeth is very ill.
   b. John plans to spend more time with Abigail.
   *c. John has had an adulterous affair.
   d. John is planning to leave Elizabeth.

4. Abigail stuck a needle into her stomach in order to
   *a. accuse Elizabeth Proctor of witchcraft.
   b. cast suspicion on Mary Warren.
   c. claim that it was John Proctor's doing.
   d. pretend that she was a witch.

5. Why does Mary say she cannot tell the truth in court?
   a. She does not want the other girls punished.
   b. She wants Elizabeth found guilty.
   *c. She is afraid that Abigail will kill her.
   d. She is too embarrassed to admit she is a fraud.

6. What does John Proctor mean when he says, "My wife will never die for me"?
   a. If he baptizes his son, his wife will be freed.
   *b. He knows his adultery has caused Elizabeth to be arrested.
   c. He knows Elizabeth is being punished for his quarrels with Parris.
   d. Hale will not release Elizabeth until Proctor attends church.

7. Goody Osburn will hang, but Sarah Good will not because
   a. Goody Osburn's conjuring was much worse.
   b. the villagers like Sarah Good better than Goody Osburn.
   c. Parris spoke up for Sarah Good.
   *d. Sarah Good confessed, but Goody Osburn did not.

## The Crucible: Act Three
### Test Generator

1. Which line best expresses the real truth behind the trials?
   a. "Is every defense an attack upon the court?"
   b. "I have evidence for the court!"
   c. "But it does not follow that everyone accused is part of it."
   *d. ". . . private vengeance is working through this testimony!"

2. Giles Corey is arrested because he refuses to
   *a. name the person who accused Putnam of grabbing land.
   b. leave the court without presenting his evidence.
   c. accuse his wife of conjuring spells.
   d. name the books his has been reading.

3. Hale begins seriously to doubt the morality and motivations of the trials when he
   a. hears John Proctor's story.
   b. talks to Giles Corey.
   *c. signs Rebecca's death sentence.
   d. reads Giles's deposition.

4. Francis Nurse is terrified when Danforth insists on questioning the people who signed his petition because he
   a. knows he will be arrested for contempt.
   b. knows the people will deny signing it.
   *c. promised no harm would come to them.
   d. feels the judge should accept his word.

5. Hale denounces the proceedings of the court because he
   a. believes that Parris has orchestrated the trials.
   b. feels that the devil will never be driven from Salem.
   c. is upset by the way John Proctor has treated Abigail.
   *d. believes the testimony of Mary Warren and John Proctor.

## The Crucible: Act Four
### Test Generator

1. What is Parris's real reason for wanting Proctor saved?
   *a. a concern for his own safety
   b. fear of hanging an innocent man
   c. fear that Hale will turn the village against him
   d. a desire for his own redemption

2. Why does Danforth refuse to postpone the hangings?
   a. He refuses to accept any suggestions from Hale.
   b. He fears the people will riot if the executions don't take place.
   *c. It might look as if he has wrongly executed innocent people.
   d. He doubts the authority of the church.

3. Giles Corey can best be described as
   a. petty.
   *b. courageous.
   c. cruel.
   d. remorseful.

4. You can infer that Abigail and Mercy have left Salem because they
   a. were asked to leave by Parris.
   b. cannot bear to see Proctor hanged.
   c. have gone to Andover for the witch trials.
   *d. fear the villagers will turn on them.

5. Cows are wandering loose on the roads of Salem because
   a. the farmers fear the trials and have left Salem.
   b. the people believe the devil has possessed the cows.
   *c. many farmers have been jailed and can't take care of their farms.
   d. the farmers are spending too much time at the trials.

6. Which line best expresses a major theme of this play?
   a. "Another judgment waits us all!"
   *b. "I am not your judge, I cannot be."
   c. "I never knew such goodness in the world!"
   d. "I cannot mount the gibbet like a saint."

## Part Two
### Speech in the Virginia Convention
### Test Generator

1. Which of the following best describes Henry's tone in this speech?
   *a. fiery
   b. smug
   c. doubtful
   d. quietly confident

2. To Henry, the situation of the colonies calls for the Convention to
   *a. take swift action.
   b. engage in lengthy debate.
   c. consult with other authorities.
   d. delay action until tempers have calmed.

3. At the beginning of the speech, Henry treats the members of the Convention whose position he opposes as
   a. bullies.
   b. traitors.
   *c. patriots.
   d. inferiors.

4. Which of the following is not something that Henry believes will aid the colonial cause against the British?
   a. a sense of unity
   b. a sense of justice
   *c. a desire for peace
   d. strength in numbers

5. Henry's use of rhetorical questions in this speech is mainly intended to make the decision facing the Convention seem
   a. trivial.
   b. complex.
   *c. clear-cut.
   d. impossible to make.

6. Which phrase in the following quotation is the best example of loaded language: "Should I keep back my opinions at such a time, through fear of giving offense, I should consider myself as guilty of treason toward my country, and of an act of disloyalty toward the majesty of heaven"?
   a. "Should I keep back my opinions"
   b. "through fear of giving offense"
   c. "I should consider myself"
   *d. "an act of disloyalty toward the majesty of heaven"

## Declaration of Independence
## Test Generator

1. The Declaration states that all men have the right to
   *a. liberty and the pursuit of happiness.
   b. protection from the British government.
   c. keep and bear arms.
   d. vote in elections.

2. What does Jefferson mean when he says that "governments are instituted among men, deriving their just powers from the consent of the governed"?
   a. People cannot be expected to make decisions about government.
   b. Only governments can decide what is right for the common people.
   *c. Governments are created and given power by the people they govern.
   d. If people do not vote, they should have no say in the government.

3. Jefferson accuses the king of
   a. creating an independent government for the colonies.
   b. refusing to tax the colonies.
   *c. making it difficult for the colonists to attend legislative meetings.
   d. not letting the colonies keep a portion of the taxes they collect.

4. Jefferson opens the Declaration by stating that, as a show of respect, the colonies will
   *a. explain the causes of their discontent.
   b. demand that all British forces leave the United States.
   c. explain why the colonies cannot fight against Britain.
   d. ask the representatives to present the king with a list of grievances.

## Letter to the Rev. Samson Occom
## Letter to John Adams
## Test Generator

1. Which of the following best describes Wheatley's attitude toward Rev. Samson Occom?
   a. timid
   b. superior
   *c. respectful
   d. affectionate

2. Wheatley believes that slavery is doomed for all of the following reasons except that
   *a. slavery is highly profitable.
   b. slavery is absurd and irrational.
   c. the desire for freedom is strong.
   d. the desire for freedom is natural.

3. All of the following are part of the tone of Adams's letter except
   a. anger.
   *b. humor.
   c. affection.
   d. impatience.

4. Which of the following is most probably the reason that Adams agreed to be separated from her husband?
   a. They would soon be reunited.
   b. It was what he wanted and he was to be obeyed.
   c. It gave her more freedom to run the household as she desired.
   *d. His service to the country was more important than anything else.

5. Why hasn't Adams written to her husband for ten days?
   a. She has been evacuated from her home.
   b. She has been too busy with domestic duties.
   *c. She hasn't been in the mood to be pleasant.
   d. She knows he is too busy to read her letters.

6. Adams believes that the work her husband is engaged in is of
   a. little interest to her.
   b. little importance to the nation.
   *c. vital importance to the nation.
   d. more interest to her than to him.

7. Which of the following does Adams believe is the source of the authority of kings?
   a. God
   b. natural law
   *c. the people
   d. the moral superiority of kings

8. What is Adams's opinion of the reaction of her husband and his colleagues to the situation in Boston?
   a. She believes that they have overreacted.
   *b. She believes that they haven't done enough.
   c. She believes that they have handled it perfectly.
   d. She believes that they have done all that they could do.

9. Why does Adams believe that her husband and his colleagues are being ungenerous to "the ladies"?
   a. They aren't keeping in touch with their wives.
   b. They aren't electing women to the Congress.
   *c. They are keeping absolute power over their wives.
   d. They are forcing their wives to take on all of their domestic duties.

10. In the letter, Adams attempts to convince her husband that
   a. men are powerless against women.
   b. men have greater power over women than men realize.
   c. women are powerless against men.
   *d. women have greater power than men give them credit for.

11. Which of the following quotations includes a metaphor?
   a. "God grant deliverance in his own way and time."
   b. "Thus do I suppress every wish and silence every murmur."
   *c. "Our country is, as it were, a secondary god and the first and greatest parent."
   d. "How many are the solitary hours I spend, ruminating upon the past and anticipating the future."

## What Is an American?
### Test Generator

1. According to Crèvecoeur, the countries that most emigrants came from weren't really their "countries" because
   *a. their labor wasn't rewarded.
   b. they didn't have equal rights.
   c. they didn't have the right to vote.
   d. they gave up their citizenship when they left.

2. According to Crèvecoeur, which of the following did real Americans leave behind in their old countries?
   a. their religious beliefs
   b. their arts and sciences
   c. their material possessions
   *d. their customs and prejudices

3. Which of the following is not something that Crèvecoeur includes in his definition of an American?
   *a. He is born in America.
   b. He is a western Pilgrim.
   c. He is European or the descendant of a European.
   d. He earns his bread in America.

4. In the letter, Crèvecoeur mainly emphasizes the idea of America as a land of
   a. ease.
   b. illusions.
   c. contrasts.
   *d. opportunity.

## Lecture to a Missionary
### Test Generator

1. What is Red Jacket's attitude toward history?
   a. scornful
   *b. attentive
   c. indifferent

2. According to Red Jacket, the Great Spirit created his people's country out of
   *a. love.
   b. pride.
   c. loneliness.

3. Red Jacket feels that his people's country
   a. will never by taken over by white settlers.
   *b. has already been taken over by white settlers.
   c. is in danger of being taken over by white settlers.

4. Who does Red Jacket believe is the creator of white people?
   a. the devil
   *b. the Great Spirit
   c. the missionary's god

## *from* Stride Toward Freedom
## Necessary to Protect Ourselves
## Test Generator

1. In *Stride Toward Freedom,* King's diction could best be described as
   *a. formal.
   b. informal.
   c. conversational.

2. In *Stride Toward Freedom,* King is mainly concerned with racial injustice as a
   a. legal issue.
   *b. moral issue.
   c. personal issue.

3. King argues in the excerpt from *Stride Toward Freedom* that injustice should be
   *a. fought.
   b. ignored.
   c. made illegal.

4. Which of the following does King imply he is willing to sacrifice for the cause of racial equality?
   a. pride and self-respect
   *b. immediate comfort and safety
   c. the concerns of "generations yet unborn"

5. King associates acquiescence, or "the freedom of exhaustion," with all of the following except
   a. cowardice.
   b. obedience.
   *c. noncooperation.

6. Which of the following is not a reason that King advocates nonviolent resistance?
   *a. He believes that it is less risky than other methods.
   b. He believes that it is more civil than other methods.
   c. He believes that it is more effective than other methods.

7. In the interview, Malcolm X compares the fight for racial justice with the
   a. Holocaust.
   *b. American Revolution.
   c. assassination of Martin Luther King, Jr.

8. In these two selections, the main agreement between King and Malcolm X concerns
   *a. the problem that needs to be addressed.
   b. the methods used to bring about a solution to the problem.
   c. the solution to the problem.

## *from* I Am Joaquín/Yo Soy Joaquín
## Test Generator Open-Book Test

1. Which of the following is part of the feelings Joaquín expresses toward "gringo society"?
   a. awe
   *b. disgust
   c. compassion
   d. grudging admiration

2. In lines 14–23, Joaquín associates financial success with cultural and spiritual
   *a. death.
   b. rebirth.
   c. survival.
   d. revolution.

3. To Joaquín, his ancestors' defeat of the Moors is a source of
   a. anguish.
   b. confusion.
   *c. inspiration.
   d. humiliation.

4. Joaquín's attitude toward the future could best be described as
   *a. optimistic.
   b. indifferent.
   c. slightly pessimistic.
   d. extremely pessimistic.

# UNIT THREE

## *Part One*
### A Psalm of Life
### Test Generator Open-Book Test

1. Of the ideas expressed in the following lines, with which does the speaker disagree?
   *a. line 2
   b. line 13
   c. line 21

2. According to the speaker, which of the following is part of human destiny?
   *a. action
   b. suffering
   c. pleasure

3. The speaker would be most likely to compliment a person for
   *a. taking risks.
   b. being cooperative.
   c. being level-headed.

4. The speaker most emphasizes the need to
   a. study the past.
   *b. live in the present.
   c. plan for the future.

5. The speaker believes that heroes tend to be
   a. ignored.
   *b. inspiring.
   c. threatening.

### The Devil and Tom Walker
### Test Generator

1. Early in the story, the narrator says that the skull Tom finds indicates that the swamp
   a. was an evil place.
   b. was Captain Kidd's burial place.
   *c. had been an Indian battleground.
   d. had been the site of human sacrifices.

2. The narrator indicates that Old Scratch doesn't frighten Tom because
   a. he doesn't look like a devil.
   b. he uses his powers to calm Tom.
   c. Tom doesn't realize who he is.
   *d. Tom's wife is more frightening.

3. As proof of the truth of his statements, Old Scratch
   a. lends Tom his ax.
   b. promises to take Tom's wife.
   c. gives Tom a piece of pirate gold.
   *d. signs Tom's forehead with a fingerprint.

4. The relationship between Tom and his wife is most similar to the typical relationship between
   a. newlyweds.
   *b. a cat and a dog.
   c. business partners.
   d. an employer and an employee.

5. Tom's wife most probably disappears because she
   a. gets lost in the swamp and dies.
   b. runs away to start a new life without Tom.
   c. tries to bribe Old Scratch to leave Tom alone.
   *d. is "taken" after trying to make a bargain with Old Scratch.

6. In what the narrator calls the "most authentic" account of the disappearance of Tom's wife, Tom finds
   a. only her apron.
   b. a skull tied up in her apron.
   *c. a heart and liver tied up in her apron.
   d. the household valuables tied up in her apron.

7. The disappearance of his wife makes Tom feel
   a. angry.
   b. fearful.
   *c. grateful.
   d. indifferent.

8. In negotiating their deal, Tom rejects Old Scratch's suggestion that he
   a. become a usurer.
   *b. become a slave trader.
   c. drive other people to Old Scratch.
   d. use the pirate treasure in Old Scratch's service.

9. An important factor contributing to Tom's success as a moneylender is
   a. his religious conversion.
   b. his generosity toward borrowers.
   *c. other people's desire to get rich quick.
   d. Old Scratch's interference in the economy.

10. So that Old Scratch can't take him by surprise, Tom, in his old age
   *a. carries a Bible in his pocket.
   b. spends most of his time in church.
   c. stops taking advantage of borrowers.
   d. gives up his money lending business.

11. At the end of the story, Old Scratch comes for Tom because
   *a. Tom hasn't fulfilled the bargain.
   b. the bargain gives him the right to Tom's soul.
   c. Old Scratch doesn't want to fulfill the bargain.
   d. Old Scratch never intended for Tom to become so successful.

12. After Tom's disappearance, all of his belongings are
   a. given to charity.
   b. buried in the swamp.
   *c. mysteriously changed or destroyed.
   d. distributed to the borrowers he cheated.

## *from* Self-Reliance
### Test Generator

1. According to Emerson, goodness
   a. is impossible to achieve.
   b. is the enemy of the individual.
   *c. results from being self-reliant.
   d. should be the chief goal of the individual.

2. According to Emerson, to achieve greatness, one must possess
   a. modesty and honesty.
   *b. individuality and self-trust.
   c. an overwhelming desire for recognition and acceptance.
   d. the ability to adapt quickly to changing attitudes and values.

3. Emerson believes that people who achieve greatness tend to live
   a. by themselves.
   b. in the world by society's rules.
   *c. in the world by their own rules.
   d. long enough for society to come to understand them.

4. According to Emerson, society encourages all of the following except
   a. uniformity.
   *b. independent thinking.
   c. sacrifice for the common good.
   d. obedience to custom and tradition.

## *from* Civil Disobedience
### Test Generator

1. Thoreau compares the government to
   *a. a machine.
   b. a wheel.
   c. a body.
   d. an army.

2. Thoreau was sent to jail because he
   a. would not join the army.
   b. refused to pay his church tax.
   c. protested before Congress.
   *d. refused to pay the poll tax.

3. Why was Thoreau freed from prison?
   a. He finally paid his tax.
   *b. Someone else paid his tax.
   c. The government agreed with his position.
   d. The people petitioned for his release.

4. According to Thoreau, if people believe a law is unjust, they should
   a. not deal with the government at all.
   *b. disobey the law and be willing to pay the penalty.
   c. take arms against the government and its representatives.
   d. leave the country.

5. Thoreau believed that
   a. the majority should always rule.
   b. the minority should always rule.
   *c. a person's conscience should always rule.
   d. a central government cannot exist.

## from **Walden**
## **Test Generator**

1. According to Thoreau, contentment is
    a. boring.
    *b. desirable.
    c. common.
    d. impossible.

2. Thoreau believes that he was wisest
    *a. when he was born.
    b. when he decided to live at Walden Pond.
    c. while he was living at Walden Pond.
    d. when he decided to leave Walden Pond.

3. Thoreau's home on Walden Pond could best be described as a
    a. tent.
    *b. cabin.
    c. mansion.
    d. houseboat.

4. Thoreau's attitude toward newspapers and letters is one of
    a. fondness.
    b. fascination.
    *c. annoyance.
    d. grudging acceptance.

5. When Thoreau says, "I have found that no exertion of the legs can bring two minds much nearer to one another," he means that physical closeness
    a. is enough.
    b. is all that people can really hope for.
    *c. doesn't guarantee intellectual or spiritual closeness.
    d. can feel the same as intellectual or spiritual closeness.

6. Thoreau decided to leave Walden Pond because he
    a. had grown lonely.
    *b. felt that it was time to do other things.
    c. didn't find what he had hoped to find there.
    d. knew that he would never truly feel at home there.

7. Which of the following quotations contains a metaphor?
    a. "I say, let your affairs be as two or three, and not a hundred or a thousand."
    b. "The upright white hewn studs and freshly planed door and window casings gave it a clean and airy look."
    *c. "Men say that a stitch in time saves nine, and so they take a thousand stitches today to save nine tomorrow."
    d. "Hardly a man takes a half hour's nap after dinner, but when he wakes he holds up his head and asks, 'What's the news?' "

8. Which of the following quotations contains a simile?
    a. "I did not wish to live what was not life, living is so dear."
    b. "Instead of three meals a day, it if be necessary eat but one."
    c. " I took up my abode . . . on Independence day, or the fourth of July, 1845."
    *d. "The very dew seemed to hang upon the trees later into the day than usual, as on the sides of mountains."

9. Which of the following quotations contains personification?
    a. "I do not wish to be any more busy with my hands than is necessary."
    *b. "As the sun arose, I saw [Walden Pond] throwing off its nightly clothing of mist"
    c. "Still we live meanly, like ants; though the fable tells us that we were long ago changed into men."
    d. "For most men, it appears to me, are in a strange uncertainty about [life], whether it is of the devil or of God."

## **Selected Poems by Whitman**
## **Test Generator Open-Book Test**

1. In "I Hear America Singing," the songs of the workers are an expression of their
    a. weariness.
    *b. individuality.
    c. restlessness.
    d. lack of seriousness.

2. How are the songs in the last two lines of "I Hear America Singing" different from the songs elsewhere in the poem?
   *a. They are songs of play.
   b. They are songs of defiance.
   c. They are songs of immigrants.
   d. They are songs of romantic love.

3. In "I Hear America Singing," the speaker's attitude toward the future of the nation is one of
   a. gloom.
   b. indifference.
   c. mild concern.
   *d. boundless optimism.

4. Which of the following is the least likely reason that the speaker of "I Sit and Look Out" is silent?
   *a. The speaker is unaware of the world's problems.
   b. The speaker is overwhelmed by the world's problems.
   c. The speaker is deeply saddened by the world's problems.
   d. The speaker is baffled by the existence of so much evil in the world.

5. Which of the following best describes the attitude of the speaker in "I Sit and Look Out" toward the subject of the poem?
   a. hopeful
   b. outraged
   *c. detached
   d. surprised

6. The speaker of "Song of Myself" would be least likely to describe death as
   *a. final.
   b. lucky.
   c. natural.
   d. meaningful.

7. Line 3 of "Song of Myself" is most probably intended to convey the speaker's feeling of being
   a. inferior to others.
   b. superior to others.
   *c. connected to others.
   d. isolated from others.

8. In "Song of Myself," what is the attitude of the speaker toward "creeds and schools" (line 10)?
   a. joyous
   b. trusting
   *c. scornful
   d. accepting

9. In "Song of Myself," nature is presented as all of the following except
   a. inspiring.
   b. mystical or spiritual.
   *c. endangered by humanity.
   d. interconnected with humanity.

10. Lines 25–30 of "Song of Myself" suggest that the speaker believes that
    a. each blade of grass has a soul.
    *b. each blade of grass represents a soul.
    c. the grass may foretell the future.
    d. the grass may be growing on people's graves.

11. Lines 52–55 of "Song of Myself" suggest that the speaker believes that, with death, he or she will
    a. cease to exist in any form.
    *b. physically become one with nature.
    c. go on exactly as if nothing had happened.
    d. discover all of the answers to life's mysteries.

**Danse Russe**

**anyone lived in a pretty how town**

**Test Generator Open-Book Test**

1. In "Danse Russe," the speaker dances
   a. for exercise.
   *b. to please himself.
   c. to entertain other people.
   d. as practice for a public performance.

2. To the speaker of "Dance Russe," his loneliness seems
   a. strange.
   b. sudden.
   *c. acceptable.
   d. depressing.

3. In "anyone lived in a pretty how town," the townspeople view "anyone" and "noone" as their
   a. betters.
   b. equals.
   *c. inferiors.
   d. own children.

4. Line 7 of "anyone lived in a pretty how town" suggests that the townspeople lead
   a. long lives.
   b. exciting lives.
   *c. ordinary lives.
   d. meaningful lives.

5. Lines 9 and 10 of "anyone lived in a pretty how town" suggest that those townspeople with insight into human nature include
   a. all of the children.
   *b. some of the children.
   c. only the oldest children.
   d. only "anyone" and "noone."

6. When "anyone" dies, the townspeople bury him
   a. with regret.
   b. with sorrow.
   c. with affection.
   *d. without fanfare.

7. The refrains in lines 3, 11, and 34 in "anyone lived in a pretty how town" communicate a sense of
   a. the present.
   *b. time passing.
   c. one single moment in time.
   d. the final moment in "anyone's" life.

# Ending Poem

## Tía Chucha

## Test Generator Open-Book Test

1. In "Ending Poem," the speaker describes her ancestors as
   a. slaves.
   *b. laborers.
   c. people of leisure.
   d. professional people.

2. The tone of "Ending Poem" could best be described as one of
   *a. pride.
   b. anger.
   c. frustration.
   d. patient acceptance.

3. The speaker of "Tía Chucha" suggests that his aunt's behavior taught him something he needed to know about how to
   *a. look at life.
   b. play the guitar.
   c. keep promises.
   d. surprise people.

4. The speaker of "Tía Chucha" suggests that his feelings and opinions about his aunt's behavior were
   a. completely positive.
   b. completely negative.
   *c. mixed, but mainly positive.
   d. mixed, but mainly negative.

# Gary Keillor

## Test Generator

1. Gary takes great pleasure in all of the following except
   a. eating.
   b. reading.
   c. going to school.
   *d. being misunderstood.

2. When Gary volunteers to be in the talent show, Deed's surprise makes him feel
   a. puzzled.
   b. flattered.
   *c. annoyed.
   d. delighted.

3. Miss Rasmussen regards Gary as
   *a. gifted.
   b. average.
   c. troublesome.
   d. the class clown.

4. From Bill Swenson's performance at the talent show, Gary learns about all of the following except the
   a. power of comedy.
   b. importance of being flexible.
   *c. need to take oneself seriously.
   d. value of leaving an audience wanting more.

## Part Two

### The Masque of the Red Death
### Test Generator

1. Which of the following did Poe least probably intend Prince Prospero to represent in this allegory?
   *a. regret
   b. privilege
   c. ignorance
   d. arrogance

2. Which of the following did Poe most probably intend the ebony clock to represent in this allegory?
   *a. fate
   b. freedom
   c. prosperity
   d. generosity

3. Which of the following did Poe least probably intend the Red Death to represent in this allegory?
   a. guilt
   b. mortality
   c. vengeance
   *d. compassion

4. The sound of the ebony clock striking the hour makes the revelers feel
   a. tired.
   b. lucky.
   *c. anxious.
   d. carefree.

5. At first, Prince Prospero reacts to the sudden appearance of the Red Death with
   *a. rage.
   b. terror.
   c. indifference.
   d. amusement.

6. What do the revelers find underneath the mask and cloth wrappings of the Red Death?
   a. blood
   *b. nothing
   c. a corpse
   d. a mummy

### The Raven
### Test Generator Open-Book Test

1. At the beginning of the poem, the speaker is immersing himself in books in an effort to
   *a. forget Lenore.
   b. forgive Lenore.
   c. punish himself.
   d. better understand what has happened.

2. At the beginning of the poem, the tapping makes the speaker feel
   a. angry.
   b. hopeful.
   c. comforted.
   *d. threatened.

3. The raven brings the speaker
   a. relief from sorrow.
   b. Lenore's forgiveness.
   *c. continual reminders of Lenore.
   d. hope of being reunited with Lenore.

4. At the end of the poem, the speaker is least probably feeling
   *a. relieved.
   b. confused.
   c. obsessed.
   d. depressed.

5. In the poem, the raven is most probably intended to represent
   a. nature.
   b. wisdom.
   c. salvation.
   *d. the finality of death.

6. In general, the words that are most often repeated throughout the poem rhyme with the word
   a. grim.
   b. raven.
   c. weary.
   *d. nevermore.

7. Which of the following is found in the first and third lines of each stanza?
   a. end rhyme only
   *b. internal rhyme only
   c. both end and internal rhyme
   d. neither end nor internal rhyme

## The Fall of the House of Usher
### Test Generator

1. The narrator first responds to Roderick Usher with
   a. anger.
   *b. sympathy.
   c. jealousy.
   d. disregard.

2. The story implies that Roderick and Madeline communicate in extraordinary ways because they are
   a. both dying.
   b. husband and wife.
   c. both ghosts.
   *d. twins.

3. The narrator says that the atmosphere in the vault is so oppressive that
   a. they cannot leave Madeline there.
   b. Roderick panics.
   *c. the torches almost go out.
   d. they decide to place Madeline in her room.

4. After Madeline is entombed, Roderick's health becomes even worse because
   a. a storm beats upon the house.
   b. the narrator insists on leaving.
   c. he desperately misses his sister.
   *d. he hears her in the vault.

5. At the end of the story, Roderick is losing his mind mainly because he
   a. knows that he is the last living Usher.
   b. is convinced that the storm will destroy the house.
   c. cannot live without his sister.
   *d. knows that his sister is alive in the tomb.

6. The actual fall of the Ushers' house is most closely connected to the
   a. poor quality of its construction.
   *b. end of the family.
   c. violence of the storm.
   d. proximity of the tarn.

## Dr. Heidegger's Experiment
### Test Generator

1. According to Dr. Heidegger, he doesn't participate in the experiment because he
   a. enjoys growing old.
   *b. doesn't want to be young again.
   c. feels obligated to maintain a professional disinterest.
   d. hasn't any idea what the outcome of the experiment will be.

2. The guests drink the Water of Youth with
   a. a great deal of guilt.
   b. a great deal of gratitude.
   *c. a great deal of eagerness.
   d. complete indifference.

3. As they appear to get younger, the guests begin to behave
   a. lovingly.
   b. fearfully.
   *c. foolishly.
   d. cooperatively.

4. The Water of Youth is spilled
   *a. accidentally, by the guests.
   b. accidentally, by Dr. Heidegger.
   c. on purpose, by the guests.
   d. on purpose, by Dr. Heidegger.

5. After the vase is broken, the rose
   *a. dries up.
   b. turns red.
   c. disappears.
   d. comes to life.

6. The results of the experiment most probably
   a. anger Dr. Heidegger.
   b. humiliate Dr. Heidegger.
   *c. fulfill Dr. Heidegger's expectations.
   d. encourage Dr. Heidegger to continue with similar experiments.

7. The Widow Wycherly would rather be
   a. dead than young.
   *b. dead than old and ugly.
   c. dead than anything else.
   d. old and ugly than young.

8. What effect does the outcome of the experiment have on Dr. Heidegger's views on youth and old age?
   a. It changes his views on both youth and old age.
   b. It changes his views on youth, but not on old age.
   c. It changes his views on old age, but not on youth.
   *d. It doesn't change his views on either youth or old age.

9. At the end of the story, Dr. Heidegger implies that he will
   *a. never again perform this experiment.
   b. never again perform any type of scientific experiment.
   c. perform the same experiment again on the guests.
   d. perform the same experiment again, but on himself instead.

## A Rose for Emily
## Test Generator

1. In the setting of this story, it is assumed that the ultimate goal of a young woman such as Miss Emily is to
   *a. marry.
   b. become wealthy.
   c. serve the community.
   d. achieve success in a profession.

2. The narrator believes that Miss Emily's father did all he could to
   a. make Miss Emily happy.
   b. find a suitable husband for Miss Emily.
   c. encourage Miss Emily to be more humble.
   *d. ensure that Miss Emily would never marry.

3. Colonel Sartoris released Miss Emily from paying taxes because he
   a. hoped to marry her.
   *b. didn't want to see her humiliated.
   c. knew the town owed her father money.
   d. felt a duty to her as a member of her family.

4. When the Board of Aldermen tried to get Miss Emily to pay her taxes, her reply was one of
   a. rage.
   b. wild despair.
   *c. calm arrogance.
   d. complete bewilderment.

5. At different points in her life, Miss Emily was considered all of the following by the townspeople except
   a. odd.
   *b. violent.
   c. pathetic.
   d. snobbish.

6. By killing Homer Barron, Miss Emily finally manages to
   a. find love.
   *b. defy her father.
   c. gain the town's pity.
   d. gain the town's respect.

7. In this story, the narrator's point of view is most representative of the views and opinions held by
   a. Miss Emily.
   b. Miss Emily's father.
   c. Homer Barron.
   *d. Colonel Sartoris.

## The Life You Save May Be Your Own
## Test Generator

1. At first, Mrs. Crater lets Mr. Shiftlet stay because she
   a. is lonely.
   b. is afraid of him.
   c. hopes he can repair the car.
   *d. wants him to fix up the place.

2. What does Mr. Shiftlet want from the beginning of his stay at the Craters'?
   a. a wife
   b. a home
   *c. the car
   d. friendship

3. What does Mr. Shiftlet give as his reason for not having married before?
   a. He's been too busy.
   b. He hasn't had enough money.
   c. No one has ever loved him enough to marry him.
   *d. The available women weren't good enough for him.

4. Mrs. Crater most probably asks Mr. Shiftlet to teach Lucynell to say "sugarpie" because Mrs. Crater
   a. knows he can't do it.
   b. knows that Lucynell gets pleasure from learning.
   c. wants to see if Lucynell is truly capable of learning.
   *d. wants to suggest a romantic relationship with Lucynell to Mr. Shiftlet.

5. The hitchhiker most probably jumps out of Mr. Shiftlet's car because the hitchhiker
   a. is afraid of Mr. Shiftlet.
   *b. is angered by Mr. Shiftlet.
   c. feels guilty about running away.
   d. realizes that Mr. Shiftlet won't take him where he wants to go.

6. Which of the following is not ironic?
   a. Mr. Shiftlet bemoans corruption and acts corruptly.
   b. Mr. Shiftlet feels that a man with a car has a responsibility to others.
   c. Mr. Shiftlet isn't happy when he gets what he thinks will make him happy.
   *d. Mr. Shiftlet pulls off his con game in an isolated area where interference is unlikely.

# UNIT FOUR

## Part One
### *from* Narrative of the Life of Frederick Douglass, an American Slave
### Test Generator

1. Why doesn't Douglass's owner, Master Thomas, do something about Douglass's situation with Covey?
   a. He is afraid of Covey.
   b. He wants Douglass to be more independent.
   *c. The situation doesn't worry him.
   d. Douglass has no evidence to back up his claims.

2. Douglass takes the root from his friend Sandy because Douglass
   a. fears Sandy's temper.
   b. shares Sandy's belief in the root's power.
   c. admires Sandy's intellect and knowledge.
   *d. appreciates Sandy's kindness and concern.

3. The fight with Covey leaves Douglass feeling
   a. dirtied.
   b. humble.
   *c. triumphant.
   d. wildly confused.

4. To Douglass, the distinction between being whipped and fighting back is parallel to the distinction between
   a. being good and being bad.
   *b. being a brute and being a human being.
   c. saving one's pride and saving one's soul.
   d. feeling physical discomfort and feeling emotional discomfort.

5. Douglass's standing up to Covey does all of the following except
   a. surprise Covey.
   b. show up Covey.
   c. earn Douglass Covey's fear or grudging respect.
   *d. make Covey ashamed of trying to "break" Douglass.

## Stanzas on Freedom
## Free Labor
### Test Generator Open-Book Test

1. In the first stanza of "Stanzas on Freedom," the speaker suggests that "Men!"
   *a. are, by their own doing, slaves.
   b. are, by the laws of nature, slaves.
   c. have little in common with slaves.
   d. have the duty and the right to take their freedom for granted.

2. In the second stanza of "Stanzas on Freedom," the speaker least appeals to "Women!" to think about their duties toward
   a. their sons.
   b. their nation.
   *c. themselves.
   d. enslaved women.

3. In the third stanza of "Stanzas on Freedom," the speaker suggests that true freedom requires
   a. solitude.
   b. individuality.
   c. forgiveness.
   *d. responsibility.

4. In the fourth stanza of "Stanzas on Freedom," the speaker suggests that all of the following are enemies of freedom except
   a. conformity.
   b. intimidation.
   c. indifference.
   *d. steadfastness.

5. The garment that the speaker of "Free Labor" wears makes her feel
   a. sad.
   b. guilty.
   *c. at ease.
   d. vulnerable.

6. The speaker of "Free Labor" would least probably describe slavery as a
   a. moral issue.
   b. political issue.
   c. spiritual issue.
   *d. complicated issue.

7. In "Free Labor," the speaker's garment least symbolizes
   a. liberty.
   *b. shame.
   c. tranquility.
   d. responsibility.

## An Occurrence at Owl Creek Bridge
## Test Generator

1. The attitude of the soldiers toward hanging Farquhar is one of
   a. sorrow.
   *b. respect.
   c. impatience.
   d. lightheartedness.

2. In this story, Farquhar is least devoted to
   a. his family.
   b. the South.
   *c. law and order.
   d. the defense of slavery.

3. All of the following phrases describe Farquhar's social position except
   a. family man.
   b. upper class.
   c. slave owner.
   *d. military officer.

4. The soldier who stops at Farquhar's home for a drink of water is actually a
   *a. spy.
   b. traitor.
   c. civilian.
   d. deserter.

5. Farquhar is most probably being hanged for
   a. spying.
   b. giving vital information to the enemy.
   *c. plotting to set fire to Owl Creek Bridge.
   d. successfully burning down Owl Creek Bridge.

6. The writer most probably intended the ending of this story to be
   a. happy.
   *b. shocking.
   c. unrealistic.
   d. humorous.

## A Mystery of Heroism
## Test Generator

1. When Collins goes for the water, the colonel and captain are shocked because
   a. they had planned to send a different soldier.
   b. Collins shows so much courage and bravery.
   *c. it seems like such a foolhardy thing to do.
   d. they know that his comrades will help him.

2. When Collins first returned, the other men most likely thought he was
   *a. heroic.
   b. boastful.
   c. insane.
   d. arrogant.

3. As Collins faced the meadow, he found it strange that
   a. he only had to run a short distance.
   b. the entire company fell silent.
   *c. he had put himself into this situation.
   d. he could barely move for fear.

4. You can infer that Collins dashed back to the dying officer's side because
   a. he desperately wanted to save the officer.
   *b. he could not deny a dying man's request.
   c. the other men pleaded with him to go back.
   d. he was too afraid to run across the meadow.

5. Collins experienced sheer terror when he
   a. heard the jeers of the other soldiers.
   b. ran toward the house.
   c. found that the well was empty.
   *d. tried to fill the canteen.

## Gettysburg Address
## Test Generator

1. The Gettysburg Address was delivered during the
   a. War of 1812.
   b. Revolutionary War.
   *c. Civil War.
   d. Mexican War.

2. According to Lincoln, the United States was founded on the principle of
   a. revenge.
   b. courage.
   *c. freedom.
   d. fairness.

3. Lincoln believed that the Civil War was the ultimate test of
   a. good over evil.
   b. the dedication of the South.
   c. the rights of individual states.
   *d. how well the nation could hold together.

4. What is the "great task" that Lincoln refers to in his speech?
   a. The North will vanquish the South.
   *b. The nation will be reborn as one free nation.
   c. The South will become its own nation.
   d. The country must elect a strong president.

5. Lincoln states that the United States embodies the idea that
   a. tyrants will receive their just rewards.
   *b. all men are created equal.
   c. only a strong government can survive.
   d. dissatisfied states can leave the Union.

## *from* Coming of Age in Mississippi
### Test Generator

1. At this point in her life, Moody's main interest is in
   *a. justice.
   b. her family.
   c. going to school.
   d. starting a career.

2. When Moody and the other "sit-inners" enter Woolworth's, they are careful to
   a. signal the press.
   b. signal the police.
   *c. avoid attracting attention.
   d. wait for all of the other shoppers to leave.

3. The waitresses at the lunch counter react to the sit-in with
   a. violence.
   b. polite courtesy.
   c. grudging respect.
   *d. surprise and fear.

4. The customers who are sitting at the lunch counter when Moody and the other "sit-inners" arrive choose
   *a. not to become involved.
   b. to take a wait-and-see attitude.
   c. to support Moody and the protest.
   d. to pretend that nothing special is happening.

5. In general, the reporters respond to Moody and the other "sit-inners" with
   a. anger.
   b. compassion.
   c. grudging admiration.
   *d. professional curiosity.

6. When the reporters at the sit-in ask Moody what she wants, she tells them that the only thing she wants is
   a. freedom.
   b. to be left alone.
   c. to be respected.
   *d. to be served at the counter.

7. The crowd of onlookers reacts to the prayers of Moody and the other "sit-inners" with
   a. shame.
   b. respect.
   *c. violence.
   d. sympathy.

## Ballad of Birmingham
### Test Generator Open-Book Test

1. Based on the mother's actions in this ballad, which of the following does she value most?
   *a. her daughter's safety
   b. her daughter's freedom
   c. her daughter's moral instruction

2. Why does the little girl go to the church?
   *a. to sing in the choir
   b. to pray for the marchers
   c. to prepare for the march

3. When the mother sends the little girl to church, the mother expects the little girl to
   a. die.
   *b. be safe.
   c. be endangered.

4. Which of the following is implied, but never stated, in the ballad?
   *a. The little girl dies in a bombing.
   b. The little girl knows she is about to die.
   c. The little girl defies her mother's order to stay away from the march.

## Part Two

### The Indian and the Hundred Cows/
### El indito de las cien vacas
### Test Generator

1. When the priest says, "You know that when you make a donation to God, He returns it a hundredfold," the priest means his statement to be taken
   a. literally.
   *b. figuratively.
   c. as a joke.
   d. as a warning.

2. How does the Indian take the priest's statement about donations to God?
   *a. literally
   b. figuratively
   c. as a joke
   d. as a warning

3. When the Indian gives the cow to the priest, he expects to
   a. be forgiven for his sins.
   b. be rewarded in heaven.
   *c. be rewarded immediately.
   d. feel better about himself.

4. From the Indian's point of view, if the priest were to take away the cows, the priest would be
   *a. stealing them.
   b. completely justified.
   c. fulfilling a duty to God.
   d. fulfilling a promise made to the Indian.

5. When the priest discovers that the Indian has taken his cows, the priest responds with
   *a. anger.
   b. forgiveness.
   c. mild annoyance.
   d. lighthearted humor.

### High Horse's Courting
### from Black Elk Speaks
### Test Generator

1. Most of all, High Horse wants
   a. marriage.
   *b. the girl.
   c. the girl's respect.
   d. the girl's father's respect.

2. High Horse's reasons for wanting to marry the girl mainly have to do with
   a. wealth.
   b. prestige.
   c. revenge.
   *d. emotions.

3. Red Deer's reasons for helping High Horse mainly have to do with
   a. wealth.
   b. prestige.
   c. revenge.
   *d. emotions.

4. It is most important to the girl that she
   a. not marry at all.
   b. not marry High Horse.
   *c. marry a man who is worthy of her.
   d. marry a man who pleases her parents.

5. It is most important to the girl's father that his daughter marry a man who is
   a. kind.
   b. wealthy.
   *c. courageous.
   d. in love with her.

### from The Autobiography of Mark Twain
### Test Generator

1. When some of the townspeople refused to believe that he had been mesmerized, the young Twain felt
   a. guilty.
   b. justified.
   c. relieved.
   *d. offended.

2. As an adult, Twain knows for a fact that
   a. he was mesmerized.
   *b. he was never mesmerized.
   c. the mesmerizer believed he had mesmerized Twain.
   d. the mesmerizer didn't believe he had mesmerized Twain.

3. As an adult, Twain looks back on the mesmerizer incident with
   a. pride.
   b. alarm.
   *c. regret.
   d. indifference.

4. Twain's mother most probably didn't object to people from the audience sticking pins in her son because she
   a. felt he deserved it for lying.
   *b. believed that he didn't feel any pain.
   c. didn't want to expose his lies in front of everyone.
   d. hoped that the pain would make him stop pretending.

## from Life on the Mississippi
## Test Generator

1. Which word best describes Twain when he first joined Mr. Bixby?
   *a. innocent
   b. sophisticated
   c. cocky
   d. confused

2. Throughout the selection, Twain used imagery that appeals mostly to the sense of
   a. touch.
   *b. sight.
   c. taste.
   d. smell.

3. Twain said that if he had known what it required to become a pilot, he would have
   a. become a writer instead.
   b. asked for a different teacher.
   c. left for the Amazon.
   *d. decided not to begin.

4. Mr. Bixby can best be described as
   a. patient.
   *b. hot-tempered.
   c. melancholy.
   d. despondent.

5. For Twain, becoming a pilot led to
   a. elation that he had learned a career.
   b. bitter competition with Mr. Bixby.
   *c. a loss of innocence.
   d. a new respect for the beauty of the Mississippi.

## The Notorious Jumping Frog of Calaveras County
## Test Generator

1. The tone of this story can best be described as
   *a. humorous.
   b. pleasant.
   c. bitter.
   d. desperate.

2. Why was Smiley so eager to catch up with the stranger?
   *a. The stranger tricked him out of his money.
   b. Smiley owed him money.
   c. The stranger left town with Dan'l Webster.
   d. Smiley wanted a rematch.

3. Dan'l Webster "was planted as solid as a church" is an example of
   a. exaggeration.
   b. irony.
   c. personification.
   *d. a simile.

4. Andrew Jackson would take a severe beating at the start of each fight so that
   a. Smiley would become upset.
   b. the fight would be stopped.
   c. more money would be bet for him to win.
   *d. Smiley could increase the bets against him.

5. The first narrator suspects that
   a. Simon Wheeler's memory is not very good.
   *b. his friend back East had set him up.
   c. Leonidas W. Smiley has moved to another town.
   d. Jim Smiley has moved on to Mexico.

6. The climax in the plot of the story about Smiley's frog occurs when
   a. Andrew Jackson loses a fight.
   b. Smiley boasts about his frog's abilities.
   *c. Smiley discovers the quail shot.
   d. Wheeler mentions the one-eyed cow.

# A Wagner Matinee
## Test Generator

1. Clark begins to vividly remember Aunt Georgiana and his childhood when he
   *a. receives the letter.
   b. sees her at the train station.
   c. talks with her about her concerns.
   d. watches her at the concert.

2. What has "stretched and twisted" Aunt Georgiana's hands?
   a. anger
   b. disease
   *c. hard work
   d. piano playing

3. Clark decides to take Aunt Georgiana to the concert in order to
   a. avoid talking to her.
   *b. give her a little pleasure.
   c. show her that the choice she made was wrong for her.
   d. demonstrate the contrast between frontier life and city life.

4. When Aunt Georgiana first gets to the concert hall, Clark sees her reaction as one of
   a. regret.
   *b. detachment.
   c. embarrassment.
   d. nervous anticipation.

5. During the concert, what does Clark realize never dies?
   a. love
   b. youth
   *c. the soul
   d. bitterness

# The Legend of Gregorio Cortez
## Test Generator

1. Which of the following "facts" about Cortez implies that he had magical or supernatural powers?
   a. No one knows exactly where he was born.
   b. No one knows exactly where he was buried.
   *c. He was the seventh son of a seventh son.
   d. He died within a year of being released from jail.

2. Which of the following does the narrator believe could have prevented all of Cortez's troubles?
   *a. nothing
   b. Román
   c. the governor
   d. Cortez himself

3. Before Román is shot, Cortez is a
   a. cultural hero.
   b. wandering adventurer.
   c. wild, rowdy young man.
   *d. quiet, hardworking family man.

4. Cortez responds to the news of Román's death with
   a. disbelief.
   b. wild anger.
   *c. acceptance.
   d. deep sadness.

# UNIT FIVE

## Part One
### Selected Poems by Dickinson
### Test Generator Open-Book Test

1. In "This is my letter to the World," what does the speaker suggest about his or her poetic efforts?
   *a. They will eventually be read.
   b. They will create an interaction with society.
   c. They will be understood only by people the speaker does not know.

2. From "Success is counted sweetest," a reader can tell that the color purple is associated with
   a. death.
   *b. triumph.
   c. struggle.

3. In "Because I could not stop for Death," the third stanza most probably represents the speaker's
   *a. life.
   b. hopes.
   c. afterlife in eternity.

4. In line 13 of "Because I could not stop for Death," the word *He* refers to
   a. Death.
   b. the journey.
   *c. the setting sun.

5. The speaker of "'Hope' is the thing with feathers" would most likely agree that hope
   *a. makes life better.
   b. is not often fulfilled.
   c. is an illusion.

6. In "Much Madness is divinest Sense," the speaker suggests that society thinks a "normal" person is one who
   a. thinks independently.
   *b. agrees with the opinions of the majority.
   c. lives apart from the community.

7. What is the subject of "My life closed twice before its close"?
   a. failure
   b. the afterlife
   *c. the loss of loved ones

8. In "I heard a Fly buzz—when I died," what does the speaker imagine?
   *a. the moment of her own death
   b. that a fly speaks to her
   c. what heaven looks like

## The Yellow Wallpaper
### Test Generator

1. The narrator and John, her husband, have moved to the country in order to
   a. save money.
   b. allow John to work.
   *c. allow the narrator to rest.
   d. allow the narrator to write.

2. At the beginning of the story, the narrator feels that the yellow wallpaper is
   a. haunted.
   b. amusing.
   c. oddly pleasant.
   *d. ugly and annoying.

3. John has all of the following reasons for refusing to replace the wallpaper except that
   *a. he likes the wallpaper.
   b. it would be expensive to replace it.
   c. the narrator's feelings about it are irrational.
   d. the narrator would then insist on other changes.

4. John behaves the way that he does because he is
   *a. convinced he knows best.
   b. too wrapped up in his work.
   c. too much in love to see clearly.
   d. resentful of his wife's condition.

5. John believes the narrator's imagination and "fancies" are
   a. clever and amusing.
   b. helpful to her recovery.
   *c. harmful to her recovery.
   d. a sign of serious mental illness.

6. The story suggests that the narrator is merely imagining the wallpaper's
   *a. smell.
   b. ugly color.
   c. confused pattern.
   d. stained and torn condition.

7. At the end of the story, John faints from
   a. fear.
   *b. shock.
   c. illness.
   d. exhaustion.

# The Story of an Hour
## Test Generator

1. Those who tell Mrs. Mallard the news are trying
   to make sure that she
   a. retains some hope.
   *b. is not suddenly shocked.
   c. does not realize the full truth.
   d. is given ample opportunity to be alone.

2. Mrs. Mallard believes that seeing her dead
   husband's body will arouse feelings of
   a. guilt.
   b. relief.
   c. triumph.
   *d. sadness.

3. Mrs. Mallard would be most likely to see a problem
   in a woman's traditional wedding vow to
   a. love her husband.
   *b. obey her husband.
   c. honor her husband.
   d. remain with her husband until death.

4. When Mrs. Mallard wants to be alone, Josephine
   is concerned that her sister is
   a. dying.
   b. denying reality.
   *c. overcome with grief.
   d. realizing that she is free.

# Seventeen Syllables
## Test Generator

1. Which of the following do Rosie's father and Mrs.
   Hayano, the woman with four daughters, most
   clearly have in common?
   a. They are cruel to their spouses.
   b. They have been mistreated by their spouses.
   *c. They seem uncomfortable with people outside
   their families.
   d. They were significantly changed by the birth of
   their first child.

2. Which of the following do Rosie's mother and Mr.
   Hayano, the man with four daughters, most clearly
   have in common?
   *a. They enjoy intellectual and artistic pursuits.
   b. Their want more for their children than they
   have had.
   c. They seem uncomfortable with people outside
   their families.
   d. They were significantly changed by the birth of
   their first child.

3. What is Rosie's strongest emotion as she goes out
   to meet Jesus?
   a. love
   b. guilt
   c. worry
   *d. excitement

4. Which of the following is lacking in Rosie's attitude
   toward her mother throughout most of the story?
   a. caring
   b. deception
   c. obedience
   *d. understanding

5. Of the following, which causes the greatest
   problem for Rosie?
   a. her parents' strictness
   b. her parents' pride in her
   c. the hard work she is expected to do
   *d. friction and conflict between her parents

6. When something is bothering him, Rosie's father
   tends to
   a. talk about it.
   *b. lash out at others.
   c. carefully think things through.
   d. pretend that nothing is wrong with him.

7. What is the strongest emotion Rosie feels when
   her mother asks if Rosie knows why she married
   Rosie's father?
   a. pity
   *b. dread
   c. sorrow
   d. curiosity

8. The marriage between Rosie's mother and father could best be described as
   *a. loveless.
   b. respectful.
   c. passionate.
   d. comfortable.

## Adolescence—III
### Test Generator Open-Book Test

1. In the first stanza, the speaker compares her body to
   *a. tomatoes.
   b. a shadow.
   c. glowing sunlight.
   d. starched cotton slips.

2. The main image in the first stanza is one of
   a. violence.
   b. hard work.
   c. rotting vegetation.
   *d. growing up and filling out.

3. The image in lines 16–19 could **least** be described as
   a. tender.
   *b. realistic.
   c. romantic.
   d. optimistic.

4. Line 20 **most** strongly suggests that the man would
   a. toy with the speaker.
   b. abandon the speaker.
   *c. heal the speaker's pain.
   d. make the speaker laugh.

## I Stand Here Ironing
### Test Generator

1. The narrator suggests that the main reason she left Emily with other people is that the narrator
   *a. had to, in order to work.
   b. knew it was best for Emily.
   c. wanted to be free of all responsibility.
   d. thought it was what Emily truly wanted.

2. The narrator says that she smiled at Emily too little because
   a. Emily was so homely.
   b. the narrator didn't truly love Emily.
   *c. the narrator was too full of anxiety.
   d. the narrator could see too much of Emily's father in her.

3. According to the narrator, she left Emily in the convalescent home so long because
   a. Emily was happy there.
   b. Emily was getting well there.
   c. the narrator wanted to be able to focus on her new baby.
   *d. the authorities wouldn't allow the narrator to take Emily home.

4. When she was a child, how did Emily react to being left alone at night?
   a. with silent pride
   b. with indifference
   *c. by asking not to be left alone
   d. by throwing temper tantrums

## Part Two
### Chicago
### Lucinda Matlock
### Test Generator Open-Book Test

1. Which of the following phrases from "Chicago" is an epithet?
   a. "city with lifted head singing"
   *b. "Freight Handler to the Nation"
   c. "Laughing even as an ignorant fighter laughs"

2. The speaker believes the bad things that people say about Chicago because the speaker
   *a. has witnessed them.
   b. has never actually been to Chicago.
   c. assumes that Chicago is no different from any other city.

3. The speaker of "Chicago" celebrates all of the following except the city's
   a. vitality.
   b. diversity.
   *c. delicacy.

4. The verbs that Sandburg uses in "Chicago" suggest
   a. slow movement.
   *b. constant movement.
   c. weariness or exhaustion.

5. The verbs that Masters uses suggest that Lucinda Matlock was
   a. always exhausted.
   *b. constantly in motion.
   c. precise and cautious in every movement.

6. Who or what is "singing to the green valleys" in line 15 of "Lucinda Matlock"?
   a. the larks
   b. Spoon River
   *c. Lucinda Matlock

7. Whom does Lucinda Matlock accuse of "sorrow and weariness"?
   a. the dead
   b. her husband
   *c. younger generations

8. With which of the following quotations would Lucinda Matlock most probably agree?
   *a. "The significance of life is life itself."—Hermann Keyserling
   b. "Life holds more disappointment than satisfaction."—Greek proverb
   c. "Youth is a blunder; manhood a struggle; old age a regret."—Benjamin Disraeli

## Selected Poems by Robinson
## Test Generator Open-Book Test

1. In "Richard Cory," how did Cory act toward the townspeople?
   *a. graciously
   b. coldly
   c. impatiently
   d. affectionately

2. While he was alive, Richard Cory inspired all of the following in the townspeople **except**
   a. envy.
   b. admiration.
   c. personal dissatisfaction.
   *d. pity.

3. In life, Richard Cory appeared to the townspeople to be
   a. spoiled and snobbish.
   b. marked by death.
   *c. everything that they wished they could be.
   d. lonely and depressed.

4. A sharp contrast is drawn between the circumstances of Richard Cory's death and
   a. his feelings.
   b. his goals.
   *c. the impression he made on others.
   d. the reality of life.

5. Which proverb best reflects the lesson implied in "Richard Cory"?
   a. Nothing succeeds like excess.
   b. You can never be too thin or too rich.
   *c. Never judge a man until you have walked a mile in his shoes.
   d. Live life to its fullest.

6. In "Miniver Cheevy," Cheevy does not succeed at his work because he
   a. is incapable of working.
   *b. spends his time dreaming.
   c. is lonely.
   d. finds the work too difficult.

7. You can infer that if Miniver Cheevy lived in the "days of old" he would
   a. find happiness.
   b. be successful.
   c. find life exciting.
   *d. still be dissatisfied.

8. What does Miniver Cheevy have difficulty facing?
   a. his friends
   *b. reality
   c. his success
   d. happiness

## Selected Poems by Dunbar
## Test Generator Open-Book Test

1. In "We Wear the Mask," the tone can best be described as
   *a. bitter.
   b. calm.
   c. hopeful.
   d. proud.

2. The people who wear "the mask" hide their feelings from
   a. themselves only.
   b. one another only.
   c. Christ only.
   *d. the world.

3. The people who wear "the mask" are **least** likely to hide feelings of
   a. bitterness.
   b. hostility.
   c. anxiety.
   *d. delight.

4. Wearing "the mask" allows people to
   a. reveal their emotions.
   b. express their individuality.
   *c. hide their ideas and thoughts.
   d. feel pride in their accomplishments.

5. In the first stanza of "Sympathy," the caged bird feels
   a. the need to sing.
   b. the need to hide from all of society.
   *c. the desire to have all that the world can offer.
   d. the protection provided by the cage.

6. In "Sympathy," the caged bird most likely beats his wing because it
   a. has a constant throbbing pain.
   *b. wants to be free.
   c. wants to return to the safety of its perch.
   d. wants to sing a song of joy.

7. You can infer that the caged bird's plea is for
   a. happiness.
   b. restraint.
   *c. freedom.
   d. conflict.

## Winter Dreams
## Test Generator

1. Judy's reaction to hitting Mr. Hedrick with her golf ball could best be described as
   a. coy.
   b. mocking.
   *c. self-centered.
   d. unusually sincere.

2. Dexter gains wealth by building a business that caters to the needs of
   a. the lower class.
   b. the middle class.
   *c. the upper class.
   d. women of all classes.

3. What realization leads Dexter to become engaged to Irene?
   *a. He will never "have" Judy.
   b. He was never in love with Judy.
   c. Judy hasn't been sincere with him.
   d. Judy isn't the right sort of woman for him.

4. Which of the following does Judy seem to want most?
   a. Dexter's respect
   *b. Dexter's devotion
   c. Dexter's happiness
   d. Dexter's wealth and status

5. Which of the following causes Dexter to feel that his youthful dreams are gone?
   a. his breaking off his engagement to Irene
   b. Judy's breaking off her engagement to him
   c. hearing about Judy's getting married to another man
   *d. hearing about the changes in Judy since her marriage

## America and I
## Test Generator

1. Before immigrating to America, the narrator saw America as a
   a. prison.
   *b. paradise.
   c. wilderness.
   d. testing ground.

2. From her first job in America, the narrator learned
   a. to speak fluent English.
   *b. not to trust Americans.
   c. not to speak up for her rights.
   d. how to wash floors, dishes, and clothes.

3. The main reason that the narrator left her first job was that she
   a. was fired.
   *b. wasn't paid.
   c. wanted more freedom.
   d. didn't like her employers.

4. With her first American wages, the narrator planned to buy
   a. food.
   b. books.
   *c. clothing.
   d. a typewriter.

5. The narrator was fired from her second job for
   a. not showing up for work.
   b. showing up late for work.
   c. demanding higher wages.
   *d. demanding better treatment.

6. Reading American history causes the narrator to identify herself with
   a. slaves.
   *b. the Pilgrims.
   c. Native Americans.
   d. Spanish conquerors.

# In the American Society

## Test Generator

1. Fernando most probably reports the immigration violations to the police because he
   a. feels guilty.
   *b. wants revenge.
   c. strongly opposes lawlessness.
   d. is afraid that the authorities will come after him.

2. It is implied in the story that the country club grants membership to
   *a. white people only.
   b. people of all races and creeds.
   c. upper-class people of any race.
   d. enthusiastic tennis players and golfers only.

3. When Mr. Chang throws the drunken man's shirt into the pool, the man responds with
   a. fear.
   b. anger.
   c. shame.
   *d. greater respect.

4. Who finds fitting into American society most difficult?
   *a. Mr. Chang
   b. Mrs. Chang
   c. the narrator
   d. the narrator's sister, Mona

# Defining the Grateful Gesture
# Refugee Ship
## Test Generator Open-Book Test

1. In "Defining the Grateful Gesture," lines 11 and 12 strongly suggest that the mother has
   a. enjoyed life to the fullest.
   *b. worked hard.
   c. been demanding of others.
   d. enjoys sharing her memories of childhood.

2. The stories that the mother tells at the dinner table are intended to arouse feelings of
   a. sympathy.
   b. pride.
   c. intimacy.
   *d. appreciation.

3. The mother sees Mrs. Perez's searching through the garbage as
   a. disgusting.
   b. tragic.
   c. funny.
   *d. admirable.

4. The speaker suggests that her family's meals tended to be
   a. meager.
   b. lively.
   *c. solemn.
   d. inspiring.

5. In "Refugee Ship," the speaker's relationship with her grandmother is
   *a. very limited.
   b. close.
   c. very loving.
   d. supportive.

6. In "Refugee Ship," lines 10–14 suggests that the speaker
   a. wants to live in Mexico.
   b. feels like a captive in the United States.
   c. wants to move away from her mother and grandmother.
   *d. does not feel she belongs to either culture.

# UNIT SIX

## Part One
## Selected Poems by Hughes
## Test Generator Open-Book Test

1. In "I, Too," the speaker's tone is best described as
   a. modest.
   b. humble.
   *c. optimistic.
   d. sarcastic.

2. When the speaker of "I, Too" is sent to "eat in the kitchen," he responds with
   *a. dignity.
   b. shame.
   c. surprise.
   d. humility.

3. In "Harlem," the speaker's tone mainly suggests a sense of
   a. fear.
   b. submission.
   c. anxiety.
   *d. frustration.

4. In "Harlem," the last line can best be interpreted as a
   *a. warning.
   b. symbol of hopelessness.
   c. reassurance.
   d. signal of faith.

5. In "Weary Blues," the first blues verse (lines 19–22) suggests that the musician is going to
   a. kill himself.
   *b. overcome his troubles.
   c. continue the same way.
   d. stop playing the piano.

6. In "The Weary Blues," which of the following is associated with the blues?
   a. coldness
   *b. darkness
   c. brilliant light
   d. contentment

## When the Negro Was in Vogue
## Test Generator

1. Which word best describes Hughes's tone toward the white audiences in the Harlem clubs?
   a. furious
   b. ambivalent
   *c. sarcastic
   d. proud

2. Many Harlemites resented the African-American owners of clubs who
   a. did not use African-American musicians.
   b. raised their prices.
   *c. barred people of their own race.
   d. refused to serve white customers.

3. Despite a sarcastic tone, Hughes's statements about Harlem suggest that he was
   a. bitter that the renaissance ended.
   *b. proud of the people's accomplishments.
   c. disillusioned by the house-rent parties.
   d. disappointed by the music.

4. What was unusual about the Cotton Club in Harlem?
   *a. African Americans could not go there.
   b. It catered to African-American audiences.
   c. Its owners encouraged African-American performers.
   d. Only white musicians could perform there.

5. You can conclude that in the 1920s, most African Americans experienced
   a. integration.
   *b. discrimination.
   c. lasting success.
   d. enduring recognition.

## My City
## Any Human to Another
## Test Generator Open-Book Test

1. In "My City," Manhattan is presented as being all of the following except
   a. lively.
   *b. lonely.
   c. diverse.
   d. crowded.

2. In "My City," the speaker
  *a. emphasizes the positive elements
      of Manhattan.
   b. emphasizes the negative elements
      of Manhattan.
   c. completely ignores the positive elements
      of Manhattan.
   d. completely ignores the negative elements
      of Manhattan.

3. In the first stanza of "Any Human to Another,"
   an arrow is compared to
   a. joy.
  *b. grief.
   c. pride.
   d. sympathy.

4. "Any Human to Another" suggests that the pain
   of grief
   a. grows slowly.
   b. is dull and heavy.
  *c. is sudden and sharp.
   d. is more physical than emotional.

5. The fourth stanza of "Any Human to Another"
   suggests that joy is
   a. universal.
  *b. uncommon.
   c. unavoidable.
   d. impossible to share.

6. With which of the following quotations would the
   speaker of "Any Human to Another" be most likely
   to agree?
   a. "Let every man mind his own business."—
      Miguel de Cervantes
   b. "Laugh, and the world laughs with you; / weep
      and you weep alone."—Ella Wheeler Wilcox
   c. "It is with sorrows as it is with countries—each
      man has his own."—François René de
      Chateaubriand
  *d. "To withhold from a child some knowledge . . .
      of the world's sorrows and wrongs is to cheat
      him of his kinship with humanity."—Agnes
      Repplier

## If We Must Die
## A Black Man Talks of Reaping
## Test Generator Open-Book Test

1. The attitude of the speaker of "If We Must Die"
   could least be described as
   a. proud.
   b. defiant.
  *c. mocking.
   d. determined.

2. The first stanza of "A Black Man Talks of
   Reaping" most strongly suggests that it
   has been the speaker's goal to achieve
   a. pity.
   b. humility.
  *c. security.
   d. revenge.

3. The second stanza of "A Black Man Talks of
   Reaping" suggests that the speaker's efforts have
   a. paid off handsomely.
  *b. far exceeded the reward.
   c. slightly exceeded the reward.
   d. rewarded him as he deserved.

4. In the third stanza of "A Black Man Talks of
   Reaping," the speaker suggests that the results
   of his efforts have been
  *a. stolen.
   b. ignored.
   c. ridiculed.
   d. shared fairly.

## How It Feels to Be Colored Me
## Test Generator

1. Hurston performed for the tourists in her
   hometown because she
   a. felt she had to.
  *b. enjoyed doing it.
   c. desperately needed the money.
   d. never got any attention at home.

2. Hurston feels that being the granddaughter of slaves
   a. puts her at a great disadvantage.
   b. makes her superior to white people.
  *c. means that she has nothing to lose by
      persevering.
   d. gives her an advantage over other African
      Americans.

3. Hurston implies that the reason her white companions don't appreciate jazz music to the extent that she does is that they
   a. have no sense of imagination.
   *b. don't feel it inside themselves.
   c. worry too much about what others will think of them.
   d. look down on it because it is an African-American art form.

4. The overall tone of this essay could best be described as
   a. bitter.
   b. tender.
   *c. positive.
   d. guarded or distant.

## My Dungeon Shook: Letter to My Nephew on the One Hundredth Anniversary of the Emancipation
### Test Generator

1. The tone of Baldwin's letter could be described as all of the following except
   a. loving.
   b. optimistic.
   *c. lighthearted.

2. Baldwin says, "You can only be destroyed by believing that you really are what the white world calls a nigger." Baldwin uses the term "nigger" in this quotation to refer to
   *a. an offensive stereotype created by whites.
   b. any African American who refuses to accept things as they are.
   c. any African American who must deal with racism on a daily basis.

3. Baldwin implies that ghettos are the direct result of
   *a. racism.
   b. democracy.
   c. widespread migration from the country to the city.

4. Baldwin believes that if his nephew studies his roots, he will
   *a. be inspired to survive.
   b. be driven by despair to give up.
   c. never again be harmed by racism.

## Selected Poems by Brooks
## Test Generator Open-Book Test

1. In "Life for My Child Is Simple," which pair of words is used to create anaphora?
   a. *or* and *life*
   *b. *or* and *and*
   c. *life* and *like*
   d. *and* and *not*

2. In "Life for My Child Is Simple," how is the child different from the speaker?
   a. He wants to be happy.
   b. He knows what he wants.
   *c. He has never been afraid.
   d. He is destined to succeed.

3. In "Life for My Child Is Simple," the child and the speaker are alike in that they both
   *a. enjoy simple pleasures.
   b. avoid testing themselves.
   c. will risk anything to reach their goals.
   d. fail to consider the consequences of their actions.

4. The last line of "Life for My Child Is Simple" suggests that a person for whom "reaching is his [or her] rule" would be most likely to avoid
   a. conflict.
   b. happiness.
   c. disappointment.
   *d. settling for too little.

5. All of the following lines help to create anaphora in "Primer for Blacks" except
   a. line 21.
   *b. line 25.
   c. line 32.
   d. line 50.

6. If someone who was not a poet wanted to say what Brooks says in the second stanza of "Primer for Blacks," he or she might say
   a. it is better to be black than it is to be white.
   b. it is better to be white than it is to be black.
   *c. the strength of blacks is being used to increase the strength of whites.
   d. the strength of blacks is being used to challenge the strength of whites.

7. In the third stanza of "Primer for Blacks," which aspect of "Blackness" does the speaker celebrate?
   a. its past
   b. its future
   *c. its diversity
   d. its standing in American society

8. Lines 40–42 of "Primer for Blacks" least emphasize the need of blacks to
   a. rejoice in being black.
   b. take pride in being black.
   c. understand what it means to be black.
   *d. educate whites about what it means to be black.

9. In line 50 of "Primer for Blacks," the speaker most strongly suggests that "self-shriveled Blacks" are
   a. inferior to other blacks.
   b. superior to other blacks.
   c. ashamed of other blacks.
   *d. connected to other blacks.

## Thoughts on the African-American Novel
## Test Generator

1. To Morrison, the birth of the novel has the least to do with
   a. human need.
   b. social change.
   c. the industrial revolution.
   *d. the invention of the printing press.

2. In this selection, Morrison is least concerned with fiction as
   a. art.
   b. instruction.
   c. inspiration.
   *d. entertainment.

3. According to Morrison, the lower classes didn't need novels because they
   a. couldn't read.
   b. couldn't afford them.
   *c. had their own art forms.
   d. hadn't the time to read them.

4. According to Morrison, which of the following brought about the need for the African-American novel?
   *a. social change
   b. greater economic opportunities
   c. greater educational opportunities
   d. increased interest in the oral tradition

5. To Morrison, black literature is any literature that
   a. is written by black people.
   b. is written in a black dialect.
   c. is written about black people.
   *d. captures the essence of black experience.

## Part Two
## Selected Poems by Frost
## Test Generator Open-Book Test

1. In "Acquainted with the Night," night is most closely associated with
   a. danger.
   *b. solitude.
   c. tranquility.

2. The tone, or speaker's attitude, of "Mending Wall" could best be described as
   a. annoyed.
   b. nostalgic.
   *c. mildly mischievous.

3. In lines 41 and 42 of "Mending Wall," darkness is associated with all of the following except
   a. tradition.
   *b. intimacy.
   c. suspicion.

4. In "Mending Wall," the wall that is being mended could represent
   a. trust.
   b. youth.
   *c. tradition.

5. In "Mending Wall," the speaker pictures the neighbor as
   a. an elf.
   b. a cow.
   *c. a stone-age "savage."

6. The speaker of "Mending Wall" seems to think that the saying of the neighbor's father should be
   a. ridiculed.
   *b. tolerated.
   c. worshipped.

7. In " 'Out, Out—,' " the first line makes the buzz saw seem
   a. bored.
   b. efficient.
   *c. threatening.

8. Which of the following best describes the attitude of the speaker of " 'Out, Out—' " toward the boy's death?
   *a. regretful
   b. indifferent
   c. mildly interested

9. Lines 15–18 of " 'Out, Out—' " imply that it is in the nature of accidents to be
   *a. confusing and unclear.
   b. thrilling and frightening.
   c. quick and straightforward.

## The Death of the Hired Man
### Test Generator Open-Book Test

1. Mary meets Warren at the door as he returns from
   a. haying.
   b. plowing.
   c. the bank.
   *d. the market.

2. According to Mary, Silas returns to Mary and Warren's home because he
   a. wants to teach Harold to bundle hay.
   b. wants to ditch the meadow.
   *c. knows that he will die soon.
   d. knows that Warren appreciates him.

3. Warren is angry with Silas because Silas
   a. is looking for a free bed.
   *b. left him when he needed Silas the most.
   c. never did a good job on the farm.
   d. did not ask his own brother for help.

4. The speaker's tone in this poem can best be described as
   *a. understanding.
   b. resentful.
   c. sarcastic.
   d. amused.

## The End of Something
### Test Generator

1. This story is told from the third-person limited point of view of
   *a. Nick.
   b. Marjorie.
   c. a person outside the story.

2. The narration in this story least reveals what the characters are
   a. doing.
   b. saying.
   *c. thinking.

3. Nick seems to find fault with Marjorie for being too
   a. needy.
   b. emotional.
   *c. predictable.

4. When Nick tells Marjorie what is wrong, she is
   *a. not especially surprised.
   b. too overcome with grief to react.
   c. relieved that they are both feeling the same way.

5. When Nick's friend Bill arrives, Bill seems to know
   a. exactly the right thing to say.
   *b. that Nick was planning to leave Marjorie.
   c. that Marjorie was planning to leave Nick.

## The Love Song of J. Alfred Prufrock
### Test Generator Open-Book Test

1. In the stanza beginning with line 15, fog is compared to a
   *a. cat.
   b. cloud.
   c. snake.
   d. smoldering fire.

2. The references to the women who "come and go / talking of Michelangelo" imply that
   a. the party is at a gallery or museum.
   b. the women are experts on Michelangelo.
   *c. the conversation at the party is shallow and pretentious.
   d. Prufrock is impressed by the women's knowledge of art.

3. Prufrock doesn't ask his question because
   a. someone else asks it first.
   *b. he fears being laughed at.
   c. he doesn't have an opportunity.
   d. he can't find the person he wants to ask.

4. Which of the following would be least appropriate to describe Prufrock?
   a. timid
   *b. decisive
   c. intelligent
   d. slightly silly

## The Jilting of Granny Weatherall
## Test Generator

1. Which sentence from the story is an example of personification?
   *a. "The trees leaned out and bowed to each other."
   b. "Light flashed on her closed eyelids."
   c. "Doctor Henry floated like a balloon around the foot of the bed."
   d. "I don't throw my money away on nonsense."

2. You can infer that the person who helped Granny most when she was jilted was
   a. her mother.
   *b. John.
   c. her father.
   d. Father Connolly.

3. When Granny realizes that her children are all there in the room because she is dying, she feels
   a. angry.
   b. comforted.
   *c. surprised.
   d. amused.

4. When Granny says, "Don't lay a hand on him [George], for my sake leave something to God," she means that
   a. she still loves him.
   b. she cannot bear to see him suffer.
   *c. God's punishment will be far worse.
   d. God will forgive him.

5. Granny's character can best be described as
   *a. headstrong and hardworking.
   b. meek and shy.
   c. lighthearted and easygoing.
   d. cynical and bitter.

## The Man Who Was Almost a Man
## Test Generator

1. Which word from the title of this story is most important in creating verbal irony?
   *a. man
   b. was
   c. almost

2. To whom does the title of this story refer?
   *a. Dave
   b. Dave's father
   c. Hawkins, Dave's employer

3. To Dave, guns are symbols of
   *a. power.
   b. oppression.
   c. irresponsibility.

4. Shooting off the remaining bullets in the gun makes Dave feel
   *a. proud.
   b. foolish.
   c. content.

5. What does Dave leave behind when he jumps on the train?
   a. the gun
   b. his problems
   *c. his responsibilities

# Mirror

## Self in 1958

## Test Generator Open-Book Test

1. In "Mirror," the speaker could be described as all of the following except
   *a. animated.
   b. detached.
   c. observant.
   d. straightforward.

2. In "Mirror," which of the following does the mirror claim to reflect?
   a. one's innermost fears
   b. one's innermost feelings
   c. exactly what one wants to see
   *d. exactly what is placed in front of it

3. In "Mirror," the speaker is compared to
   a. a blank wall.
   b. "a terrible fish."
   *c. "the eye of a little god."
   d. "the candles or the moon."

4. The image of the fish in the last line of "Mirror" is one of
   a. rebirth.
   *b. disgust.
   c. whimsy.
   d. jealousy.

5. In the last line of "Mirror," the phrase "like a terrible fish" refers to the reflection of
   a. a young girl.
   *b. an old woman.
   c. an actual fish in the lake.
   d. any unhappy woman.

6. Which of the following features would you be least likely to find on an actual doll based on the speaker of "Self in 1958"?
   a. fashionable clothes
   *b. eyes that produce tears
   c. eyes that open and close
   d. arms and legs that move

# UNIT SEVEN

## Part One
### Armistice
### Test Generator

1. Which of the following is least responsible for Morris's feelings toward the Nazis?
   a. patriotism
   b. his childhood memories
   c. the fact that he is Jewish
   *d. the fact that Gus admires the Nazis

2. In Morris's dreams, he is a
   a. Nazi.
   b. hero.
   *c. victim.
   d. conqueror.

3. Gus's presence tends to make Leonard, Morris's son, feel
   *a. uneasy.
   b. jealous.
   c. outraged.
   d. ashamed.

4. In this story, the armistice between Morris and Gus could best be described as
   a. cruel. .
   *b. flimsy.
   c. cordial.
   d. shattered.

## The Death of the Ball Turret Gunner
## Why Soldiers Won't Talk
### Test Generator

1. The speaker of "The Death of the Ball Turret Gunner" is
   *a. dead.
   b. dying.
   c. traumatized by war, but alive.

2. The speaker of "The Death of the Ball Turret Gunner" suggests that the State's attitude toward his life is one of
   a. guilt.
   b. gratitude.
   *c. indifference.

3. In "Why Soldiers Won't Talk," Steinbeck argues that soldiers don't tend to discuss their combat experiences because
   a. of shell-shock, or trauma.
   b. of consideration for others.
   *c. they don't actually recall them.

4. In "Why Soldiers Won't Talk," Steinbeck argues that the body's natural reaction to stress
   *a. increases one's ability to survive that stress.
   b. decreases one's ability to survive that stress.
   c. has little, if any, effect on one's ability to survive that stress.

## Letter from Paradise, 21° 19' N., 157° 52' W.
## In Response to Executive Order 9066
### Test Generator

1. All of the following might be used to describe the tone, or writer's attitude, of "Letter from Paradise . . ." except
   a. sad.
   b. serious.
   *c. objective.
   d. thoughtful.

2. In "Letter from Paradise . . . ," as the tour boat leaves for Pearl Harbor, the atmosphere reminds Didion of
   *a. a tacky tourist trap.
   b. a classic war movie.
   c. the attack on Pearl Harbor.
   d. the National Memorial Cemetery of the Pacific.

3. In "Letter from Paradise . . . ," Didion doesn't observe how other people react to the site of the *Utah* and the *Arizona* because she
   a. can't bear to visit the sites.
   *b. is too caught up in her own reaction to notice.
   c. is too busy writing down her own reaction to notice.
   d. is too afraid of discovering that people really don't care.

4. In "Letter from Paradise . . . ," Didion watches with wonder and curiosity as a couple places leis on the grave of a soldier who died
   a. in Vietnam.
   b. in World War I.
   *c. in World War II.
   d. during peacetime.

5. In "In Response to Executive Order 9066," the father's saying that the tomato seeds won't grow where the family is going most strongly suggests that that place will be
a. urban.
*b. barren.
c. familiar.
d. faraway.

6. In "In Response to Executive Order 9066," the speaker gives Denise a packet of tomato seeds to express the speaker's
*a. love.
b. guilt.
c. patriotism.
d. individuality.

## Ambush
## Test Generator

1. The narrator responds to his daughter's question by
*a. lying.
b. telling the truth.
c. telling her a story.

2. The narrator implies that the most important factor in determining the answer he gives to his daughter's question is
*a. her age.
b. her mood.
c. his mood.

3. The narrator's answer to his young daughter's question is intended to
*a. reassure her.
b. entertain her.
c. enlighten her.

4. At the time that the narrator killed the young soldier, the narrator was
a. off-duty.
b. in the middle of a battle.
*c. keeping watch over his platoon.

5. Which of the following seems to have driven the narrator to kill the young soldier?
*a. fear
b. hatred
c. a misunderstanding

6. Kiowa, the narrator's friend, seems to have believed that the narrator's killing the young soldier was
a. odd.
b. wrong.
*c. reasonable.

7. In the narrator's daydreams, the narrator
*a. allows the young soldier to live.
b. is forgiven by the young soldier.
c. is attacked by the young soldier.

## Camouflaging the Chimera
## Deciding
## Test Generator Open-Book Test

1. The imagery in lines 5–7 of "Camouflaging the Chimera" conveys the soldiers' desire to
a. fly away.
b. conquer nature.
c. contemplate nature.
*d. blend into the scenery.

2. In "Camouflaging the Chimera," the image of the soldiers' waiting "till something almost broke / inside us" suggests that the soldiers feel
a. guilty.
b. numb.
c. heroic.
*d. anxious.

3. In making her decision, the speaker of "Deciding" is most concerned about the needs of
a. herself alone.
*b. herself and her loved ones.
c. her employers.
d. her native country.

4. Which of the following least complicates the decision that the speaker of "Deciding" must make?
a. family considerations
b. political considerations
c. financial considerations
*d. religious considerations

5. In Line 14 of "Deciding," the word *they* most probably refers to the
a. military.
*b. Americans.
c. communists.
d. Vietnamese who oppose the communists.

## At the Justice Department, November 15, 1969

### Test Generator Open-Book Test

1. As described in this poem, the tear gas makes everything look
   a. bright.
   *b. indistinct.
   c. transparent.
   d. brilliant.

2. The speaker wants what is happening to her to
   *a. be happening.
   b. stop immediately.
   c. go on forever.
   d. fade away.

3. The speaker believes that the protesters
   a. will win the struggle.
   b. hope to lose the struggle.
   c. do not really want to win the struggle.
   *d. have little chance of winning the struggle.

4. Where does the event described in this poem take place?
   a. Saigon
   *b. Washington, D.C.
   c. Hanoi
   d. New York City

5. From the poem, you can infer that the speaker
   a. is very conservative.
   b. is strongly influenced by others.
   *c. has strong commitments.
   d. looks out only for herself.

## Part Two

### Letter from Birmingham Jail

### Test Generator

1. In his letter, King's main purpose is to
   a. urge the protesters to go home.
   b. insist that he broke no laws.
   c. demand an apology from the clergymen.
   *d. explain his actions.

2. According to King, what is the fourth basic step in any nonviolent campaign?
   a. negotiation
   b. self-purification
   c. collection of facts
   *d. direct action

3. King explicitly compares himself with
   *a. the apostle Paul.
   b. Martin Buber.
   c. Reinhold Niebuhr.
   d. Paul Tillich.

4. This letter can best be described as
   a. an apology.
   b. a summary.
   *c. a defense.
   d. an accusation.

5. King warns that if "repressed emotions are not released in a nonviolent way," they will
   a. destroy the nation's basic doctrines.
   b. die and be forgotten forever.
   *c. seek expression through violence.
   d. be forgotten by the world.

6. King's tone in the first paragraph establishes that he is
   a. extremely angry with the clergymen.
   *b. a very busy and important man.
   c. not willing to acknowledge their position.
   d. in need of a secretary.

## Wandering

### Test Generator

1. She portrays all of the following characters except Him's
   a. wife.
   b. mother.
   *c. daughter.

2. Between themselves, He and She tend to
   *a. agree.
   b. disagree.
   c. pretend to agree.

3. In their various relationships with Him, He and She tend to be
   *a. critical of Him.
   b. amused by Him.
   c. supportive of Him.

4. Who views "wandering" as a positive activity?
   *a. Him only
   b. He and She only
   c. all three characters

5. Him seems to have sought all his life to be
   *a. a good person.
   b. a troublemaker.
   c. an ordinary person.

6. At the end of his life, Him seems to have
   a. stopped caring about the meaning of life.
   b. figured out everything there is to know about life.
   *c. some remaining questions about how to live his life.

## The Writer in the Family
## Test Generator

1. The walks that Jonathan and his father took to Canal Street hint at
   a. the conflicts between the two families.
   b. the illness that his father suffered with.
   *c. his father's dream of the sea and travel.
   d. his father's need to get away from the family.

2. You can infer that Jonathan did not want his father's old suits because
   a. he did not want secondhand clothing.
   *b. they reminded him of his father's illness.
   c. they were too big.
   d. his mother would be upset.

3. Aunt Frances wanted Jonathan to write letters from his father mainly to
   a. annoy Jonathan's mother.
   *b. comfort his grandmother.
   c. help Jonathan accept his father's death.
   d. make his father appear to be successful.

4. Jonathan is very much like his father in that he
   a. dreams of a life at sea and traveling to foreign lands.
   b. defends his mother just as his father did.
   c. sides with his father's family.
   *d. does not take a stand on the arguments between the families.

5. What motivated Jonathan to write the last letter?
   *a. an uneasy suspicion that he was being used by the family
   b. respect for his mother's wishes
   c. a desire to please Aunt Frances
   d. a need to please his grandmother

6. What has Jonathan learned by the end of the story?
   a. Harold is extremely critical of him.
   b. Aunt Frances is completely right about his mother.
   *c. His parents are individuals, with good and bad qualities.
   d. His grandmother always loved his mother.

## Teenage Wasteland
## Test Generator

1. Whose thoughts and feelings about Donny's problems are best known to the reader?
   a. Cal's
   *b. Daisy's
   c. Donny's
   d. the principal's

2. Donny's grades improve when
   *a. Daisy begins tutoring him.
   b. Daisy stops tutoring him.
   c. Cal begins tutoring him.
   d. Cal stops tutoring him.

3. Daisy worries a great deal about how the time she spends with Donny affects her
   a. husband.
   *b. daughter.
   c. housework.
   d. own well-being.

4. Daisy and Donny are alike in that both of them
   a. demand attention.
   *b. lack self-confidence.
   c. lack respect for authority.
   d. run away from problems.

## Separating
### Test Generator

1. Which of the following is true of Richard and Joan's relationship?
   a. It ends suddenly without warning.
   *b. It ends when Richard finds it unsatisfying.
   c. Joan knows that it is over before Richard does.
   d. Joan is more visibly upset about its ending than Richard is.

2. How does Richard feel about telling the children about the separation?
   *a. He dreads it.
   b. He looks forward to it.
   c. He is unable to feel anything at all.
   d. It strikes him as being somewhat humorous.

3. All of the following is true of Joan's plan to tell the children about the separation except that
   a. Richard agrees to it.
   *b. it is the plan that is carried out.
   c. it may be intended to punish Richard.
   d. it is intended to recognize the individuality of the children.

4. How does Joan handle the situation once the news of the separation has been broken to the children at dinnertime?
   a. She acts as if the whole thing is just a joke.
   b. She breaks down and weeps uncontrollably.
   *c. She attempts to calm and reassure the children.
   d. She blames Richard and tries to turn the children against him.

## Mexicans Begin Jogging
## Legal Alien
### Test Generator Open-Book Test

1. Who has problems with being stereotyped by Americans?
   *a. both speakers
   b. neither speaker
   c. the speaker of "Legal Alien"
   d. the speaker of "Mexicans Begin Jogging"

2. Who has problems with being stereotyped by Mexicans?
   a. both speakers
   b. neither speaker
   *c. the speaker of "Legal Alien"
   d. the speaker of "Mexicans Begin Jogging"

3. In "Mexicans Begin Jogging," the attitude that Soto takes toward being stereotyped by his boss could best be described as
   a. proud.
   b. defiant.
   *c. mischievous.
   d. embarrassed.

4. Which of the following best describes the speaker's grin in line 21 of "Mexicans Begin Jogging"?
   a. hidden
   *b. genuine
   c. sarcastic
   d. dangerous

5. In "Legal Alien," the speaker suggests that she moves back and forth between her two cultures with
   *a. intellectual ease but emotional difficulty.
   b. emotional ease but intellectual difficulty.
   c. great ease, both emotionally and intellectually.
   d. great difficulty, both emotionally and intellectually.

6. In "Legal Alien," the phrase "a handy token" (line 16) refers to
   *a. the speaker herself.
   b. the speaker's smile.
   c. the speaker's biculturalism.
   d. a judgment made about the speaker.

7. Which of the following best describes the speaker's smile referred to in line 19 of "Legal Alien"?
   a. intense
   *b. artificial
   c. genuine
   d. judgmental

## Hostage

### Test Generator

1. Before the incident with the madman, the attitude of the other children toward Bruno tends to be one of
   *a. awe.
   b. scorn.
   c. affection.
   d. indifference.

2. Before the incident with the madman, the narrator and Bruno could best be described as
   a. kin.
   b. rivals.
   c. friends.
   *d. acquaintances.

3. Why doesn't the narrator attempt to escape from the madman?
   a. He has a knife.
   *b. She feels paralyzed.
   c. She knows she can't escape his grip.
   d. She thinks it would be safer to reason with him.

4. Looking back on the incident with the madman, the narrator believes that she should have
   a. killed him.
   *b. fought back.
   c. given in to him.
   d. tried to reason with him.

5. Which of the following statements would the narrator be most likely to say is completely true?
   a. Bruno acted heroically.
   *b. Bruno saved her from the madman.
   c. Bruno knifed the madman in self-defense.
   d. Bruno's motivations in attacking the madman were completely selfless.

## Mother Tongue

### Test Generator

1. The main theme of this essay suggests that
   a. it is important for everyone to speak at least two languages.
   *b. language shapes a person and his or her relationships.
   c. one should never be embarrassed by one's language.
   d. the results of standardized tests should not be trusted.

2. Tan's mother can best be described as
   a. reclusive.
   b. frustrated.
   c. shy.
   *d. determined.

3. Tan seems to believe that her best critic is
   a. herself.
   b. her husband.
   *c. her mother.
   d. her publisher.

4. When she was young, Tan was ashamed of her mother's English because
   *a. she believed it reflected the quality of her mother's thoughts.
   b. none of her friend's mothers spoke that way.
   c. she thought it limited the opportunities available to her.
   d. her mother always said the wrong thing.

5. Tan suggests that Asian Americans might do better on math tests than on English tests because
   a. Asian Americans take more math courses.
   *b. languages spoken at home may influence how they think.
   c. Asian languages are much easier to learn than English.
   d. math is a more difficult subject than English.

# The Latin Deli: An Ars Poetica
## Test Generator Open-Book Test

1. What does the speaker mean when she says that the deli owner sells "canned memories"?
   a. The memories are very painful.
   b. The owner is deceiving the customers.
   c. The memories are artificial.
   *d. The cans of food remind people of their native homes.

2. In this poem, lines 1–7 suggest a sense of
   a. political intrigue.
   *b. religious devotion.
   c. nervous apprehension.
   d. strict discipline.

3. Who is the "Patroness of Exiles"?
   a. the speaker of the poem
   b. one of the customers
   c. a Latin American saint
   *d. the deli owner

4. The theme of this poem is mainly concerned with
   *a. how immigrants feel.
   b. forgetting one's past.
   c. how people shop for food.
   d. following one's dreams.

5. In the last line of the poem, the phrase "closed ports" refers to
   a. harbors in other countries.
   *b. memories of places that no longer exist.
   c. people who have died.
   d. closed doors.

# Straw into Gold
## Test Generator Open-Book Test

1. Cisneros's attitude toward her parents is best described as
   *a. appreciative.
   b. distant.
   c. uncomfortable.
   d. resentful.

2. Which word best describes Cisneros's tone in this essay?
   a. humorous
   b. confrontational
   c. formal
   *d. casual

3. Cisneros seems to believe that
   a. traveling is not an important experience.
   b. poverty held her back.
   *c. all her experiences helped to shape her as a writer.
   d. nothing can help you spin straw into gold.

4. As an example of her shyness, the author mentions
   a. her experience making tortillas.
   b. what it has been like traveling all over the world.
   c. her life with other artists in France.
   *d. what her life was like at age 11.

5. In her family's culture, it was traditionally acceptable for a young woman to leave home only if she was
   *a. committed to a marriage.
   b. going to college.
   c. leaving after the eldest child was gone.
   d. planning to elope.

# Writing Assessment

## Contents

# To the Teacher

This section provides several different tools to help you conduct holistic evaluations of your students' writing. Holistic evaluation is a quick, guided method for evaluating writing. An evaluator reads the piece through, considers certain important features, and immediately assigns a grade. The grade may be a single rating for the entire piece of writing or a set of ratings for the different features being considered.

- **Holistic Scoring Guide** (301–302) Helps you rate papers objectively and consistently. This guide can be used to assign an overall rating after you have analyzed a paper using the General Rubric or a mode-specific rubric. To adapt to a three-point rating system, focus on the level designations (strong, average, weak).

- **General Rubric** (303) Demonstrates a multi-rating type of holistic evaluation, based on a list of major attributes of content and form that characterizes most types of writing. This rubric is useful for almost any type of writing.

- **Writing Prompts** (304–308) Available to help your students prepare for essay tests.

For guidance in evaluating your students' writing, you can refer to the scored student models and rubrics that appear in the Unit Resource Books.

# Holistic Scoring Guide

The following 6-point scale shows the features that tend to appear in a range of student papers representing various levels of accomplishment. The aim of the scale is to guide teachers in the evaluation of student papers according to a set of standards that are similar to those used in large-scale evaluations of student writing all across the country. A single student's paper may not include all the characteristics identified with any one score point, but it can be assigned a score by looking for the description that most nearly matches its features or its dominant impression. Some allowance should be made for minor errors in style, usage, mechanics, and spelling on the unit assessment, since that test does not provide time for revision.

## Level: Strong

| Exceptional — 6 points | Commendable — 5 points |
|---|---|
| A paper at score point 6 <br><br> • Has a clear and consistent focus <br><br> • Has a logical organization <br><br> • Uses transitions to connects ideas <br><br> • Supports ideas with details, quotations, examples, and/or other evidence <br><br> • Exhibits well-formed sentences varying in structure <br><br> • Exhibits a rich vocabulary, including precise language that is appropriate for the purpose and audience of the paper <br><br> • Contains almost no errors in usage, mechanics, and spelling | A paper at score point 5 has the same general features of organization and effective elaboration as a 6-point paper, but it represents a somewhat less accomplished performance. It may, for example, <br><br> • Have an organization that is predictable or unnecessarily mechanical <br><br> • Lack the depth and logical precision of a 6-point paper in presenting its argument and supporting evidence <br><br> • Exhibit appropriate sentence variety and vocabulary but without the control and richness of a 6-point paper <br><br> • Contain a few errors in usage, mechanics, and spelling |

# Level: Average

| Proficient | 4 points | Basic | 3 points |
|---|---|---|---|

A paper at score point 4

- Has a fairly clear focus that may occasionally become obscured

- Shows an organizational pattern, but relationships between ideas may sometimes be difficult to understand

- Contains supporting evidence that may lack effect and so only superficially develops ideas

- Has complete and varied sentences most of the time

- Contains some errors in usage, mechanics, and spelling but which do not confuse meaning

A paper at score point 3

- Has a vague focus and so may contain irrelevant details or digressions

- Shows an attempt at organization, but connections between ideas are difficult to understand

- Lacks important supporting evidence, or the evidence cited does not sufficiently develop ideas

- Shows little sentence variety

- Contains several serious errors in usage, mechanics, and spelling which causes distraction and some confusion about meaning

# Level: Weak

| Limited | 2 points | Minimal | 1 point |
|---|---|---|---|

A paper at score point 2

- Has a topic but does not include any elaboration

- Lacks plausible support for ideas

- Shows limited word choice

- Contains serious and numerous errors in usage, mechanics, and spelling which leads to confusion about meaning

A paper at score point 1

- Only minimally addresses the topic and lacks a discernible idea

- Has only a few simple sentences

- Shows minimal word choice

- May be incoherent and/or have serious errors in almost every sentence

A paper is unable to be scored if it is
- illegible
- unrelated to the topic
- only a rewording of the prompt
- written in a foreign language
- not written at all

# General Rubric

| Ideas and Content | Weak | Average | Strong |
|---|---|---|---|
| 1. Contains an engaging introduction that identifies the topic | | | |
| 2. Develops a writing topic appropriate to the assignment | | | |
| 3. Fulfills the writer's general purpose and specific goals | | | |
| 4. States ideas clearly and elaborates on them with specific supporting details and examples | | | |
| 5. Uses vivid, precise language that is appropriate to the audience and the writing type | | | |
| 6. Includes an effective conclusion | | | |

| Structure and Form | | | |
|---|---|---|---|
| 7. Includes a well-developed introduction, body, and conclusion | | | |
| 8. Demonstrates proper and effective paragraphing | | | |
| 9. Uses a logical, effective organizational strategy consistent with the writing type | | | |
| 10. Includes transitional words and phrases to show relationships among ideas and maintain coherence within and between paragraphs | | | |
| 11. Uses a variety of sentence structures | | | |

| Grammar, Usage, and Mechanics | | | |
|---|---|---|---|
| 12. Contains no more than two or three minor errors in grammar and usage | | | |
| 13. Contains no more than two or three minor errors in spelling, capitalization, and punctuation | | | |

## Additional Comments

_____

_____

# Prompts for Personal and Expressive Writing

Your impressions of your parents or family have changed over time and will continue to change. Write a personal essay relating how your view of your parents or family today differs from your childhood view of them.

Are you a perfectionist? a loner? the class clown? Choose an autobiographical incident that reveals something about your basic character or personality and write an essay discussing this incident.

All of us have been helped by another person at one time or another. Write a reflective essay narrating a personal experience in which someone helped you. Draw conclusions about how the assistance affected you and what it meant to you.

Think about a special childhood memory you have. It might be something that you experienced or learned alone, or it might be a special moment that was shared with someone else. Write a memoir relating that experience.

# Prompts for Observation and Description

Think of a person who fascinates you—perhaps a relative, a friend, or someone you only know from a distance, such as a bus driver or newspaper vendor. Write a character sketch of that person for your friends, inventing details about your character's life, if necessary.

For your class magazine, write a "day-in-the-life" study, focusing on someone in an intriguing situation or with an interesting occupation. Use vivid language and dialogue to make the person come alive for your readers.

Write a description to explain your appearance to a teenager twenty-five years from now. How do you dress? How do you style your hair? What overall "look" do you try to project?

Observe a person completely engrossed in work or play. For example, watch a construction worker walking a beam high above the street, someone practicing a musical instrument, or a child jumping rope. Write a description of the person and the activity he or she is engaged in for an audience of your peers. In your writing, try to convey the individual's involvement with his or her activity.

# Prompts for Narrative and Literary Writing

Imagine that you have witnessed firsthand an important event in history, such as the invention of the wheel, the eruption of Mount Vesuvius that destroyed Pompeii, or the landing of the first man on the moon. Write a letter to a friend or relative describing the event and the importance you think it will have for humanity.

Pretend you are a literary character that you know well. For your school literary magazine, write a diary entry narrating an important event—either personal or political—and your reactions to it.

Think of a conflict you have experienced. Then write a short narrative in which you explore that conflict through the interactions of two or three characters in a specific setting.

For your drama club, write a scene dramatizing a teenager's weekend experience hanging out at a shopping mall or other popular gathering place.

# Prompts for Informative Writing

Has our notion of a hero changed over time or remained largely the same? Write an article for your school newspaper in which you identify a modern-day hero or heroine, indicating the criteria on which you base your selection. Also consider whether these criteria would apply to a specific hero from the past.

You have probably undergone many changes in your values, attitudes, and beliefs over the years. In an essay for a general audience, analyze the evolution in your attitude about something important to you.

Physicians, professional athletes, and entertainers are paid high salaries; teachers, social workers, and nurses are not. What factors do you think should influence the determination of salaries? For example, what weight should be given to innate talent, amount of education required, risk involved, contribution to the betterment of humanity, or supply and demand? Write an essay for a sports magazine discussing the criteria on which salaries should be based.

What changes would you like to institute for your school? Write a letter to your school principal identifying one or more key improvements and justifying the need for addressing them.

# Prompts for Persuasion

In an effort to reduce the number of fatalities and injuries caused by drunken drivers, some local police forces have set up roadblocks and randomly check drivers' sobriety. While some people feel this is an effective way to protect the public, others feel that the practice violates individual freedom. Write a letter to the chief of police at your local law enforcement agency expressing your opinion on this issue.

Should welfare recipients who are capable of working be required to hold jobs as a condition for receiving public aid? Write a letter to your representative in the state legislature expressing your point of view. Support your arguments with facts and examples.

The health hazards of smoking have been widely publicized. Should the federal government pass a law prohibiting the sale of tobacco, or should individuals have the right to choose whether or not to smoke? Write a letter to your state representative supporting your opinion on the subject.

What political leader do you most admire? Imagine that this person is running for reelection or for election to a different office. Write a few paragraphs for a campaign leaflet for the candidate, directing it to eligible voters.

# Standardized Test Practice

## Contents

# To the Teacher

This section provides opportunities for your students to develop strategies for performing well on standardized tests. Practice items are included for areas typically found on standardized tests: analogies, sentence completion, error identification, error correction, revision-in-context passages, and critical reading passages.

Each set of practice items explains the purpose of that particular test, provides an example, and describes specific strategies students can use to be successful. The To the Student form on the facing page provides general test-taking strategies. You may wish to duplicate this form, distribute it to your students, and discuss the strategies.

# To the Student

During the next few years you will be taking many standardized tests that evaluate your understanding of English. No matter what type of test you are facing, there are steps you can take beforehand to maximize your performance. As you work on the sample test questions in this booklet, you will begin to develop strategies that will help you perform well. You might also want to try using the following general strategies, which work for many people.

## Physical and Emotional Preparation

- Before the test get at least eight hours of sleep and eat a good breakfast and/or lunch.

- Wear comfortable clothes.

- Try to relax and maintain a positive attitude.

## Taking the Test

- When you receive the test, glance over it, noting the types of questions and the number of points to be awarded for each.

- Read and listen to directions carefully.

- Budget your time, making sure that you do not spend too much time on any single question.

- Read each question and all answer choices before answering. Many items include choices that may seem right at first glance but are actually wrong.

- Complete the questions that you can answer easily. Then go back to the more difficult items.

- Do not make wild guesses. Since points are deducted for incorrect answers on many standardized tests, random guessing can harm your score. If you can eliminate one or two of the answer choices, however, your chance of choosing the correct answer is increased.

# Analogies

**Analogies** involve pairs of related words. In many analogy questions you are given two words and are asked to find another pair of words that are related in the same way. Here is a typical question:

> MICROSCOPE : GERMS : : (A) doctor : illness  (B) shot : serum
>      (C) patient : nurse  (D) vision : glasses  (E) telescope : stars

The analogy can be expressed this way: "A *microscope* is to *germs* as a _?_ is to _?_."

The following strategies can help you answer analogy questions:

- Determine the relationship expressed by the original pair of words. State that relationship in a sentence:
  "A *microscope* is an apparatus used to view and study *germs*."

- Decide which other pair of words expresses a similar relationship. Test your choice by substituting those words in your sentence:
  "A *telescope* is an apparatus used to view and study *stars*."

Here are the most common types of relationships used in analogies:

| Type of Analogy | Example |
|---|---|
| cause to effect | virus : disease : : carelessness : error |
| part to whole | finger : hand : : spoke : wheel |
| object to purpose | car : transportation : : lamp : illumination |
| action to object | dribble : basketball : : push : wheelbarrow |
| item to category | giraffe : mammal : : grasshopper : insect |
| item to characteristic | owl : nocturnal : : lion : carnivorous |
| word to synonym | accumulate : increase : : squander : decrease |
| word to antonym | cold : hot : : arctic : tropical |
| worker to creation | composer : symphony : : author : novel |
| time sequence | infant : child : : adolescent : adult |
| spatial sequence | ceiling : floor : : sky : ground |
| word to grammatical variant | go : went : : lose : lost |

Choose the letter of the pair of words that best completes each analogy.

1. JUICE : ORANGE : : (A) beef : meat (B) apple : core (C) pie : bakery
   (D) clouds : rain (E) milk : cow

2. TRIGGER : GUN : : (A) ignition : car (B) crossbow : arrow (C) rifle : bullet
   (D) bullet : target (E) umbrella : handle

3. CORRAL : ENCLOSURE : : (A) grass : lawn (B) saddle : horse (C) food : cook
   (D) boat : dock (E) box : container

4. ACIDITY : LEMON : : (A) air : atmosphere (B) element : fire
   (C) water : evaporation (D) salinity : ocean (E) sediment : mud

5. MILLION : QUANTITY : : (A) conservation : wilderness (B) teacher : desk
   (C) anger : emotion (D) fish : net (E) ten : hundred

6. AUTHOR : MANUSCRIPT : : (A) book : pages (B) writing : stories
   (C) actor : stage (D) sculptor : clay (E) artist : painting

7. WOOD : BENCH : : (A) cloth : suit (B) thread : button (C) lock : door
   (D) paper : clip (E) glass : reflection

8. STUBBORN : YIELD : : (A) strong : bully (B) withdrawn : socialize
   (C) eager : begin (D) hungry : cook (E) angry : fight

9. IMPOSE : EXPOSE : : (A) depress : express (B) impress : depress
   (C) impress : express (D) invade : escape (E) expel : impel

10. NEGLECTED : SQUALID : : (A) tidiness : tidy (B) clean : dirty
    (C) careful : forgetful (D) sloppy : sloping (E) neat : spotless

11. MILITANT : AGGRESSIVE : : (A) nonviolent : peaceful (B) lazy : active
    (C) warlike : victorious (D) selfish : generous (E) military : civilian

12. SCISSORS : CUT : : (A) measure : ruler (B) hammer : pound (C) water : drink
    (D) write : computer (E) nail : hammer

13. INTERMITTENTLY : CONTINUOUSLY : : (A) legally : legitimately
    (B) occasionally : always (C) infrequently : seldom (D) always : constantly
    (E) usually : generally

14. OVERWORK : STRESS : : (A) relaxation : anxiety (B) gardening : lawn
    (C) starvation : hunger (D) sport : leisure (E) dreaming : sleep

15. RECALL : PAST : : (A) anticipate : prediction (B) forget : reminder
    (C) foretell : future (D) foresee : hindsight (E) guess : luck

16. AGENT : ACTOR : : (A) proprietor : property (B) lawyer : client
    (C) banker : investment (D) employee : employer (E) dentist : doctor

17. GENERATE : ELECTRICITY : : (A) mine : gold   (B) conduct : orchestra
    (C) invent : patent   (D) radiate : light   (E) heat : fire

18. EXISTENCE : EXIST : : (A) assume : assumption   (B) recreation : swim
    (C) painting : create   (D) transportation : travel   (E) domination : dominate

19. CAUSE : EFFECT : : (A) accident : car   (B) snow : ice   (C) spring : weather
    (D) scream : fear   (E) lightning : thunder

20. HISTORY : MYTH : : (A) fact : fiction   (B) truth : newspaper   (C) narrative : story
    (D) moral : fable   (E) science fiction : fiction

21. APPRECIATION : GRATITUDE : : (A) love : hatred   (B) business : profit
    (C) advocate : supporter   (D) testimony : jury   (E) success : succession

22. WEAPON : ARSENAL : : (A) tool : toolbox   (B) kitchen : cabinet
    (C) closet : hanger   (D) gun : ammunition   (E) army : warfare

23. DUPLICITY : HONESTY : : (A) fragility : delicacy   (B) aggression : passivity
    (C) deterioration : recuperation   (D) twin : quadruplet   (E) agriculture : tractor

24. PROTEIN : NUTRIENT : : (A) food : vegetable   (B) lunch : meal   (C) egg : chicken
    (D) diet : hunger   (E) carnivore : meat

25. MASK : DISGUISE : : (A) helmet : protect   (B) ghost : appear
    (C) costume : mask   (D) sword : fence   (E) kidnapper : seek

26. SKIN : BODY : : (A) nail : finger   (B) body : clothes   (C) root : tree   (D) yolk : egg
    (E) bark : trunk

27. SUN : SOLAR : : (A) planet : terrestrial   (B) universe : galactic   (C) moon : lunar
    (D) meteor : temporary   (E) warmth : heater

28. PHYSICIAN : SYRINGE : : (A) artist : painting   (B) banker : wealth
    (C) engineer : caboose   (D) writer : word processor   (E) teacher : grade

29. GRAPE : VINE : : (A) pear : fruit   (B) cherry : tree   (C) flower : pot
    (D) orchard : apple   (E) root : leaf

30. PROPHET : PROFIT : : (A) emigration : immigration   (B) moral : morale
    (C) flair : flare   (D) verse : curse   (E) learning : earning

31. YESTERDAY : TODAY : : (A) decade : century   (B) day : month   (C) past : present
    (D) Sunday : Saturday   (E) memory : dream

32. TERMINATE : END : : (A) argue : agree   (B) authorize : permit
    (C) prevent : incite   (D) rain : snow   (E) swim : wade

33. TRAITOR : BETRAYAL : : (A) hijacker : flight   (B) consumer : product
    (C) vandal : defacement   (D) artist : canvas   (E) spy : investigation

34. MONKEY : AGILITY : : (A) snail : sluggishness  (B) smirk : smile  (C) stealth : fox
(D) dog : Dalmatian  (E) robbery : thief

35. GRACE : GYMNAST : : (A) politeness : politician  (B) subtlety : spy
(C) organization : typist  (D) predictability : magician  (E) affluence : accountant

36. MIRROR : GLASS : : (A) song : notes  (B) calendar : date
(C) ice cream : milkshake  (D) glove : leather  (E) sofa : cushion

37. DISTILL : WATER : : (A) shred : paper  (B) exhaust : fume  (C) refine : oil
(D) alloy : metal  (E) melt : ice

38. LIBRARY : BOOK : : (A) title : chapter  (B) sentence : paragraph
(C) camera : film  (D) pharmacy : medicine  (E) data : computer

39. HOSPITAL : SURGEON : : (A) teacher : school  (B) courtroom : lawyer
(C) store : shopper  (D) library : book  (E) water : duck

40. SERVITUDE : SLAVERY : : (A) king : queen  (B) latitude : longitude
(C) limitation : restriction  (D) dependence : loneliness  (E) bandage : wound

41. CONTEMPORARY : PAST : : (A) first : last  (B) late : early  (C) ancestral : future
(D) current : former  (E) old-fashioned : modern

42. COMPASS : NAVIGATE : : (A) pencil : educate  (B) scalpel : stitch
(C) thermometer : convalesce  (D) odometer : travel  (E) calculator : compute

43. APERTURE : CAMERA : : (A) doorway : exit  (B) film : photograph
(C) lips : mouth  (D) window : building  (E) fence : gate

44. BOILING : EVAPORATION : : (A) freezing : condensation  (B) eating : hunger
(C) burning : oxidation  (D) forgetting : memorization  (E) hypothesizing : truth

45. ARM : HAND : : (A) hat : head  (B) leg : foot  (C) wrist : ankle  (D) nail : finger
(E) bow : arrow

46. CALF : WHALE : : (A) pup : seal  (B) cow : calf  (C) robin : egg  (D) bee : drone
(E) butterfly : caterpillar

47. TIPTOE : WALK : : (A) babble : chatter  (B) whisper : talk  (C) scurry : stroll
(D) speak : drawl  (E) caress : strike

48. UNIFORMITY : UNIQUENESS : : (A) quantity : quality  (B) deformity : infirmity
(C) reformation : information  (D) conformity : individuality
(E) simplicity : directness

49. IMMODERATE : EXCESSIVE : : (A) immature : adult  (B) reasonable : irrational
(C) immodesty : modesty  (D) immobile : stationary  (E) moderate : extreme

50. MECHANIZATION : PRODUCTIVITY : : (A) invention : discovery  (B) regulation : rules
(C) industry : automation  (D) system : confusion  (E) organization : efficiency

# Sentence Completion

**Sentence completion** questions test your ability to understand words and to recognize relationships among parts of a sentence. You are given a sentence with one or more words missing and are asked to choose the word or words that best complete the sentence. Here is a typical question:

> The argument _____, but Aaron felt his anger _____.
> (A) proceeded . . . grow  (B) exploded . . . simmer
> (C) continued . . . diminish  (D) regressed . . . disappear
> (E) ended . . . slightly

The following strategies can help you answer sentence completion questions:

- Read the entire sentence carefully, paying particular attention to words that indicate relationships such as contrast *(but, although, however)* and similarity *(and, another, likewise)*. For example, the word *but* in the sample question is a clue that the correct pair of words will express a contrast. The correct answer is C, *continued . . . diminish.*

- Look for grammatical clues. Does the structure of the sentence require a noun? a verb? an adjective or adverb? If a verb is needed, what tense and number must it be?

- Try each of the choices in the sentence. Eliminate those that do not make sense, are grammatically incorrect, or contradict information in the sentence.

Choose the word or words that best complete each sentence.

## Part A

1. Julio was impressed with the _____ of the mountain bike.
   - (A) mediocrity
   - (B) predictability
   - (C) technique
   - (D) quality
   - (E) expense

2. The white shark we encountered while swimming was a(n) _____ to our safety.
   - (A) predator
   - (B) threat
   - (C) prey
   - (D) surprise
   - (E) inducement

3. Because of their _____ and hostility, the two apes in the zoo had to be separated.
   - (A) remoteness
   - (B) resourcefulness
   - (C) aggressiveness
   - (D) age
   - (E) playfulness

4. The _____ in the directions for preparing the dessert made several outcomes possible.

   (A) uniformity
   (B) diversion
   (C) mistakes
   (D) transcription
   (E) ambiguity

5. The flaw in the diamond was so imperceptible that several jewelers _____ it in their appraisal.

   (A) overlooked
   (B) disguised
   (C) extolled
   (D) mentioned
   (E) fixed

6. Sonia was very apprehensive about the _____ task that was facing her.

   (A) exciting
   (B) recognizable
   (C) daunting
   (D) forgotten
   (E) pleasant

7. Scientists do _____ in the laboratory to determine how new drugs might work in the human body.

   (A) recycling
   (B) practice
   (C) experiments
   (D) hypotheses
   (E) anticipation

8. The main character in the story is intense, solitary, _____, and pessimistic, but at the same time likable.

   (A) abominable
   (B) brooding
   (C) benign
   (D) personable
   (E) sparkling

9. The company _____ huge profits from the sale of its popular new video program.

   (A) comprised
   (B) deducted
   (C) adapted
   (D) realized
   (E) lost

10. During the debate, Raphael forcefully _____ his team's position.

   (A) remembered
   (B) deduced
   (C) confounded
   (D) forgot
   (E) articulated

11. The colony's people expressed their yearning for self-government by denouncing the _____ with which the colonial power treated them.

(A) integrity
(B) doggedness
(C) stealth
(D) paternalism
(E) comradeship

12. Lara behaves so _____ that she makes all her friends feel inadequate.

(A) unpredictably
(B) haughtily
(C) spiritually
(D) childishly
(E) retroactively

13. To avoid muscle strain, exercise in _____.

(A) moderation
(B) daylight
(C) sweat pants
(D) company
(E) repetition

14. Before attempting to move to the United States, Li studied its _____ laws.

(A) dietary
(B) traffic
(C) unwritten
(D) immigration
(E) new

15. The vaulter's pole acts as a _____ to launch him over the bar.

(A) cataract
(B) catapult
(C) lever
(D) support
(E) reminder

16. Psychologists say that it is better to express your feelings than to keep them _____ inside.

(A) mottled
(B) festering
(C) expressive
(D) discernible
(E) perceptive

17. A good _____ to promote comprehension and retention of what you read is to skim the material first, noting main headings, and then to study the text carefully.

(A) reminder
(B) improvement
(C) distraction
(D) approximation
(E) strategy

18. At the end of the term, we took a _____ exam covering everything we had studied.
    (A) confusing
    (B) conservative
    (C) comprehensive
    (D) corollary
    (E) commencement

19. After examining all the evidence, the detective _____ that the suspect could not have committed the burglary.
    (A) interpreted
    (B) aspired
    (C) concluded
    (D) reconciled
    (E) appropriated

20. One of the _____ for admission to a university is a high school diploma.
    (A) benefits
    (B) prerequisites
    (C) causes
    (D) deliberations
    (E) achievements

21. Traditionally, robins are said to _____ the arrival of spring.
    (A) estimate
    (B) herald
    (C) maintain
    (D) overtake
    (E) enjoy

22. Advertisements tend to _____ even the most unexciting products and make them seem desirable.
    (A) glamorize
    (B) expose
    (C) avoid
    (D) mention
    (E) correct

23. Keeping taxes low while also providing good services is a _____ problem in city management.
    (A) perpetual
    (B) prestigious
    (C) pessimistic
    (D) risky
    (E) responsible

24. The capacity for self-preservation is a(n) _____ quality of the wild dog.
    (A) tenuous
    (B) sporadic
    (C) inherent
    (D) undesirable
    (E) unconscious

25. The newcomer's _____ solution to the problem astonished all those who had been working on it fruitlessly for months.
   (A) insolent
   (B) incomprehensible
   (C) inept
   (D) ingenious
   (E) identical

## Part B

1. As a(n) _____ to shoppers with children, the shopping mall _____ a free child-care center.
   (A) reminder . . . had discouraged
   (B) authorization . . . employs
   (C) enticement . . . offers
   (D) empowerment . . . described
   (E) inspiration . . . will have planned

2. Naomi lives in a(n) _____ neighborhood; almost everyone has a similar _____.
   (A) large . . . aspiration
   (B) sinister . . . tactical
   (C) remote . . . mobility
   (D) ethnic . . . heritage
   (E) important . . . memory

3. The critic wrote with _____ about the performance, _____ that the play was not worth the price of admission.
   (A) indictment . . . ascertaining
   (B) approval . . . envisioned
   (C) exertion . . . remembering
   (D) derision . . . proclaiming
   (E) qualification . . . predicting

4. The lecture was so _____ that I could not _____ on what the speaker was saying.
   (A) interminable . . . concentrate
   (B) revealing . . . understand
   (C) stimulating . . . expanded
   (D) unexpected . . . dispute
   (E) symbolic . . . illuminate

5. Luis did not know the _____ of the rumor, but he _____ that Jorge had started it.
   (A) source . . . suspects
   (B) reason . . . knew
   (C) humor . . . hopes
   (D) probability . . . doubted
   (E) origin . . . thought

6. The delegation from the unaligned nation _____ between _____ and supporting the resolution.
    (A) dispute . . . approval
    (B) vacillated . . . opposing
    (C) intensified . . . restoring
    (D) questioned . . . apprehending
    (E) circumscribed . . . applause

7. _____ behavior is not _____ in the classroom.
    (A) Superlative . . . memorable
    (B) Disruptive . . . tolerated
    (C) Hostile . . . contemptuous
    (D) Mediocrity . . . important
    (E) Immature . . . suspected

8. Unauthorized or _____ use of certain common medications can be _____ to your health.
    (A) urgency . . . acceptable
    (B) compulsive . . . restorative
    (C) immoderate . . . hazardous
    (D) lawlessly . . . tragic
    (E) immoral . . . comforting

9. The natural _____ of the buffalo was destroyed as _____ plains were brought under cultivation by farmers.
    (A) equality . . . luxuriant
    (B) significance . . . flooded
    (C) nutritional . . . extinct
    (D) family . . . uninhabited
    (E) habitat . . . vast

10. As Alexis descended the stairs to the subway, she _____ to be a(n) _____ to the commuters who were trying to exit.
    (A) proved . . . obstacle
    (B) is trying . . . example
    (C) proposes . . . guide
    (D) has hoped . . . distraction
    (E) ceased . . . interruption

11. It would have been impossible for our ancestors to have _____ today's _____.
    (A) appreciating . . . progress
    (B) understood . . . comparison
    (C) envisioned . . . technology
    (D) encounter . . . ecology
    (E) realized . . . history

12. The caterpillar's _____ into a butterfly takes place _____, not abruptly.
    (A) arrangement . . . quickly
    (B) disintegration . . . absolutely
    (C) metamorphosis . . . gradually
    (D) turning . . . inevitable
    (E) assemblage . . . consequently

13. The Renaissance was a(n) _____ when the arts and sciences _____.
    (A) atmosphere . . . implode
    (B) experience . . . disagrees
    (C) government . . . consulted
    (D) era . . . flourished
    (E) fantasy . . . floundered

14. The union hoped to _____ a pay raise that would _____ three dollars an hour.
    (A) intellectualize . . . precede
    (B) compete . . . comprise
    (C) forgo . . . expose
    (D) negotiate . . . exceed
    (E) manifest . . . deny

15. The family's _____ situation was so good that they were able to _____ in a new home.
    (A) unhealthy . . . lived
    (B) debt . . . survive
    (C) financial . . . invest
    (D) domestic . . . communicate
    (E) intellectual . . . calculating

16. _____ plant growth could not be _____ by such an arid climate.
    (A) Abundant . . . supported
    (B) Perpetual . . . uprooted
    (C) Stunted . . . described
    (D) Useless . . . appreciated
    (E) Annually . . . interrupted

17. It would be nice if the world were an ideal place where everyone _____; unfortunately, this is not the _____.
    (A) communicates . . . implication
    (B) survived . . . opportunity
    (C) agree . . . reality
    (D) prospered . . . case
    (E) existed . . . intuition

18. During a(n) _____ of two previously _____ companies, new operating policies must be developed for the new entity.
    (A) shortage . . . hostile
    (B) merger . . . independent
    (C) alternation . . . commercial
    (D) examination . . . enterprising
    (E) communicating . . . construction

19. The psychologist was _____ in her analysis of a person's _____.
    (A) uncomplicated . . . finances
    (B) distinguishable . . . style
    (C) analytical . . . memorization
    (D) disapproval . . . habits
    (E) perceptive . . . character

20. It was easy to _____ laughter from the children, who were basically uninhibited and _____.
    (A) force . . . repressed
    (B) evoke . . . effusive
    (C) adopt . . . adaptably
    (D) persuading . . . hyperactive
    (E) negate . . . serious

21. The coach _____ a(n) _____ exercise program in preparation for the upcoming triathlon.
    (A) ends . . . forgivable
    (B) commented . . . leisurely
    (C) launched . . . rigorous
    (D) practiced . . . sophisticated
    (E) recommended . . . exemplary

22. Living in a(n) _____, essentially undeveloped part of the country _____ few of the creature comforts offered by modern society.
    (A) urban . . . extols
    (B) forgotten . . . establish
    (C) remote . . . provides
    (D) sedimentary . . . manifest
    (E) mountainous . . . interprets

23. The transparent lake and the cloudless sky are so _____ that they could _____ even the most troubled mind.
    (A) visionary . . . revere
    (B) serene . . . soothe
    (C) theoretical . . . approximately
    (D) glorious . . . condemn
    (E) unbelievably . . . convince

24. The criminal _____ the state border and _____ north to Canada.
    (A) crossed . . . headed
    (B) intersected . . . calculates
    (C) misses . . . sneaked
    (D) canceled . . . vanished
    (E) lengthened . . . disgruntled

25. The shy hero _____ his accomplishment, _____ saying that anyone could have done what he did.
    (A) preserved . . . unmercifully
    (B) ennobles . . . grotesquely
    (C) brandished . . . courageous
    (D) dismantled . . . urgently
    (E) minimized . . . modestly

# Error Identification

**Error identification** questions test your ability to recognize errors in standard English usage. In each sentence four words or phrases are underlined and marked with letters. You are asked to choose the underlined part that needs correction or to mark **E** if the sentence contains no error. Here is a typical question:

Many a music lover <u>believe</u> that <u>Mozart's</u> music is the <u>most beautiful</u> ever
               A            B                 C

<u>written</u>. <u>No error</u>
  D     E

The following strategies can help you answer error identification questions:

- Read the entire sentence carefully.

- Reexamine the underlined parts. Check for lack of agreement, errors in capitalization and punctuation, improper sentence construction, incorrect forms, and inappropriate word choice. In the sample question, the subject of the sentence, *Many a music lover,* is singular and therefore requires a singular verb. Since the verb *believe* is plural, the answer is **A.**

Choose the letter that indicates an error. If the sentence is correct, mark **E.**

1. Each of the <u>women</u> <u>has brought</u> <u>her</u> own <u>scissors.</u> <u>No error</u>
            A        B     C      D     E

2. <u>Having been spoke</u> in biblical <u>times,</u> Hebrew is one of the <u>world's</u> <u>oldest living</u>
       A                   B                        C      D

   languages. <u>No error</u>
          E

3. <u>Him</u> singing <u>"Danny Boy"</u> and other ethnic songs <u>was</u> the highlight of the
  A          B                        C

   evening for my family and <u>me.</u> <u>No error</u>
                     D     E

4. Smallpox <u>was</u> <u>one of the worse diseases</u> in history, but <u>it</u>
          A             B                     C

   <u>has been virtually wiped out</u> by a worldwide vaccination campaign. <u>No error</u>
              D                                               E

5. Neither Sasha nor Isabel <u>enjoys</u> mysteries; <u>neither one</u> <u>can never guess</u> <u>who</u>
                              A                   B        C      D

   the murderer is. <u>No error</u>
               E

6. One of the many differences between the letters of our alphabet <u>is</u> their
                                                                    A

   <u>age; for example,</u> o is <u>thousands'</u> of years old, whereas j and v <u>came</u> into
   B                           C                                            D

   the language about 1630. <u>No error</u>
                            E

7. When each of the witnesses <u>takes</u> the witness stand, <u>he or she</u> <u>looks</u>
                              A                            B         C

   nervously at <u>we jury members</u>. <u>No error</u>
                D                    E

8. Columbus <u>Day,</u> along with certain other <u>holidays,</u> <u>are</u> now celebrated on
            A                                 B          C

   a Monday in order to create a <u>three-day weekend</u>. <u>No error</u>
                                 D                     E

9. Although <u>Captain William Kidd</u> was employed by England to fight <u>piracy,</u> he
            A                                                         B

   became a pirate <u>himself</u> and was ultimately executed by the government that
                   C

   <u>has once employed</u> him. <u>No error</u>
   D                          E

10. Neither the host nor the guests <u>have found</u> <u>Mr. Harris's sunglasses,</u>
                                    A              B

    <u>which were</u> <u>laying</u> on the kitchen table a few hours ago. <u>No error</u>
    C          D                                                 E

11. In 1981 twenty cents <u>was</u> the price of a first-class <u>stamp; by</u> 1991 the
                         A                                 B

    price  <u>had risen</u> to <u>twenty-nine cents</u>. <u>No error</u>
           C                D                     E

12. Caring for contact lenses <u>are</u> <u>more difficult</u> than <u>caring for glasses, but</u>
                              A    B                        C

    contact lenses can be <u>more convenient</u> to wear. <u>No error</u>
                          D                            E

13. *War and Peace* <u>presents</u> an intimate picture of <u>Russian society</u> during
                    A                                    B

    the <u>wars with Napoleon, in fact</u> some critics have declared Tolstoy's
        C

    novel  <u>the best ever written</u>. <u>No error</u>
           D                         E

14. Because the orchestra sounded <u>so beautifully, we chorus members</u>
                                   A                        B

    <u>were inspired</u> to perform <u>our very best</u>. <u>No error</u>
         C                            D            E

15. The <u>Japanese beetle,</u> an insect harmful to <u>many kinds of plants,</u> <u>comes</u>
           A                                          B                          C

    to the United States <u>accidentally</u> in about 1916, carried on a plant from
                             D

    Japan. <u>No error</u>
              E

16. <u>Neither of the mice</u> <u>has found</u> <u>its way</u> through the <u>cleverly constructed</u>
          A                    B           C                        D

    maze yet. <u>No error</u>
                  E

17. Of all the <u>peanut-growing states,</u> <u>the state of Georgia</u> <u>is</u> the <u>more productive</u>.
                 A                            B                       C         D

    <u>No error</u>
        E

18. Early <u>operas</u> <u>were based</u> on myths and legends, but <u>more realistic</u>
            A          B                                          C

    subjects <u>have been</u> becoming popular in the nineteenth century. <u>No error</u>
                 D                                                           E

19. <u>My friend Huang</u> and his brother <u>claim</u> that no theme park <u>isn't</u> <u>more famous</u>
          A                                 B                           C        D

    than Walt Disney World. <u>No error</u>
                                E

20. Visitors to Peru <u>learn</u> that many of its inhabitants <u>are</u> <u>Quechua Indians,</u> <u>whose</u>
                       A                                       B        C                   D

    ancestors established the great Inca Empire in that mountainous country

    hundreds of years ago. <u>No error</u>
                               E

21. The <u>coach's</u> daughter <u>taught</u> <u>Mitsuo and myself</u> some basketball
          A                     B           C

    strategies that we <u>can use</u> in tomorrow's game. <u>No error</u>
                           D                                 E

22. Fossils are <u>seen</u> by <u>paleontologists scientists</u> who study ancient life
              A                          B

   <u>forms,</u> as records of <u>earlier</u> times. <u>No error</u>
    C                 D          E

23. As soon as one of the onlookers <u>shouted, "Look,</u> <u>there's</u> the stunt planes
                                        A         B

   <u>now!" everyone</u> in the crowd <u>scanned</u> the sky intently. <u>No error</u>
       C                       D                   E

24. Despite the fact that my <u>uncle and aunt's</u> new car includes <u>all sorts of</u> special
                              A                            B

   features, it <u>doesn't handle</u> very <u>well</u>. <u>No error</u>
               C            D   E

25. "<u>Were</u> any of the tourists surprised to hear Catalan spoken in the streets of
   A

   <u>Barcelona," Xavier asked,</u> "<u>Especially</u> since they had been told to study
         B                    C

   <u>Castilian Spanish?"</u> <u>No error</u>
        D         E

26. Petra is the <u>most highly skilled</u> player on our <u>team; nevertheless,</u> the coach
                  A                                B

   <u>doesn't expect</u> that the state champion <u>will be her</u>. <u>No error</u>
       C                          D      E

27. Rebecca sang <u>well</u> last night, but <u>you're voice</u> sounded even <u>better</u> than
               A                     B               C

   hers. <u>No error</u>
    D    E

28. Every job applicant <u>has already</u> filled out <u>their application</u> and <u>has taken</u> <u>it</u>
                      A                   B            C  D

   to the appropriate office. <u>No error</u>
                     E

29. Most of the world <u>was unaware</u> of the existence of Hawaii until
                  A

   <u>Captain James Cook</u> <u>lands</u> there in <u>January 1778</u>. <u>No error</u>
        B          C              D        E

30. Although I <u>have known</u> our <u>village</u> librarian all my life, she <u>hardly never</u>
                A          B                           C

   speaks to <u>either my brother or me</u>. <u>No error</u>
                 D              E

# Error Correction

**Error correction** questions can appear in a variety of formats. One of the most common is the paragraph format shown below. These questions test your ability to recognize and correct errors in sentence construction, grammar, and usage.

In each paragraph certain words are underlined and numbered. You are asked to choose the correct version of each numbered word or phrase from the choices at the right or, if the original is correct, to mark **A** or **F**. Here is a typical paragraph:

Vast <u>ranches, which</u> breed cattle, sheep, and
1

other domesticated animals have operated

successfully for centuries. Now ranches for wild game

are becoming popular as well, especially in Africa. In

Botswana, for example, ostriches <u>are being raised</u>
2

profitably on ranches.

1. A. No change
   B. ranches, that
   C. ranches that
   D. ranches, and which

2. F. No change
   G. are rose
   H. are risen
   J. are rising

The following strategies can help you answer these questions:

- Read the entire paragraph carefully.

- Then reread each sentence, paying special attention to each underlined part.

- Decide whether the underlined part contains an error and, if so, which rewording at the right corrects the error. In number 1 of the example, *ranches, which* indicates that the clause following the comma is nonessential. However, the clause actually presents essential information, so it should be introduced by *that* and no comma. The correct rewording of number 1, therefore, is *C, ranches that*.

- If the underlined part is correct, select the first choice. In number 2, the underlined words are correct, so the answer is *F, No change*.

Choose the letter that indicates the best revision of the underlined word or words. If there is no error, mark **A** or **F.**

The growth of radio, television, <u>newspapers and</u>
1
other media <u>have drawn</u> many artists and performers
2
to the attention of the public. For every famous and

generously paid rock star or <u>sculptor, however,</u> there
3
are thousands of other highly talented <u>artists which</u>
4
remain relatively unknown. Perhaps no area of

artistic endeavor receives <u>as little</u> recognition as folk
5
art. This lack of widespread appreciation for the

indigenous arts is particularly sad in a country like the

United States, <u>with it's</u> rich tapestry of cultures.
6
In formal recognition of America's folk art, the

National Endowment for the Arts awards $5,000 grants

to exceptional artists who <u>have chose</u> to use
7
traditional art forms. Those honored by the program

include a Hispanic carver of saints, a Cajun fiddler, a

quilter from Missouri, <u>a Appalachian</u> ballad singer, a
8
group of African-American gospel singers, an

Ojibwa storyteller, and a Pueblo potter. One cannot

<u>help and be</u> struck by the magnificent diversity of
9
the art forms, a phenomenon <u>that reflect</u> the diversity
10
of the American heritage.

1. A. No change
   B. newspapers, and
   C. newspapers; and
   D. newspapers also

2. F. No change
   G. have drawed
   H. had drew
   J. has drawn

3. A. No change
   B. sculptor; however
   C. sculptor although
   D. sculptor and also

4. F. No change
   G. artists, which
   H. artists who
   J. artists that

5. A. No change
   B. as less
   C. less
   D. as least

6. F. No change
   G. with its
   H. with our
   J. with their

7. A. No change
   B. choose
   C. had chose
   D. will be choosing

8. F. No change
   G. a appalachian
   H. an Appalachian
   J. the Appalachian

9. A. No change
   B. help and been
   C. help, and be
   D. help being

10. F. No change
    G. that reflects
    H. which reflect
    J. which, reflect

You are <u>their</u> in geography class, watching the teacher
11
point to a map of the world. Daydreaming a <u>little. You</u>
12
gaze at the shapes on the map. Suddenly you notice

that the bulge on the <u>East Coast</u> of South America looks
13
as if it would <u>fit neat</u> into the indented coast of western
14
Africa across the ocean.

Most scientists who study the earth now believe

<u>that, in fact,</u> these continents were joined until about 100
15
million years ago. They base this belief on rock layers and

fossils <u>common to</u> both South America and Africa. Further
16
support is provided by the theory of plate tectonics, which

states that the outer shell of the earth always has been and

still <u>is being</u> constantly in motion.
17
According to this theory, the outer shell of the earth

is broken up into large chunks, called tectonic <u>plates these</u>
18
move slowly on the partially molten rock that <u>lays</u> beneath
19
them. About 200 million years ago, there was a single

landmass, called Pangaea. Over a period of 65 million years,

Pangaea broke up into two smaller masses—Gondwanaland

and Laurasia. South America and Africa were originally part of

Gondwanaland, but they too began to drift apart, eventually

arriving at <u>its</u> current positions on the globe.
20

11. A. No change
    B. hey're
    C. there
    D. here

12. F. No change
    G. little you
    H. little, you
    J. little; you

13. A. No change
    B. East coast
    C. east Coast
    D. east coast

14. F. No change
    G. be fitting neatly
    H. have fitted neat
    J. fit neatly

15. A. No change
    B. that, factually
    C. that in fact
    D. that, in fact

16. F. No change
    G. in common to
    H. uncommon to
    J. commonly in

17. A. No change
    B. is having been
    C. was
    D. is

18. F. No change
    G. plates, these
    H. plates. These
    J. plates those

19. A. No change
    B. has lain
    C. lies
    D. had laid

20. F. No change
    G. it's
    H. there
    J. their

Have you ever <u>wondered? Why</u> dogs bark?
21

Sometimes <u>them barking</u> serves as a warning, a threat,
22

a greeting, or a complaint. Although barking is a

complicated communication system, dogs often seem

to bark just because they <u>feel like it.</u>
23

Different breeds of dogs have different barking

habits. <u>Only some bark</u> rarely, but others find it
24

difficult to be silent. For example, <u>terriers they</u>
25

tend to bark more than most other dogs. No matter

what their particular habits, however, dogs apparently

can't help <u>but bark</u>.
26

Scientists have been investigating this noisy

phenomenon for some time; however, they have yet

to come up with a definitive explanation. Some data

suggest a link between an <u>animals' tameness</u> and its
27

tendency to bark. When researchers in the Soviet

Union <u>bred unusually</u> tame foxes, they found that
28

those animals behaved, looked, and sounded <u>not like</u>
29

wild foxes but like dogs! One theory proposes that

barking is a juvenile behavior, along with dependence

and tameness. According to this theory, the barking dog

is a case of <u>revolutionary</u> immaturity. The dog has
30

simply not developed as far as its wild cousin, the

nonbarking wolf.

21. A. No change
    B. wondered why
    C. wondered, why
    D. wondered: why

22. F. No change
    G. they barking
    H. their barking
    J. those barking

23. A. No change
    B. felt like it
    C. feel about it
    D. were feeling it

24. F. No change
    G. Only, some bark
    H. some only bark
    J. Some bark only

25. A. No change
    B. them terriers
    C. terriers
    D. a terrier

26. F. No change
    G. but be barkers
    H. but being barkers
    J. barking

27. A. No change
    B. animal tameness
    C. animals tameness
    D. animal's tameness

28. F. No change
    G. not bred usually
    H. bread unusual
    J. bred unusual

29. A. No change
    B. not alike
    C. not unlike
    D. alike

30. F. No change
    G. evolutionary
    H. revolving
    J. voluntary

# Revision-in-Context

On certain tests you may find questions that provide part of the first draft of a composition and ask you to revise it. These **revision-in-context** questions ask you to make decisions about logic, organization, sentence structure, and basic English usage. The following strategies can help you perform well on these types of questions:

- Read the entire passage carefully.

- Reread the passage, noting specific problems in the composition.

- Read each question and the answer choices provided. If necessary, go back and reread the indicated portion in the context of the whole composition.

- Choose the revision that makes the intended meaning clearest and follows the rules of standard English usage.

*The passages that follow are the first drafts of students' compositions. Some of the ideas may not be well developed or precisely expressed. For each question, choose the answer that best conveys the writer's intended meaning.*

## Passage I

(1) I am physically challenged. (2) I was born with cerebral palsy. (3) I have been attending public schools since I was six years old. (4) My brother, who doesn't have cerebral palsy, was just six years old in March. (5) Physically challenged children have the same needs as any other children—education, recreation, socialization, and recognition—and the public schools can meet those needs.

(6) Today there are physically challenged children in the public schools in all fifty states. (7) It hasn't always been this way, however. (8) Physically challenged used to be sent off to private schools. (9) Then, in the mid-1970's, the federal government passed a law for physically challenged children to attend public schools. (10) The law also stated that therapy and other services should be provided in the schools.

(11) Attending public schools gives physically challenged children an opportunity to learn to their full potential. (12) These schools can provide the special help children like me need and can also challenge us to do our best. (13) At public schools, we get a chance to socialize with other physically challenged teens. (14) It was nice for me to find out that there were other teens with the same problems who can understand what you're going through. (15) We also need to interact with people who are not physically challenged. (16) Attending public schools lets us get to know the kids in our neighborhood and makes us a part of the community.

(17) Recreation is also important for physically challenged young people. (18) We need to play games and have fun like anybody else. (19) Physical education classes like adaptive PE are very helpful. (20) They allow us to do what we can and to feel good about ourselves, which we need.

(21) In conclusion, physically challenged young people are like anybody else. (22) We just want the opportunity to prove what we can do, and attending public schools helps us achieve that goal.

1. Which is the best way to combine sentences 2 and 3?
   (A) Being born with cerebral palsy, I have been attending public schools since I was six years old.
   (B) I was born with cerebral palsy: consequently I have been attending public schools since I was six years old.
   (C) Although I was born with cerebral palsy, I have been attending public schools since I was six years old.
   (D) Because I have been attending public schools since I was six years old, I was born with cerebral palsy.
   (E) I was born with cerebral palsy and, as such, I have been attending public schools since I was six years old.

2. Which sentence does not belong in this essay?
   (A) sentence 4
   (B) sentence 12
   (C) sentence 16
   (D) sentence 20
   (E) sentence 22

3. Which is the best revision of the underlined part of sentence 9?
   *Then, in the mid-1970's, the federal government passed a law for physically challenged children to attend public schools.*
   (A) a law telling physically challenged children that public schools must be attended to
   (B) a law requiring public schools to accommodate physically challenged children
   (C) a law in terms of which physically challenged children could attend public schools
   (D) a law for public schools that had physically challenged children in attendance
   (E) a law that must be attended to regarding public schools

4. Which is the best revision of the underlined part of sentence 14?
   *It was nice for me to find out that there were other teens with the same problems who can understand what you're going through.*
   (A) that are understanding of what you're going through
   (B) who could understand what I was going through
   (C) who have an understanding of where you have gone
   (D) who are standing where you were
   (E) that share your understanding of goings on

5. Which of the following best describes the student's purpose in writing this composition?
   (A) to make friends
   (B) to tell an entertaining story about growing up
   (C) to describe cerebral palsy
   (D) to educate readers about the needs of handicapped people and how they can best be met
   (E) to ask for sympathy

## Passage II

(1) The birds along the lake shore were singing in the brisk, cool morning. (2) I will never forget that clear, piercing sound and the crispness of the air. (3) These, along with many other wonderful recollections, made my Memorial Day camping trip memorable and worth sharing. (4) The trip began with a nine-hour drive along winding country roads. (5) We set up the tents and went right to bed, so we had no idea of the beauty that surrounded us. (6) When we got up in the morning, the sun had just risen over the towering mountains and was shimmering against the awesome blue lake. (7) Because we had a flat tire, we didn't arrive at the campsite until after dark. (8) As I stepped out of my tent, and noticed all the incredibly gorgeous wildlife in the area. (9) I hated to tear myself away from the scenery to cook breakfast, but I was suddenly very hungry. (10) Then I made a fire, sat down to eat, and enjoyed a wonderful feeling as the sun shone it's warmth on me. (11) It was the most peacefulest moment of my life.

(12) After eating, I went for a long hike. (13) I found a secluded spot where I dropped my fishing pole in the water and lay in the sun not even caring if I got a bite. (14) I returned to the campsite sunburned, tired, and happy. (15) I had had a long, fun-filled day. (16) I sat down in front of a crackling campfire. (17) I roasted three plump, white, sweet marshmallows. (18) As I ate them and felt the warmth of the fire, I thought of how wonderful it all has been.

6. Which sentence in the composition is out of place, and how would you reposition it?

    (A) sentence 1; put it after sentence 15.
    (B) sentence 7; put it after sentence 4.
    (C) sentence 8; put it after sentence 9.
    (D) sentence 12; put it after sentence 13.
    (E) sentence 18; put it after sentence 17.

7. Where would you begin a new paragraph to separate the introduction from the body of the composition?

    (A) no paragraph necessary
    (B) after sentence 1
    (C) after sentence 2
    (D) after sentence 3
    (E) after sentence 5

8. Which is the best title for this composition?

    (A) The Marshmallow Roast
    (B) Sunset and Sunrise
    (C) A Memorial Day to Remember
    (D) How to Camp
    (E) Birds of the Northeast

9. Which is the best revision of sentence 8?

    (A) As I stepped out of my tent, I was dazzled by a variety of wildlife.
    (B) Stepping out of my tent and I couldn't believe the wildlife.
    (C) Because I couldn't believe the gorgeous wildlife in the area, I stepped out of my tent.
    (D) Until I stepped out of my tent, the wildlife was incredibly gorgeous.
    (E) As I was stepping out of my tent in the area and noticing all the incredibly gorgeous wildlife.

10. Which is the best revision of the underlined part of sentence 10?
*Then I made a fire, sat down to eat, and enjoyed a wonderful feeling <u>as the sun shone it's warmth on me</u>.*

    (A) although the sun was shining its warmth on me
    (B) after which I was shining as warmly as the sun
    (C) as the sun warmed me
    (D) as the shining sun it warmed me
    (E) until the warm sun shone down on me

11. Which is the best revision of sentence 11?

    (A) The moment of my life which was the more peaceful was that one.
    (B) In my life it was the peacefulest moment.
    (C) Until that moment I haven't known what peaceful meant.
    (D) My life, in that moment, was inundated with peacefulness.
    (E) It was the most peaceful moment of my life.

12. Which details would you include to make the scene described in this composition seem more real to readers?

(A) accurate instructions on how to get to the camp
(B) specific descriptions of sights, sounds, smells, and feelings
(C) biographical facts about the writer
(D) actual names of people and places
(E) the year, day, and time of the camping trip

13. Which is the best way to combine sentences 15, 16, and 17?

(A) I had had a long, fun-filled day; having sat down in front of a crackling campfire roasting three plump, white, sweet marshmallows.
(B) Then, after a long, fun-filled day, I sat down in front of a crackling campfire and roasted three plump, white, sweet marshmallows.
(C) I had had a long, fun-filled day, as a result of which I was sitting down in front of a crackling campfire with three plump, white, sweet roasted marshmallows.
(D) I had had a long, fun-filled day sitting down in front of a crackling campfire roasting three plump, white, sweet marshmallows.
(E) I sat down in front of a crackling campfire pursuant to having had a long, fun-filled day during which I roasted three plump, white, sweet marshmallows.

14. Which specific word would best replace *awesome* in sentence 6?

(A) awful
(B) shimmering
(C) watery
(D) deeply
(E) translucent

15. Which is the best revision of the underlined part of sentence 18?
*As I ate them and felt the warmth of the fire, I thought of how wonderful it all has been.*

(A) I would think of the wondrousness of the totality of all of it
(B) I wondered about how I would think about all of this later
(C) I accepted that this would be a wondering memory
(D) I realized how wonderful the day had been
(E) I thought how wonderful that this all has been

# Critical Reading

**Critical-reading** questions test your ability to comprehend written material and to draw inferences from what you read. The following strategies can help you answer these types of questions:

- Skim the entire passage quickly.

- Read the questions that follow the passage.

- Reread the passage carefully, keeping the questions you will have to answer in mind.

- Reread each question carefully. Then choose the response that best answers the question. If necessary, go back and reread the relevant parts of the passage.

## *Passage I*

*The following passage is from the short story "Louisa, Please Come Home" by the American author Shirley Jackson. The story is narrated by Louisa Tether, a young woman who ran away from home three years ago. She is now returning with her old next-door neighbor, Paul, to confront her family.*

    I wondered if they were watching us from the window. It was hard for me to imagine how my mother and father would behave in a situation like this, because they always made such a point of being quiet and dignified and proper; . . . the front door ahead was still tight shut. I wondered if we would have to ring the
5  doorbell; I had never had to ring this doorbell before. I was still wondering when Carol opened the door for us. "Carol!" I said. I was shocked because she looked so old, and then I thought that of course it had been three years since I had seen her, and she probably thought that I looked older, too. "Carol," I said, "Oh, Carol!" I was honestly glad to see her.
10    She looked at me hard and then stepped back, and my mother and father were standing there, waiting for me to come in. If I had not stopped to think, I would have run to them, but I hesitated, not quite sure what to do, or whether they were angry with me, or hurt, or only just happy that I was back, and of course once I stopped to think about it, all I could find to do was just stand there and say,
15  "Mother?" kind of uncertainly.
    She came over to me and put her hands on my shoulders and looked into my face for a long time. There were tears running down her cheeks, and I thought that before, when it didn't matter, I had been ready enough to cry, but now, when crying would make me look better, all I wanted to do was giggle. She looked old, and sad,
20  and I felt simply foolish. Then she turned to Paul and said, "Oh, *Paul*—how can you do this to me again?"

Paul was frightened; I could see it. "Mrs. Tether—" he said.

"What is your name, dear?" my mother asked me.

"Louisa Tether," I said stupidly.

25     "No, dear," she said, very gently, "your real name?"

Now I could cry, but now I did not think it was going to help matters any.

"Louisa Tether," I said. "That's my name."

1. Who is the "I" in this passage?

   (A) Carol

   (B) Louisa's father

   (C) Louisa

   (D) a girl pretending to be Louisa

   (E) Louisa's psychiatrist

2. Which pair of adjectives best describes the tone of this passage?

   (A) angry and resentful

   (B) lighthearted and humorous

   (C) warm and nostalgic

   (D) awkward and confused

   (E) detached and analytic

3. Considering that Louisa ran from home and that her family doesn't seem to recognize her when she returns, what might you infer about the relationship between them?

   (A) Louisa is an adopted child

   (B) Louisa's family ignored her and never realized that she had run away.

   (C) Louisa's parents and sister are blind and resent the fact that Louisa can see.

   (D) Louisa had plastic surgery while she was gone because she didn't want to look like her family.

   (E) Louisa's family has never really "seen" her or known her as a person.

4. Which statement best explains the meaning of the clause "I had never had to ring this doorbell before" (line 5) in the context of this passage?

   (A) Until she ran away, she had lived in that house and could come and go freely.

   (B) She has never lost her key to the house before.

   (C) She has always used the back door, which doesn't have a bell.

   (D) She used to just knock on the door when she forgot her key.

   (E) Her parents installed the doorbell after she left home.

5. Which statement best describes why Louisa is shocked that her sister Carol looks so old (lines 6–8)?
   (A) She has forgotten what Carol looks like.
   (B) She has assumed that nothing and no one would have changed during the three years she was gone.
   (C) Carol has been sick with worry since Louisa's disappearance.
   (D) Carol has begun to look like her mother.
   (E) Carol has forgotten what Louisa looks like.

6. Which statement best explains the meaning of "crying would make me look better" (lines 18–19) in the context of this passage?
   (A) Tears would make her eyes glisten and sparkle prettily.
   (B) Crying would show how she really felt about being home.
   (C) Tears would cleanse her eyes so that she could see more clearly.
   (D) She would look more like her mother, who was crying.
   (E) She looks better when she is crying than when she is giggling.

7. Which phrase has the same meaning as "matters" (line 26) in the context of this passage?
   (A) spiritual concerns
   (B) angry feelings
   (C) cares about
   (D) the situation
   (E) concrete objects

8. A tether is a rope or a chain used to tie something. Which statement best describes the possible significance of the author's choice of this word as Louisa's last name?
   (A) It was the author's maiden name.
   (B) It was chosen at random and has no significance.
   (C) It suggests the complex ties that bind parents and children.
   (D) It is not the same as her parents' last name and therefore proves she is not really their child.
   (E) It has the same number of letters as does her first name.

9. How does Louisa's father react to her return?
   (A) His reaction cannot be determined from the information given in this passage.
   (B) He echoes his wife's reaction.
   (C) He is indifferent.
   (D) He is angry.
   (E) He is overjoyed.

10. To which type of literature does this passage belong?
    (A) science fiction
    (B) autobiography
    (C) nonfiction
    (D) fantasy
    (E) first-person narrative

## Passage II

*The following passage is from an article published in* Discover *magazine. It presents the results of recent research on domestic cats and their wild ancestors.*

To anyone who has stared into the deep and unwavering blankness of a house cat's eyes, or has watched his beloved pet stand motionless in the center of a room, waiting for a thought to enter its plum-sized brain—to such a person, the news will be no surprise: compared with its wild ancestor, the domestic cat
5   has about one-third fewer neurons [nerve cells]. The cat's brain has shrunk during the course of evolution, and it has shrunk by losing neurons.

[The researchers Robert Williams of the University of Tennessee at Memphis and Carmen Cavada and Fernando Reinoso-Suárez of the Universidad Autónoma de Madrid] compared the brain of *Felis catus* with that of the Spanish wildcat.
10  Spanish wildcats are living fossils—rare survivors of the species that gave rise to domesticated cats 15,000 to 20,000 years ago. While the domestic cat's line has evolved rapidly since then, the Spanish wildcat has barely changed.

Williams and his colleagues found that the domestic cat's brain is 20 to 30 percent lighter than a Spanish wildcat's brain. (Its whole body is about half the size
15  of the wildcat's body.) To find out whether the domestic cat had smaller neurons, more tightly packed neurons, or simply fewer neurons, the researchers decided to actually count the number of neurons in a small section of the feline brain—the visual pathway.

They found that the Spanish wildcat had half again as many cone cells—the
20  cells that allow for daytime and color vision—in the retina; 50 percent more signal-transmitting axons in the optic nerve; and 50 percent more cells in the lateral geniculate nucleus, a clump of neurons in the brain that sorts the signals from the optic nerve. If one extrapolates these findings to the whole brain, says Williams, this means that domestic cats have lost about a third of their neurons during
25  evolution.

The intriguing thing is that each domestic cat seems to start out with all its ancestral neurons. . . . [A large] number of the domestic cat's cells, however, die as the fetus develops. "The death of brain cells often happens in mammals," says Williams. "The human retina initially has 2.5 million ganglion cells, and then half
30  are lost. But the domestic cat makes close to a million and keeps only 160,000." If you're going to evolve a smaller brain, he adds, the cat's strategy is probably a good one: "It has a built-in flexibility. If conditions were to change rapidly in a few thousand years, an animal could take advantage and stop losing as many cells."

Why the domestic cat should want to lose brain cells in the first place,
35 however, the researchers can't say. But they warn against drawing facile
conclusions concerning the animal's intelligence. "In some respects I'm sure
a wildcat is a much more competent animal," says Williams. "But domestic
cats are much smarter at coping with humans than are wildcats—so in that
respect, a domestic cat is obviously a genius."

11. Which statement best summarizes the main point of this passage?
   (A) Wildcats would make good pets because they're so smart.
   (B) Keeping cats as pets causes people to lose their brain cells.
   (C) Mammals become less intelligent as they evolve.
   (D) Although domestic cats have lost a third of their brain cells during evolution,
       they are still smart enough to deal effectively with their environment.
   (E) Domestic cats should be returned to the wild so that they can regain their lost
       brain cells.

12. Which statement best reflects the researchers' findings?
   (A) Domestic cats have more tightly packed neurons than do Spanish wildcats.
   (B) Spanish wildcats' color vision is much better than their daytime vision.
   (C) Domestic cats have smaller neurons than do Spanish wildcats.
   (D) Domestic cats and wildcats start out with the same number of neurons, but
       domestic cats lose more of theirs as they develop.
   (E) The neurons of all cats are concentrated in their visual pathway.

13. What is the meaning of "living fossils" (line 10) in the context of this passage?
   (A) petrified animals that have been miraculously revived
   (B) animals that are hopelessly out-of-date
   (C) ancient animal species that have survived unchanged
   (D) ancient rocks that look like present-day cats
   (E) animals that feed on extinct species

14. What is the meaning of "extrapolates" (line 23) in the context of this passage?
   (A) transports to the North or South Pole
   (B) projects or extends
   (C) adds more neurons
   (D) takes out of context
   (E) exaggerates

15. Why, according to the researchers, do domestic cats lose their brain cells?

    (A) The researchers don't know.

    (B) Domestic cats don't need so many cells, because human beings take care of them.

    (C) Their wild ancestors had too many brain cells.

    (D) Their brains are too small to hold all their brain cells.

    (E) The cats don't lose the cells: the researchers counted wrong.

16. How long ago did domestic cats evolve from wildcats?

    (A) Domestic cats didn't evolve from wildcats; they're an entirely different species.

    (B) 15,000 to 20,000 years ago

    (C) 160,000 years ago

    (D) 2.5 million years ago

    (E) The passage doesn't provide that information.

17. What is the meaning of the phrase "all its ancestral neurons" (lines 26–27) in the context of this passage?

    (A) the total number of neurons in all its ancestors' brains

    (B) its oldest neurons

    (C) the same number of neurons its ancestors had

    (D) the neurons it will pass on to its children

    (E) the neurons that are related to its own

18. Which adjective best describes the tone of this passage?

    (A) disgusted

    (B) humorous

    (C) pleading

    (D) threatening

    (E) objective

19. What is the meaning of "facile" (line 35) in the context of this passage?

    (A) funny

    (B) docile

    (C) complicated

    (D) easy

    (E) misunderstood

20. Why does a researcher state that "a domestic cat is obviously a genius" (line 39) even though it has one-third fewer neurons than a wildcat?

    (A) This is a sarcastic comment that means just the opposite.

    (B) Brain cells have nothing to do with intelligence.

    (C) Domestic cats are much better at coping with humans than are wildcats.

    (D) Domestic cats perform better than wildcats on IQ tests.

    (E) Domestic cats learn to use a litter box at an early age, but wildcats never do.

*The following two passages address the issue of recognition of individual identity. The first is from the autobiographical essay "Darkness at Noon" by Harold Krents, whose life inspired the Broadway play and movie* Butterflies Are Free. *The second is the poem "Thumbprint" by the poet and playwright Eve Merriam.*

## Passage I—Darkness at Noon

Blind from birth, I have never had the opportunity to see myself and have been completely dependent on the image I create in the eye of the observer. . . .

There are those who assume that since I can't see, I obviously also cannot hear. Very often people will converse with me at the top of their lungs, enunciating each
5    word very carefully. Conversely, people will often whisper, assuming that since my eyes don't work, my ears don't either. . . .

The toughest misconception of all is the view that because I can't see, I can't work. I was turned down by over forty law firms because of my blindness, even though my qualifications included a cum laude degree from Harvard College and a
10   good ranking in my Harvard Law School class.

The attempt to find employment, the continuous frustration of being told that it was impossible for a blind person to practice law, the rejection letters, not based on my lack of ability but rather on my disability, will always remain one of the most disillusioning experiences in my life.

## Passage II—Thumbprint

15   In the heel of my thumb
     are whorls, whirls, wheels
     in a unique design:
     mine alone.
     What a treasure to own!
20   My own flesh, my own feelings.
     No other, however grand or base,
     can ever contain the same.
     My signature,
     thumbing the pages of my time.
25   My universe key,
     my singularity.
     Impress, implant,
     I am myself,
     of all my atom parts I am the sum.
30   And out of my blood and my brain
     I make my own interior weather,
     my own sun and rain.
     Imprint my mark upon the world,
     whatever I shall become.

21. Which set of adjectives best characterizes the tone of the two passages?
    (A) I—hesitant; II—angry
    (B) I—whining; II—defiant
    (C) I—angry; II—exultant
    (D) I—optimistic; II—pessimistic
    (E) I—detached; II—anxious

22. How does Harold Krents feel about "the image I create in the eye of the observer" (line 2)?
    (A) He is angry that people do not see him as a real person because he is handicapped.
    (B) He has no feelings about other people's image of him, because he can't see it.
    (C) He accepts other people's image of him.
    (D) He tries to live up to others' image of him.
    (E) He doesn't understand how other people see him.

23. What is the meaning of "not based on my lack of ability but rather on my disability" (lines 12–13) in the context of passage I?
    (A) not because he wasn't capable of doing the job, but only because he was blind
    (B) not because he wasn't capable of doing the job, but because he didn't use the ability he had
    (C) not because he was blind, but because he didn't have the ability to do the job
    (D) not because he was blind, but because he also couldn't hear
    (E) because he was blind and he also wasn't capable of doing the job

24. What is the meaning of "disillusioning" (line 14) in the context of passage I?
    (A) unreal
    (B) disgusting
    (C) disabling
    (D) unexpected
    (E) eye-opening

25. Which statement best summarizes Harold Krents's attitude toward his blindness?
    (A) He resents it and is jealous of people who can see.
    (B) He thinks that the problem is not his blindness but the fact that other people don't see him as a capable individual.
    (C) He ignores it.
    (D) He refuses to accept it and pretends that he can see.
    (E) He doesn't realize that he is blind.

26. Which statement best describes the way the speaker in passage II perceives herself?
    (A) as a large thumb
    (B) as a person stamped out of a mold
    (C) as a barometer of the weather
    (D) as a unique individual with a special contribution to make
    (E) as a person unsure of her own identity

27. What does the image of the "whorls, whirls, wheels [on my thumb] in a unique design" (lines 16–17) signify in the context of passage II?

    (A) someone squashing an insect
    (B) someone hitchhiking
    (C) the distinctiveness of every person
    (D) It was included for sound, not for meaning.
    (E) the confusion of someone going around in circles

28. What does "I make my own interior weather" (line 31) imply in the context of passage II?

    (A) The narrator lives in a climate-controlled house.
    (B) The narrator takes her temperature regularly.
    (C) The narrator determines her own destiny.
    (D) The narrator can predict the weather.
    (E) The narrator is like a reptile, whose body temperature is determined by that of its environment.

29. Which statement best characterizes the views of personal identity presented in the two passages?

    (A) I—people must not accept other people's image of them but must fight to be recognized as individuals; II—people imprint their individual personalities joyously and freely on the world.
    (B) I—people can never see themselves clearly; II—people can never really understand one another because they are so different.
    (C) I and II—people are concerned only with themselves.
    (D) I—people with disabilities aren't really people; II—everyone has some kind of disability.
    (E) I—people are blind; II—people live in their own separate worlds.

30. Which phrases from the two passages best summarize their themes?

    (A) I—"because I can't see, I can't work"; II—"of all my atom parts I am the sum"
    (B) I—"continuous frustration"; II—"I am myself"
    (C) I—"Blind from birth"; II—"What a treasure to own!"
    (D) I—"the rejection letters"; II—"whatever I shall become"
    (E) I—"one of the most disillusioning experiences in my life"; II—"thumbing the pages of my time"

# Answer Key

## Contents

### *The Language of Literature* Test Answers

### Standardized Test Practice Answers

# Unit One

## The World on the Turtle's Back
Selection Test, pp. 7–8
**A.** (8 points each)
1. Notes will vary. Students could rank "to instill a sense of awe toward the universe" as moderately or completely unimportant because
   a. by explaining many aspects of the universe, the myth takes away from its awesomeness.
   b. The Great Tree in the sky is the only element of the universe that appears to inspire awe in the characters and the narrator.
2. Notes will vary. Students could rank "to explain the workings of the natural world" as very important because the myth attempts to explain
   a. how the world was created.
   b. how people were created.
   c. why human nature contains constructive and destructive aspects.
3. Notes will vary. Students could rank "to support and validate customs" as moderately important because the myth explains
   a. the meaning behind certain rituals and ceremonies.
   b. the need to continue practicing those rituals and ceremonies.
4. Notes will vary. Students could rank "to guide people through the trials of living" as moderately or completely unimportant because the myth
   a. doesn't directly tell people how to lead their lives.
   b. doesn't focus on the behavior of ordinary humans.

**B.** (6 points each)
1. a
2. d
3. b

**C.** (4 points each)
1. a
2. b
3. c
4. a
5. b

**D.** (15 points; students should answer one of the two)
1. Answers will vary widely but should reflect students' understanding that
   a. this ritual is a part of their culture.
   b. the Iroquois believe that the left-handed twin was involved in their creation and the creation of the world.
   c. they are grateful for their world and their lives.
   d. they don't view the left-handed twin in such simplistic terms as evil or bad.

e. they don't believe that the left-handed twin is less worthy of their gratitude than the right-handed twin
f. they have tolerance for the deviant and unconventional.
2. Answers will vary widely. Most students will make points similar to the following:
   a. The Iroquois seem to believe that human nature is more reasonable or upright than it is unreasonable or devious.
   b. This belief is reflected by the fact that the right-handed brother, who is more upright than his brother, has a greater hand in creating people.
   c. The Iroquois believe that human nature is fundamentally constructive and destructive; people cannot be only one or the other.
   d. This belief is reflected by the fact that the left-handed brother, who is crooked and devious, has at least something of a role in the creation of people.

**E.** (15 points) Answers will vary widely, depending on students' personal experiences, situations, and viewpoint. Accept any answers that address the concern of the question and are elaborated by examples or details from the literature or from life.

## Song of the Sky Loom
## Hunting Song/Dinni-e Sin
Selection Test, p. 9
**A.** (15 points each)
1. Notes will vary widely. Students who choose the line "Oh our Mother the Earth, oh our Father the Sky" might write notes suggesting that the repetition emphasizes
   a. the speaker's reverence for the Earth and Sky.
   b. the superiority of the Earth and Sky over people.
Students who choose the line "Then weave for us a garment of brightness" might write notes suggesting that the repetition emphasizes
   a. the intensity of the speaker's desire for the garment.
   b. the speaker's love of nature and beauty.
Students who choose the phrase "May the . . . be . . ." could write notes suggesting that the repetition emphasizes
   a. the intensity of the speaker's wishes.
   b. the relationship between the blessings requested in the four lines beginning with that phrase.
Students who choose the phrase "That we may walk fittingly where . . ." might write notes suggesting that the repetition emphasizes
   a. the blessings that would result from granting the speaker's requests.
   b. the speaker's reverence for nature.
2. Notes will vary widely. Students who choose the line

"Comes the deer to my singing, / Comes the deer to my song, / Comes the deer to my singing" may write notes suggesting that the repetition

a. emphasizes the hunter's faith in the song.
b. reinforces for the listener/reader the movements of the deer toward the hunter.
c. creates a lulling effect that re-creates for the listener/reader the effect that the song has on the deer.

Students who choose the words *from* or *through* might write notes suggesting that the repetition emphasizes

a. the movements of the deer.
b. the song's function as a guiding force for the deer.

**B.** (10 points each)
1. a
2. c

**C.** (25 points; students should answer one of the two)
1. Answers will vary. Among the possibilities for which students could find support in the poem are the following:
   a. A way of life.
   b. The world itself.
   c. A shelter or refuge.
   d. Prosperity.
   e. Harmony.
   f. Sunshine, rain, and fertility.
2. Answers will vary, but students could say that the hunter feels blessed because
   a. the hunt is successful.
   b. the hunter doesn't feel entirely responsible for the outcome of the hunt.

**D.** (25 points) Answers will vary widely, depending on students' personal experiences, situations, and viewpoints. Accept any answers that address the concern of the question and are elaborated by examples or details from the literature or from life.

## Coyote and the Buffalo/Fox and Coyote and Whale

Selection Test, pp. 11–12
**A.** (15 points each)
1. Notes will vary, but most students will write notes suggesting that Coyote is presented as a numskull because
   a. he needs to call on his spirit power to get him out of his predicament with Bull Buffalo.
   b. he is fooled by birds, an old woman, and a young cow.
   c. the Okanogan credit his greed and foolishness for the fact that no buffalo live on their lands.

Other answers should be supported with appropriate details from the story.
2. Notes will vary, but most students will write notes suggesting that Fox is presented as a clever deceiver

because he
   a. disguises himself as a Water Maiden.
   b. deceives the Water People.
   c. successfully recovers his wife.

Other answers should be supported with appropriate details from the story.
**B.** (6 points each)
1. d
2. d
3. a

**C.** (10 points each)
1. Notes will vary. Students who choose Bull Buffalo might write notes suggesting that his power is greatest because
   a. he gets what he wants without losing anything.
   b. his flexibility leads him to make a deal with Coyote.
   c. his decision is what causes the Okanogan to have to travel outside of their lands to hunt buffalo.
   d. he has the power to bring himself and the cow back to life.
   e. he conquers Young Buffalo.
2. Notes will vary. Students who choose Fox might write notes suggesting that his power is greatest because he
   a. outsmarts and kills the more physically powerful Whale.
   b. fools the Water People.
   c. manages to get his wife back and regain her love.
   d. is responsible for Whale's inability to live in fresh water.

Students who choose Whale might write notes suggesting that
   a. he is more physically powerful than Fox.
   b. the point of the myth is that wiliness and deception help the weaker (Fox) to defeat the more powerful (Whale).

**D.** (16 points; students should answer one of the two)
1. Answers will vary. Students could say that the following character traits are rewarded:
   a. flexibility. (It allows Bull Buffalo to regain power.)
   b. cleverness. (It allows the old woman to fool Coyote.)
   c. honesty or fairness. (Even though they don't always serve Bull Buffalo well in his dealings with Coyote, they don't hurt him in the end.)
   d. wisdom. (It prevents the cow from returning to Coyote.)
   e. vengeance. (It drives Bull Buffalo to regain his leadership of the herd.)

Students could say that the following character traits are punished:
   a. bravado. (It gets Coyote into trouble with Bull Buffalo.)

b. disloyalty and greed. (After promising not to kill the cow, Coyote goes back on his word because he desires more, and ends up with nothing to eat.)

c. vanity. (It allows the old woman to fool Coyote.)

d. foolishness. (Coyote fails to understand the error of his ways.)

e. vengeance. (It drives Coyote to disgrace Bull Buffalo's bones, for which he is punished.)

Other answers should be supported with appropriate reference to the story.

2. Answers will vary, but students could say that the myth

a. explains why the Water People and the Land People don't get along.

b. explains why whales live in the sea.

c. explains why a particular waterfall is so dangerous.

d. is entertaining.

e. imparts lessons concerning love, loyalty, cleverness, and the power of determination in face of overwhelming odds.

**E.** (16 points) Answers will vary widely, depending on students' personal experiences, situations, and viewpoints. Accept any answers that address the concern of the question and are elaborated by examples or details from the literature or from life.

## The Man to Send Rain Clouds

Selection Test, pp. 13–14

**A.** (8 points each) Notes will vary, depending on the conflicts that students choose to discuss. Model answers for Father Paul's internal conflict and for the external conflict between Father Paul and Leon follow.

1. Internal: Father Paul
   External: Father Paul and Leon

2. Internal: Concerns sprinkling holy water on Teofilo's grave
   External: Concerns the religious rites for Teofilo's burial

3. Internal: Holy water isn't supposed to be used when the Last Rites haven't been administered. Father Paul wants to respect Teofilo's wishes, but he doesn't want to go against his own beliefs and his duties as a priest.
   External: Father Paul wants Teofilo to have Christian rites because Father Paul is a Christian; Leon wants Teofilo to have Laguna rites because Leon is a Laguna.

4. Internal: The conflict is resolved when Father Paul decides to sprinkle holy water on the grave.
   External: The conflict isn't resolved because both men remain true to their faith. Instead, it becomes unimportant because Father Paul accepts the situation and Teofilo is buried.

5. Internal: Father Paul becomes weary and saddened.
   External: Father Paul becomes weary and saddened; Leon feels happy and satisfied.

**B.** (4 points each)
1. a
2. a
3. c

**C.** (4 points each)
1. a
2. b
3. c
4. c
5. a

**D.** (14 points; students should answer one of the two)
1. Answers will vary. Students could say that Leon
   a. wants Teofilo to have a traditional Laguna burial.
   b. knows that Father Paul will want Teofilo to have a Christian burial.
   c. doesn't want to invite Father Paul's interference in the matter.
   d. wants to avoid conflict with Father Paul.
   e. may not want to hurt Father Paul.

2. Answers will vary. Students could say that
   a. Father Paul probably would have felt bad about disappointing Teofilo's family at such a time.
   b. Father Paul might have come to feel guilty about neglecting his duty to Teofilo and God.
   c. Teofilo's family would have been saddened and disappointed.
   d. the family's memory of Teofilo would have been marred by this controversy and by worry over his spirit's welfare.
   e. the community might have become divided by the controversy.
   f. the community might have lost respect for Father Paul.

**E.** (14 points) Answers will vary widely, depending on students' personal experiences, situations, and viewpoints. Accept any answers that address the concern of the question and are elaborated by examples or details from the literature or from life.

## *from* The Way to Rainy Mountain

Selection Test, pp. 15–16

**A.** (8 points each) Notes will vary but should include points similar to the following:

1. High Country:
   a. the mountain country is "the top of the world, a region of deep lakes and dark timber, canyons, and waterfalls"; ". . . The skyline in all directions is close at hand . . ."; "The Kiowas reckoned their stature by the distance they could see, and they were bent and blind in the wilderness." These images appeal to the senses of sight and touch.

Mood: The mood suggests that the place is beautiful but dark and somewhat confining.

2. Descent to the Plains:
   a. ". . . the highland meadows are a stairway to the plain. . . . the inland slope of the Rockies is luxuriant. . . . Clusters of trees, and animals grazing far in the distance, cause the vision to reach away. . . . The sky is immense . . . Sweet clover takes hold of the hills. . . ." These images appeal to the senses of sight and smell.

Mood: The mood is expansive. The reader leaves the lush, dark, and deep forest and suddenly steps into a wide open space with an explosion of color and the smell of sweet clover.

3. Oklahoma/Rainy Mountain:
   a. "The hardest weather in the world is there . . ." with blizzards, tornadoes, and hot summers. "The grass turns brittle and brown, and it cracks under your feet. . . ."; ". . . the steaming foliage seems almost to writhe in fire. Great green and yellow grasshoppers . . ."; ". . . the birds sang out of the shadows. The long yellow grass on the mountain shone in the bright light. . . ." These images appeal to the senses of sight, hearing, and touch.

Mood: The author's use of words and images suggest a place that is harsh, hot, and uncomfortable, with a sense of loneliness in this vast space. Yet, even though the setting seems inhospitable, the author still sees beauty in the land.

**B.** (5 points each)
1. c
2. c
3. a
4. d

**C.** (4 points each)
1. a
2. c
3. a
4. b
5. c

**D.** (20 points; students should answer one of the two)
1. Answers will vary but should include points similar to the following:
   a. He focuses on descriptions of nature and the landscape, which reflect his love and reverence for the land.
   b. His views of nature help to reflect the relationship of the Kiowa to the land, as in his description of Devil's Tower and the Kiowa tale that went along with it.
   c. Momaday does not describe details of his trip related to time or technology: how long it took, what towns he passed by, or even his method of transportation. These omissions suggest a kind of timeless journey, or a journey through a place that looks the same as it did when the Kiowa saw it.

2. Answers will vary but should include points similar to the following:
   a. Momaday's grandmother had lived through a remarkable history, which he respected and tried to appreciate (". . . in death her face was that of a child. I like to think of her as a child").
   b. She had long black hair, always braided, and he remembers certain actions: standing at the wood stove cooking, bent over beadwork; looking down into the folds of her hands; walking with a cane; praying.
   c. He fondly remembers the comings and goings at his grandmother's home, the feasting, and the talk. He sees that as the weather gets warmer, the Kiowa "cannot hold still; an old love of going returns upon them."
   d. She is the inspiration for his pilgrimage: ". . . the immense landscape of the continental interior lay like memory in her blood." Her native beliefs were never completely lost; she never forgot her birthright and always had a reverence for the sun. The natural world was always part of his grandmother's life. Momaday respects his grandmother and her respect and sense of comfort with the natural world, and he associates her with the Kiowa in general.

**E.** (16 points) Answers will vary widely, depending on students' personal experiences, situations, and viewpoints. Accept any answers that address the concern of the question and are elaborated by examples or details from the literature or from life.

**Unit One, Part One Test**
pp. 17–18
**A.** (5 points each) Answers may vary but should include points similar to the following:
1. It is intended to explain how the world came to be; how plants, animals, humans, and other elements of nature came to be; and why there are different kinds of people who act in different ways.
2. The setting is the Great Plains reservation lands of the Kiowa people; it is significant in this selection because the author is telling the story of his father's and grandmother's people, who lived on this land.
3. The main conflict is between pagan beliefs and Christianity: Leon wants Father Paul to sprinkle holy water on Teofilo's body to help bring rain, but Father Paul says that a proper Christian burial would require a funeral mass and Last Rites.
4. The Kiowa left the dark mountains and descended to the plains, where the "sun is at home." They learned the culture of the plains and acquired Tai-me, the sacred Sun Dance doll, from the Crows.

**B.** (20 points) Notes will vary. A model answer for "The Man to Send Rain Clouds" follows.

By contrasting Leon's beliefs and Father Paul's beliefs, the writer communicates
  a. how Laguna religious beliefs differ from Christian beliefs.
  b. how people are affected by clashing systems of beliefs.
  c. how it feels to be patronized.
  d. how people benefit from making reasonable compromises.

**C.** (20 points each; students should answer two of the four)
  1. Answers will vary. A model answer for the speaker of "Hunting Song" and Father Paul in "The Man to Send Rain Clouds" follows.

By leading a life in harmony with nature, the speaker of "Hunting Song"
  a. is able to attract and kill a deer.
  b. is able to meet his or her need for food.
  c. feels blessed.

By not leading a life in harmony with nature, Father Paul
  a. feels isolated from the people he serves.
  b. is uncomfortable about sprinkling holy water on Teofilo.
  c. suspects that Leon and the others are trying to trick him into some pagan ritual.
  d. has little understanding of what has happened.

  2. Answers will vary. A model answer for "Song of the Sky Loom" follows.

This sacred song reveals that the Tewa
  a. value nature and try to live in harmony with it.
  b. have religious beliefs that are closely tied to nature.
  c. probably have democratic social values in that the song reveals the necessity of cooperation and respect for others.
  d. believe their well-being depends on their pleasing the deities, Mother Earth and Father Sky.
  e. value hard work in that the speaker notes that the people have "tired backs."

  3. Answers will vary. A model answer for "Hunting Song," "My Father's Song," and "The World on the Turtle's Back" follows.

For "Hunting Song," students might include
  a. the words *Navajo, deer, mountain, beauty, nature, harmony, hunt, blessed.*
  b. the lines "Comes the deer to my singing, / Comes the deer to my song, / Comes the deer to my singing."
  c. a symbol of nature, prayer, song, and blessings.
  d. an image of Navajos, hunters, and nature.

For "My Father's Song," students might include
  a. the words *father, son, wanting to say things, soft*

*damp sand, gently, tiny pink animals, remembering, love, missing.*
  b. symbols of love, fathers and sons, nature, and loneliness.
  c. an image of an older man farming and sharing with his son.
  d. the image of small pink mice sitting in a man's palm.
  e. an image of a young man remembering better times.

For "The World on the Turtle's Back," students might include:
  a. the words *Sky-World, earth, balance.*
  b. a sea tortoise floating on the surface of the ocean as a woman falls from a hole at the top of the sky.
  c. a muskrat bringing up earth from the bottom of the ocean.
  d. an island growing from the earth on the turtle's back.
  e. twin boys, with some indication of right-handed and left-handed.
  f. the world above (light) and the world below (dark).

  4. Answers will vary. A model answer for "Coyote and the Buffalo" follows.

In "Coyote and the Buffalo,"
  a. the message is that greed and foolishness don't pay, or "don't kill the goose that lays the golden eggs." When Coyote's greed leads him to slaughter the cow that provides him with unlimited nourishment, he loses the cow altogether and gains nothing from it.
  b. the lesson can be applied to any modern-day situations in which people are driven by greed.
  c. the lesson, for example, could apply to a situation in which an employee steals from the company that provides his or her salary. If caught, the employee not only loses his or her job but also gets into serious legal trouble.

**D.** (20 points) Notes will vary widely. A model answer for "Fox and Coyote and Whale" could include notes suggesting the following:
  a. New ending: Whale kills Fox and Coyote.
  b. New lesson: Trickery and cunning can only get you so far. They can't overcome all obstacles, including that of a physically superior being.

### *from* La Relación
Selection Test, pp. 19–20
**A.** (8 points each) Notes will vary widely. Model answers follow.
  1. Character trait: perseverance
     How it helped: When there seemed to be no hope of reaching land and most of the crew were dying, his perseverance would not allow him to quit his efforts to reach land.

2. Action: blessed the sick Karankawas
   How it helped: In return, he received food to feed his crew.
3. Character trait: compassion
   How it helped: It led the Karankawas to feed and house the Spanish.
4. Action: brought the Spanish to their homes
   How it helped: It saved the Spanish from dying of exposure.

**B.** (6 points each)
1. b
2. b
3. a

**C.** (4 points each)
1. b
2. c
3. c
4. a
5. b

**D.** (15 points; students should answer one of the two)
1. Answers will vary but should include some of the following points:
   a. The Spanish desperately needed help, and the Karankawas were simply too compassionate to ignore their needs.
   b. The Karankawas had too much respect for human life to allow the Spanish to die. They grieved over the drowned Spanish strangers and continued to care for the Spanish even after they spread a deadly disease.
   c. The Karankawas were intrigued by the gifts the Spanish gave them.
   d. The Karankawas outnumbered the Spanish and so had little to fear from helping them.
   e. The Karankawas apparently grew to respect the Spanish. They believed that the Spanish were powerful enough to cure the sick.
   f. After the Spanish appeared to cure some of their people, the Karankawas cared for the Spanish out of gratitude and fairness.
2. Answers will vary but should include points similar to the following:
   a. Both groups benefited by gaining friendship, exchanging ideas, and experiencing a different culture.
   b. The Spanish were able to survive.
   c. The Karankawas received gifts that pleased them.
   d. For the Spanish, the major drawback was that their dependence on the Karankawas forced them to do things that made them uncomfortable, such as attempting to treat the ill.

who might be interesting t
terms of genealogy or his
the first child born, the
(6 points each)

**B.** (6 points each)
1. b
2. a
3. d

**C.** (4 points each)
1. c
2. a
3. b
4. c
5. b

**D.** (15 poin
1. Answe
"barb
a.
b

po...
1. a. b
   abou...
   encounte...
   peace agreeme...
   group survived. He ...
   because he was there.
   b. Williams provides factual into...
   women and children survived, w...
   and how many children they produce...
   provide this information by researching bir...
   death records and other primary sources.
2. a. Bradford was a deeply religious man who attributed the Pilgrims' successes to God; he also assumed that the Indians would rather kill them than help them. These biases can be attributed to the time in which he lived.
   b. Williams, a genealogist who wrote her work in 1993, was biased toward the interests of genealogy and the plight of women in the group.
3. a. Bradford viewed the land as harsh and inhospitable, the Indians as barbarians, and his fellow Pilgrims as remarkable people who sacrificed themselves to help one another survive. He describes the events as a governor might, praising his soldiers and explaining relations with the Indians.
   b. Williams also viewed the land as inhospitable, but her information was secondhand. She seems to view the events as sources of romantic adventures (the courtship of Priscilla Mullins) and intrigue (John Billington's hanging), and she views the integrity of Bradford's account with some skepticism (rumors of Dorothy Bradford's suicide).
4. a. Bradford was responsible for the welfare of the people and the success of the colony. From his point of view, then, he might have glossed over the failures and deaths and emphasized the positive achievements in his account.
   b. Williams views things from a distance of several hundred years and is writing for a very different audience; she tends to report events and people

modern readers in
...story (the first marriage,
...first execution).

...s; students should answer one of the two)
...rs will vary. Students might find evidence of
..."...barism" in
...ne Native Americans' manner of dress.
... stories that Bradford may have heard about their
behavior.
...me students may also point to the attack described in
...The First Encounter," although others will feel that the
defense of one's territory is not usually considered barbaric.
Most students will probably feel that the selection does
not adequately support the "savage barbarian" claim
because
  a. Bradford doesn't appear to have actually witnessed
     one instance of savage behavior on the part of any
     Native American.
  b. Bradford's point of view is clearly biased. When the
     Native Americans took tools that they later returned,
     Bradford called this "stealing," yet he found no fault
     with the Pilgrims who took corn and beans without
     permission because they paid for them six months
     later.
  c. Samoset approached the colonists and offered, in
     English, considerable information and assistance.
  d. Massasoit agreed to, and then adhered to, a peace
     compact.
  e. Squanto lived with the Pilgrims until his death,
     acting as interpreter, guide, and teacher. The
     Pilgrims considered him an instrument of God.
2. Answers will vary widely but should reflect students'
   understanding that
   a. as of the writing of the selection, the compact had
      been in effect for 24 years. This seems to indicate
      that both parties found it reasonable.
   b. not all of the clauses were reciprocal. This could
      indicate unfairness, but not necessarily.
**E.** (15 points) Answers will vary widely, depending on
students' personal experiences, situations, and viewpoints.
Accept any answers that address the concern of the
question and are elaborated by examples or details
from the literature or from life.

*from* **The Interesting Narrative of the Life
of Olaudah Equiano**
Selection Test, pp. 23–24
**A**. (10 points each) Notes will vary. Model answers follow.
  1. Sense: smell
     Feeling: disgust
  2. Sense: sight
     Feeling: fear, horror
  3. Sense: hearing
     Feeling: horror
**B.** (6 points each)
  1. b
  2. b
  3. d
**C.** (4 points each)
  1. a
  2. b
  3. a
  4. a
  5. c
**D.** (16 points; students should answer one of the two)
  1. Answers will vary. Students might say that the white
     Europeans
     a. were evil.
     b. did not believe that the black Africans were human
        beings.
     c. ignored all evidence that the black Africans were
        quite human.
     d. were raised to believe that slavery was acceptable
        and natural.
     e. valued money above human life.
     f. bought, sold, and traded black Africans because it
        was highly profitable.
     g. feared the Africans because the Africans
        outnumbered them and the Europeans assumed
        they were dangerous savages.
  2. Answers will vary. Students could find evidence in
     the selection to support the ideas that those who
     preferred slavery to death may have
     a. simply preferred life under any conditions to death.
     b. been unable to conceive what slavery would entail.
     c. had loved ones who needed them.
     d. retained the hope of escape.
In addition, students could find evidence in the selection
to support the ideas that those who preferred death to
slavery may have been too
     a. weakened by disease to care.
     b. depressed by their separation from their loved
        ones and their land to go on living.
     c. demoralized and terrified by their treatment to
        have retained the hope that their lives would
        ever improve.

**E.** (16 points) Answers will vary widely, depending on students' personal experiences, situations, and viewpoints. Accept any answers that address the concern of the question and are elaborated by examples or details from the literature or from life.

### from **Blue Highways**
Selection Test, pp. 25–26
**A.** (12 points each)
  1. Ratings will vary. The best answers will be similar to the following:
     a. To inform: important, perhaps very important
     b. To entertain: at least semi-important
     c. To express: important, perhaps very important
     d. To persuade: at least semi-important
  2. Notes will vary but could suggest the following reasons for the ratings given above:
     a. To inform: Heat-Moon includes a great deal of information about the Hopi.
     b. To entertain: The selection is entertaining only in that its subject is fascinating.
     c. To express: Heat-Moon relates not only his experience with Fritz but also what Heat-Moon himself said to Fritz.
     d. To persuade: Heat-Moon presents important issues and misperceptions that he wants the reader to consider from his and from Fritz's point of view.
**B.** (5 points each)
  1. b
  2. c
  3. b
  4. a
**C.** (4 points each)
  1. b
  2. a
  3. a
  4. c
  5. b
**D.** (18 points; students should answer one of the two)
  1. Answers will vary. Students could say that Fritz
     a. is testing Heat-Moon to ensure that he is truly interested in the Hopi Way and isn't just being a "tourist."
     b. may want Heat-Moon not only to hear about the Hopi Way but to actually feel and experience a part of it by tasting the bread.
  2. Answers will vary. Students could say that Heat-Moon seems to have been
     a. searching for meaning in his own life.
     b. seeking to connect with others.
     c. seeking to connect with his own Native American heritage.

In addition, students could say that Heat-Moon's decision to travel back roads implies that he
     a. was in no hurry.
     b. wanted to meet ordinary people and talk to them.
     c. was more interested in the journey than in reaching any specific destination.
     d. wanted to avoid tourist traps and urban areas.
**E.** (18 points) Answers will vary widely, depending on students' personal experiences, situations, and viewpoints. Accept any answers that address the concern of the question and are elaborated by examples or details from the literature or from life.

### My Sojourn in the Lands of My Ancestors
Selection Test, pp. 27–28
**A.** (12 points each)
  1. Notes will vary. Most students will write notes suggesting that the interruption provides the reader with the background necessary to understand Angelou's
     a. strong feelings toward the castles.
     b. decision not to tour them.
  2. Notes will vary but could suggest that the flashback
     a. angers the reader.
     b. depresses the reader.
     c. deepens the reader's understanding of Angelou's feelings.
     d. encourages the reader to empathize with Angelou.
     e. informs the reader about Angelou's roots.
**B.** (8 points each)
  1. c
  2. d
  3. a
**C.** (4 points each)
  1. c
  2. a
  3. b
  4. a
  5. b
**D.** (16 points; students should answer one of the two)
  1. Answers will vary. Students could say that Angelou's memories of Stamps help her to
     a. understand the culture and customs of Dunkwa.
     b. know how to behave in Dunkwa.
     c. understand the people there better than she otherwise would.
     d. know that she should praise the host for cooking food that was brought by others.
     e. know that she shouldn't offer payment for hospitality.
     f. know that she should offer gifts to the children.
     g. feel safer and more comfortable with the people of Dunkwa.

In addition, students could say that by relating the foreign customs of Dunkwa to the more recognizable customs of an American community, the Stamps flashback

    a. gives the reader a better understanding of Dunkwa and Angelou's attraction to it.

    b. explains how Angelou is able to get along so well in a place that is foreign to her.

  2. Answers will vary but should reflect students' understanding that Angelou gains the acceptance of the people of Dunkwa and, thereby, their companionship and hospitality. Most students will probably feel that she loses little, if anything, by not telling the truth. They might say that she loses only the experience of having to sleep overnight in her car. Some students may feel that Angelou loses her self-respect, noting that she is slightly ashamed of her lie.

**E.** (16 points) Answers will vary widely, depending on students' personal experiences, situations, and viewpoints. Accept any answers that address the concern of the questions and are elaborated by examples or details from the literature or from life.

### Unit One, Part Two Test

pp. 29–30

**A.** (5 points each)

  1. b

  2. d

  3. c

  4. a

**B.** (20 points) Notes will vary. A model answer for the Pilgrims (*Of Plymouth Plantation*) follows.

This journey involves

    a. traveling by sea from Europe to the East Coast of North America.

    b. hardships such as stormy seas, sickness, starvation, inhospitable weather, and hostile neighbors.

    c. creating a new home in the wilderness.

    d. blessings such as bountiful food sources and friendly neighbors.

The purpose of this journey is to

    a. carve out a new home for themselves.

    b. obtain the freedom to worship as they please.

The Pilgrims were affected by this journey in that it

    a. killed or nearly killed all of them.

    b. allowed them to worship freely.

    c. gave a greater sense of purpose to their lives.

**C.** (20 points each; students should answer two of the three)

  1. Answers will vary. A model answer for "The Interesting Narrative of the Life of Olaudah Equiano" and *Blue Highways* follows.

In "The Interesting Narrative . . . ," Equiano addresses the oppression of enslaved black Africans because he

    a. personally experiences being a slave.

    b. finds slavery inhumane and cruel.

    c. believes that slavery is immoral.

    d. may feel that, by sharing his experiences, he can help to abolish the system of slavery.

Equiano concludes that

    a. oppression harms people and leaves them without hope.

    b. freedom is necessary to happiness and, in many cases, to survival.

In *Blue Highways,* Heat-Moon addresses the oppression of Native Americans today because

    a. he is part Native American.

    b. he is on a personal journey in search of his identity.

    c. he becomes engaged in conversation with another Native American.

    d. he is fascinated by Fritz's experiences as a Native American and his knowledge of Hopi belief.

    e. the issue of oppression is a vital one to Fritz and a topic he is interested in discussing.

Heat-Moon concludes that

    a. oppression stifles individuality.

    b. oppression impedes the ability of people to communicate.

    c. oppression unnecessarily complicates the lives of individuals.

    d. freedom makes people feel better about themselves and others.

    e. freedom helps people get along.

  2. Answers will vary. A model answer for Bradford (*Of Plymouth Plantation*) and Fritz (*Blue Highways*) follows.

The connections that the men feel toward a greater power are similar in that both

    a. perceive the good things in their lives as gifts bestowed on them by a greater power.

    b. feel thankful for the gifts granted by the greater powers.

    c. see evidence in everyday things of a greater power at work.

    d. believe that a greater power actively takes part in human affairs.

    e. feel dependent on the greater power for their well-being.

The connections that the men feel are different in that

    a. Bradford views the power as something outside himself; Fritz sees the power as something inside him that connects him to all other living things.

    b. Bradford views himself, at least symbolically, as the child of a greater power. Fritz's greater power doesn't include a "father figure."

    c. Fritz doesn't seem to feel as undeserving of the greater power's blessings as Bradford does.

d. Fritz doesn't seem to feel as great a sense of awe and fear as Bradford does toward the greater power.

e. Fritz's connection to a greater power ties him more closely to nature and people unlike himself than Bradford's seems to.

3. Answers will vary. A model answer for the main characters of "My Sojourn in the Lands of My Ancestors" and "The Interesting Narrative . . ." follows.

Maya Angelou has the greatest ability to control her destiny because

a. she lives in the United States and has the freedom to travel.

b. she is able to learn new languages that enable her to communicate with the people she meets.

c. she can choose where she wants to go and when.

d. her appearance helps her fit in with the people of Ghana.

Equiano has the least ability to control his destiny in that

a. the only hope of escaping the ship is death.

b. even those who prefer life have little control over whether they survive the trip or not.

c. he has free will but lacks the freedom to exercise it.

d. the destiny that he faces is complex and will require a great deal of effort and good fortune to significantly change.

**D.** (20 points) Notes will vary. A model answer for Olaudah Equiano and the people of Dunkwa follows.

Equiano and the people of Dunkwa are similar in that they

a. are black Africans.

b. value family ties.

c. come from civilized societies.

d. are used to being around compassionate, reasonable people.

e. are distrustful of strangers.

f. have little use for white people.

g. are religious.

h. are superstitious.

i. believe in the existence of supernatural beings.

j. are very observant.

Differences could include the following:

a. Equiano is a slave; the people of Dunkwa are free.

b. Equiano lived in the eighteenth century; the people of Dunkwa in the selection are from the twentieth century.

c. Equiano was born into a society in which the threat of slavery existed; slavery does not threaten the people of Dunkwa.

d. Equiano is miserable; the people of Dunkwa are happy.

e. Equiano has no hope; the people of Dunkwa do.

f. Equiano is unlikely to see Africa again; no one in Dunkwa appears to have ever left Africa.

# Unit Two

## Selected Poems by Bradstreet

Selection Test, pp. 31–32

**A.** (15 points each)

1. "To My Dear and Loving Husband":

Students' choice of the element that appeals the most will vary. A model answer for "emotions" follows.

a. The speaker expresses strong emotions of passion and love.

b. The poet uses sensory images to emphasize the speaker's emotions ("all the riches that the East doth hold"; "such that rivers cannot quench").

2. "Upon the Burning of Our House . . .":

Students' choice of the element that appeals the most will vary. A model answer for "intellect" follows.

a. The speaker's reaction to her devastating loss is unusual in modern times.

b. Her reaction to the loss is related to her belief that the fire was God's will.

**B.** (5 points each)

1. c

2. c

3. c

4. a

5. d

6. b

**C.** (20 points; students should answer one of the two)

1. Answers will vary widely. In describing the relationship, students may use such terms as

a. passionate, full of feeling.

b. loving, caring, or warm.

c. devoted, tender, or affectionate.

2. Answers will vary but should reflect students' understanding that the speaker

a. believes that everything she has ever had was a gift from God (lines 17–18).

b. believes that God has the right to take everything away from her (lines 19–20).

c. feels fortunate that God has left her what little she still has (line 20).

**D.** (20 points) Answers will vary widely, depending on students' personal experiences, situations, and viewpoints. Accept any answers that address the concern of the question and are elaborated by examples or details from the literature or from life.

## The Examination of Sarah Good

Selection Test, pp. 33–34

**A.** (15 points each) The three examples of language and notes will vary but should resemble the following examples:

a. Language: "Why do you hurt these children?"
Bias: The examiner doesn't ask Sarah if she is hurting the children. To him, it is a foregone conclusion that she is.
  b. Language: "Her answers were in a very wicked and spiteful manner. . . ."
Bias: The transcripts show only that Sarah Good denied the charges against her. Her denials could only be considered wicked if her examiners considered her guilty to begin with.
  c. Language: "He answered no, not in this nature, but it was in her bad carriage to him. . . ."
Bias: The husband has no actual evidence that his wife is a witch, but because they have not been getting along, he states that she must be one.

**B.** (5 points each)
  1. a
  2. d
  3. a
  4. d
  5. d
  6. c

**C.** (15 points; students should answer one of the two)
  1. Answers will vary but could include points similar to the following:
     a. Religion was very much a part of everyday life. The documents reveal that there was no separation of church and state, and that a person's lack of religious conviction was taken as evidence of criminal behavior.
     b. The atmosphere was restrictive and stifling in that eccentric people, such as Sarah Good, were endangered by their lack of conformity.
     c. The atmosphere was dangerous in that people were extremely suspicious and fearful. Even spouses, such as Mr. Good, couldn't necessarily be counted on for support.
     d. Superstition was very much a part of everyday life. People were inclined to seek supernatural answers to their problems. The court officers assume that the young women's problems are caused by witchcraft.
  2. Answers will vary but should reflect students' knowledge that, at that time
     a. justice was subjective, unfair, and not based on sound reason.
     b. the accused could be assumed guilty before he or she was tried.
     c. hard evidence wasn't needed to obtain convictions.
     d. the accused didn't have the right to be represented by a lawyer.

Possible answers for how our current system of justice differs could include the following points:
  a. Justice today is based on evidence rather than accusation.
  b. Justice today is based on the idea that there must be no "reasonable doubt" to find someone guilty.
  c. Justice today is based on the principle that people are innocent until proven guilty.
**D.** (15 points) Answers will vary widely, depending on students' personal experiences, situations, and viewpoints. Accept any answers that address the concern of the question and are elaborated by examples or details from the literature or from life.

### *from* Sinners in the Hands of an Angry God
Selection Test, pp. 35–36
**A.** (10 points each) Quotations selected by students will vary but should resemble the following examples:
  1. a. "God has so many different unsearchable ways of taking wicked men out of the world and sending them to hell. . . ."
     b. This sentence is intended to make listeners feel fearful of death.
     c. Edwards's goal is to persuade listeners that anyone may die at any time, and too many are unprepared to meet their Maker.
  2. a. "The God that holds you over the pit of hell, much as one holds a spider, or some loathsome insect over the fire, abhors you, and is dreadfully provoked. . . ."
     b. This sentence is intended to invoke fear, dread, and meekness.
     c. Edwards's goal is to make listeners feel insignificant, disgusting, and contemptible before God.
  3. a. "To see so many rejoicing and singing for joy of heart, while you have cause to mourn for sorrow of heart, and howl for vexation of spirit!"
     b. This sentence is intended to make listeners feel sorry for or ashamed of themselves.
     c. Edwards's goal is to persuade listeners to repent and be "born again" so they may feel the "joy of heart" that others have achieved.
**B.** (6 points each)
  1. b
  2. c
  3. a
**C.** (4 points each)
  1. b
  2. c
  3. a
  4. b
  5. b

**D.** (16 points; students should answer one of the two)
  1. Answers will vary widely. Students who feel that the
     sermon appeals primarily to the emotions may say
     that it
     a. uses highly emotional language and images.
     b. seems designed to create fear in the audience.
     c. does not present particularly developed or
        reasonable arguments.
Students who feel that the sermon appeals primarily
to the senses may say that it uses sensory images that
create vivid illustrations of the torments of hell and
God's power and wrath.
Students who feel that the sermon appeals primarily to
the intellect should support their view with appropriate
reasons.
  2. Answers will vary but should reflect students'
     understanding that Edwards asks his audience to
     a. think about their own lives.
     b. recognize their sinfulness.
     c. become born again.
     d. devote their lives to God.
In exchange for these things, Edwards offers
     a. a religious awakening.
     b. the security of the Mediator, Jesus Christ.
     c. the salvation of their souls.
**E.** (16 points) Answers will vary widely, depending on
students' personal experiences, situations, and viewpoints.
Accept any answers that address the concern of the
question and are elaborated by examples or details
from the literature or from life.

## The Crucible: Act One

Selection Test, pp. 37–38
**A.** (10 points each)
  1. Answers will vary but should include points similar to
     the following:
The details of the setting include:
     a. a *small* bedroom
     b. a *narrow* window with leaded panes
     c. a candle burning near the bed
     d. a chest; a chair; a *small* table
     e. exposed roof rafters
  2. Answers will vary but should include points similar to
     the following:
     a. These details create a mood that is harsh, spare,
        and restrictive. The room is described as having the
        "air of clean sparseness."
     b. These details of setting help to reinforce the
        restrictive atmosphere of Puritan life.
**B.** (5 points each)
  1. d
  2. b
  3. c
  4. b

**C.** (4 points each)
  1. c
  2. c
  3. b
  4. b
  5. a
**D.** (20 points; students should answer one of the two)
  1. Answers will vary but should include points similar to
     the following:
As fear grows, Rebecca and Proctor seem to be the only
villagers who are levelheaded and calm. Their calmness
contrasts with and emphasizes the growing hysteria in
Salem.
     a. Examples: Unlike the villagers making the pilgrimage
        to Parris's house, Rebecca is there to help Betty. Her
        very presence seems to quiet Betty. Rebecca refers
        to Betty's state as "children . . . having their silly
        seasons. . . ." She tries to convince others to dismiss
        the thought of witchcraft: "A child's spirit is like a
        child, you can never catch it by running after it; you
        must stand still, and, for love, it will soon itself
        come back."
     b. Unlike the others, she sees the imminent dangers
        to come: "There is a prodigious danger in the
        seeking of loose spirits."
     c. Rebecca leaves the room in disgust when
        Reverend Hale talks of having to "rip and tear to get
        her [Betty] free."
     d. Like Rebecca, Proctor doubts that witchcraft is to
        blame for the children's state. He knows Abigail
        and the other girls are not victims of witchcraft
        but of their own mischief.
     e. He does not hesitate to speak his mind to Parris or
        Putnam. Proctor demands to know why Parris and
        Putnam have called in Hale without a meeting of
        the wardens. Proctor is not afraid to question
        authority ("I like not the smell of this 'authority'"),
        but such "anarchy" is not allowed in the Puritan
        form of government.
  2. Answers may vary but should include points similar to
     the following:
     a. At first, Parris evokes feelings of pity and sympathy.
        His daughter is afflicted and may be dying, and he is
        beside himself with worry. He seems terrified and,
        perhaps justifiably, worried about his standing in Salem.
     b. As the play progresses, Parris no longer evokes
        feelings of pity or sympathy. The audience sees
        that he cares more about his reputation and
        position than about his daughter's health. He
        wants to know the truth about what happened
        in the woods not to help the souls of the poor
        girls but to make sure his enemies cannot use
        the events against him.

c. By the end of Act One, Parris appears to be self-centered, pompous, and far from the paragon of a good and benevolent minister.

d. The audience learns that he is petty and not overly concerned with the spiritual welfare of his parish. Parris demanded the deed to the house and, as Proctor says of his sermon, ". . . you spent so long on deeds and mortgages I thought it were an auction."

**E.** (20 points) Answers will vary widely, depending on students' personal experiences, situations, and viewpoints. Accept any answers that address the concern of the question and are elaborated by examples or details from the literature or from life.

## The Crucible: Act Two
Selection Test, pp. 39–40
**A.** (10 points each) Notes will vary but should include points similar to the following:

1. Mary Warren: Although she has acquired some power, she is intimidated by Proctor. She rightfully fears physical abuse by Proctor. She uses her power to protect Elizabeth to keep him from whipping her, which he has done before. She is superstitious, in that she does believe in witchcraft.

2. Proctor: Although perhaps not superstitious, he can be cruel and quick to anger. He feels superior to Mary Warren and believes that he can intimidate her into obeying his wishes.

3. Elizabeth: She tries to be a peacemaker. She wants to protect Mary, but she doesn't want to confront Proctor. She is quiet and feels vulnerable.

**B.** (5 points each)
1. b
2. d
3. b

**C.** (5 points each)
1. b
2. a
3. c
4. b

**D.** (20 points; students should answer one of the two)
1. Answers will vary but should include points similar to the following:
a. Hale seems to be a man of some intelligence and integrity, but he is following his orders to investigate people and does not question the rightness of his actions. He knows that Proctor has his own reasons for not attending the church regularly, but still implies that Proctor's lack of attendance is a "softness" in his record.
b. Hale can see from the evidence of the poppet and Mary Warren's statement that Elizabeth is not guilty

of bewitching Abigail, but he does not stand up for her and does not question the authority or the morality of the men who come to arrest her.

c. Proctor can be considered cowardly because he does not want to be involved. At this point, he is willing to leave it up to other people to stop the madness in Salem.

d. Proctor may have been reluctant to confront Abigail because of his affair with her, but he, like Hale, is also a coward. People are going to be hanged, and it is his responsibility to stop it. Even after his wife has been arrested, he still tries to make Mary go to court and openly accuse Abigail. Proctor holds firm to his views about witchcraft and what is really happening in the town, but he does not want to step forward and be the one who stops it.

2. Answers will vary but should include points similar to the following:
a. Mary Warren continues to accuse people because she knows that the only way to stop the madness is to contradict or confront Abigail; she is terrified that the other girls will turn on her and Abigail will kill her if she does this.
b. Mary knows that if she testifies against Abigail, she could easily become accused of witchcraft herself and be hanged as a result.
c. Mary feels important because she believes she is an "official of the court" and is doing "God's work." Her position gives her power over John Proctor; up to this point, he has been her master and has probably used the whip on her before.

**E.** (15 points) Answers will vary widely, depending on students' personal experiences, situations, and viewpoints. Accept any answers that address the concern of the question and are elaborated by examples or details from the literature or from life.

## The Crucible: Act Three
Selection Test, pp. 41–42
**A.** (6 points each) Notes will vary but should include points similar to the following:
1. Abigail is extremely self-confident. She knows that she controls the other girls and, in fact, the entire village. She also knows that Mary cannot threaten her. When Mary tries to expose Abigail as a fraud, Abigail merely accuses her.
Foil: Mary attempts to do the right thing, despite her fear of Abigail and the court. But her lack of self-confidence sharpens the contrast between her naiveté and Abigail's ruthlessness.
2. Abigail is so manipulative that she concocts the plan to implicate Elizabeth by actually jabbing a needle into

her stomach. Mary would never be able to conceive or implement such a plan.

Foil: Mary is easily manipulated. She quickly falls in with the other girls and accuses innocent people of witchcraft, but she is like a person under a spell. She begins to believe that what she is feeling is real. Again, Mary's naiveté heightens the calculating coldness of Abigail.

3. Abigail begins by wanting to get rid of Elizabeth so she can be with John. But when Abigail is spurned by John, she becomes vindictive: now she wants to accuse Elizabeth at any cost, even if it means heartbreak or worse for John.

Foil: Mary has also been overcome with her new power and the respect she gets from the villagers. But she never imagined that people were really going to die. Mary's dawning awareness of what is happening to the village contrasts with Abigail's growing cruelty.

4. Abigail actually has the arrogance to threaten Danforth, who does become a bit apprehensive.

Foil: Mary's trembling and fearfulness in front of Danforth makes Abigail's growing arrogance and power even more frightening. Nothing will stop Abigail now.

**B.** (5 points each)
1. a
2. d
3. c
4. c

**C.** (4 points each)
1. c
2. b
3. a
4. b
5. b

**D.** (20 points; students should answer one of the two)
1. Answers will vary but should include points similar to the following:
   a. Danforth fears that anyone who disputes the trials is really there to overthrow the court's authority. This is obvious when he carefully asks Proctor if he has told anyone in the village his story.
   b. Danforth balks at the thought that the girls are frauds. After all, he has arrested nearly 400 people and condemned 72. He worries about his reputation and refuses to accept that the trials might not be about witchcraft but about greed and revenge. Danforth's behavior undermines the legal system because he does not allow any opposition.
   c. He denies Proctor the right to a lawyer; abuses his authority by tricking Giles into a charge of contempt; says that "no uncorrupted man may fear

this court" and then arrests an innocent Giles; he gives Mary no choices: she will go to jail for having lied in the past or go to jail for lying now. Danforth will do all he can to make sure none of his rulings are overturned and the trials are not stopped.

2. Answers will vary but should include points similar to the following:
   a. Proctor realizes he must become involved to fight evil when Danforth tries to make a deal with him to spare Elizabeth for a year. Proctor could accept the deal, but his friend's wives are also being accused, so the truth of the girls' pretense must be told.
   b. When Mary's testimony is undermined, Proctor knows he must ignore his reputation and admit his affair with Abigail. He acts on his belief, and his agreement with the statement about indifference to evil, by admitting his adultery. He thinks that this will settle the case once and for all, but Danforth does not believe him.

**E.** (16 points) Answers will vary widely, depending on students' personal experiences, situations, and viewpoints. Accept any answers that address the concern of the question and are elaborated by examples or details from the literature or from life.

## The Crucible: Act Four
Selection Test, pp. 43–44

**A.** (8 points each) Notes will vary but should include points similar to the following:

1. External conflict with Hale: When Danforth hears that Hale is trying to get Rebecca and Proctor to confess, he is at first surprised and then relieved. Somewhere in his mind he suspects that Hale might be right about the motivations for many of the charges, but to give in and agree with Hale would mean that Danforth has been wrong. He decides that more innocent people should die to justify the deaths of those already killed: "I cannot pardon these when twelve are already hanged for the same crime. It is not just."

2. External conflict with society: It is obvious that the news about Andover frightens Danforth. The people have had enough of these trials, and the deaths of two more fine people (Rebecca and Proctor) might instigate a rebellion against the court in Salem.

3. Internal conflict: Danforth is alarmed when he hears that Abigail and Mercy have run away. His own doubts begin to get stronger, and he begins to suspect that his only hope now is with Rebecca's and Proctor's confessions. Ultimately, he squelches any doubts: he believes in his authority, and he feels that any attempt to overthrow his authority is also an attempt to overthrow the authority of the church.

**B.** (5 points each)
1. d
2. b
3. b
4. c

**C.** (4 points each)
1. a
2. c
3. c
4. a
5. b

**D.** (20 points; students should answer one of the two)
1. Answers will vary but should include points similar to the following:
  a. The test the characters had to pass was to face their own consciences and come to terms with their shortcomings or personal weaknesses.
  b. Many never passed the test. Most did not confront their weaknesses and found it easier to blame the devil and witchcraft for their own ambition, lust, or greed. Examples: Thomas Putnam used the trials to obtain more land and to seek vengeance against those he believed slighted him. His wife, Ann, was jealous of Rebecca and blamed her for the deaths of her children. Parris was always driven by fear and greed—fear of what people would think, fear for his life, and greed for material things. Proctor's lust drove him to commit adultery. Abigail's desire for Proctor drove her to accuse Elizabeth. Abigail reveled in her power to accuse innocent people. Danforth's pride and arrogance compelled him to convict innocent people and circumvent the legal process.
  c. Those who did pass the test were true to themselves and their beliefs. Despite the consequences, they did what they believed was right and just. Examples: Rebecca refused to confess to a lie, even though it meant her death. Giles endured a brutal death rather than betray a friend or give up his land to his enemies. Elizabeth confessed her own faults at the end and saw the goodness in her husband. Reverend Hale realized the truth and condemned the trials. John Proctor destroyed his false confession and chose death rather than to give credence to the witch trials.
2. Answers will vary but should include points similar to the following:
  a. Parris, at first, appears to believe in the innocence of Rebecca and Proctor. As Act Four progresses, we learn that he is not motivated by the knowledge that the trials are a farce. Rather, he is worried that the villagers will rebel and oust him—or worse (he has already had a death threat).
  b. Hale, who once believed that the devil lurked in Salem, now knows that the trials are based on greed and revenge.
  c. Hale's justification for asking that Proctor lie: ". . . cleave no faith when faith brings blood. It is a mistaken law that leads you to sacrifice . . . for it may well be God damns a liar less than he that throws his life away for pride." Hale does not want an innocent man to die.

**E.** (16 points) Answers will vary widely, depending on students' personal experiences, situations, and viewpoints. Accept any answers that address the concern of the question and are elaborated by examples or details from the literature or from life.

## Unit Two, Part One Test
pp. 45–46

**A.** (5 points each)
1. b
2. d
3. a
4. c

**B.** (20 points) Notes will vary. A model answer for Danforth in *The Crucible* follows.
Danforth is intolerant of anyone who:
  a. disagrees with him or questions his decisions.
  b. questions authority.
  c. expresses a belief or opinion that differs from Christian principles.
Example: Danforth refuses to listen to contrary evidence or differing opinions that might invalidate his assumptions and decisions. "But you must understand, sir, that a person is either with this court or he must be counted against it." Reasons for his intolerance include the following:
  a. He is a judge who decides cases based on religious beliefs; any questioning of those beliefs or acceptance of different beliefs would undermine the law and his authority.
  b. He believes that questioning beliefs or the authority of the church will undermine the church's control of society and could lead to rebellion.
  c. He does not want to look like he made a mistake in hanging 12 people condemned as witches, so he cannot tolerate the suggestion that the witch hunt might have been a hoax from the beginning.
  d. Since he believes so strongly in the Christian faith, he cannot accept the possibility that different ideas might be valid or worthy of consideration.

**C.** (20 points each; students should answer two of the three)
1. Answers will vary. A model answer for "To My Dear and Loving Husband," "Upon the Burning of Our House," and *The Crucible* follows. Puritan ideals of

womanhood appear to include
  a. married love and fidelity in marriage before and after death ("To My Dear and Loving Husband").
  b. faith in and devotion to God ("Upon the Burning of Our House").
  c. patience and acceptance of hardship ("Upon the Burning of Our House").
  d. conformity (*The Crucible*).
  e. purity and chastity (*The Crucible*).
  f. conservative dress and behavior (*The Crucible*).

2. Answers will vary. A model answer for "Upon the Burning of Our House" and "Sinners in the Hands of an Angry God" follows. Distinguishing characteristics of the Puritan view of their relationship to God include the following:
  a. The relationship between God and people is immediate and a part of everyday life ("Upon the Burning of Our House").
  b. All that people have is given to them by God and, therefore, can be taken away by God at any time ("Upon the Burning of Our House").
  c. In heaven, God will compensate good people for their trials on earth ("Upon the Burning of Our House").
  d. God sits in constant judgment of people ("Sinners in the Hands of an Angry God").
  e. God is angry with people and finds it incredibly easy to cast them into hell ("Sinners . . .").
  f. God's powers are far greater than those of people ("Upon the Burning of Our House" and "Sinners . . .").
  g. It is the responsibility of people to please God, but it is not the responsibility of God to please people ("Upon the Burning of Our House" and "Sinners . . .").

3. Answers will vary. A model answer for "To My Dear and Loving Husband" and *The Crucible* follows. In "To My Dear and Loving Husband," the Puritans are presented favorably in that
  a. the speaker's love for her husband and his for her is highly admirable in an age in which love so often comes second to other concerns.
  b. the speaker's devotion and fidelity to her husband is highly admirable in an age in which divorce and marital infidelity is quite common.

In *The Crucible,* the Puritans are presented unfavorably in that
  a. their better judgment gives way to hysteria.
  b. their hysteria results in the deaths of many people.
  c. their courtroom procedures fail to reflect any interest in uncovering the truth.
  d. their arrogant faith in themselves makes them look all the more foolish and mean-spirited.
  e. their means of punishment are barbaric.

**D.** (20 points) Notes will vary. A model answer for "Sinners in the Hands of an Angry God" follows. The event is a sermon. Ideas expressed include the following:

  a. God is more angry with the living than the dead.
  b. God holds everyone at the brink of hell.
  c. The wrath of God is everlasting and miserable.
  d. God is angry with those people who are not converted or born again.
  e. Sinners have the chance to repent and fill their hearts with love.

**Speech in the Virginia Convention**
Selection Test, pp. 47–48
**A.** (8 points each)
  1. Notes will vary but should reflect students' understanding that the lesson concerns
    a. the human tendency to choose pleasure over pain.
    b. the dangers of relying on false hope.
    c. the idea that reason is what separates humans from animals.
  2. Notes will vary but should reflect students' understanding that the allusion relates to the colonists' situation in that
    a. some colonists believe that reconciliation with the British remains a possibility.
    b. this belief endangers the colonists because it prevents them from preparing for the inevitable war with the British.
  3. Notes will vary but should reflect students' understanding that the lesson concerns
    a. the fallacy of the belief that military might and physical strength are all that is needed to be victorious or to achieve success.
    b. the power of virtue.
  4. Notes will vary but should reflect students' understanding that the allusion relates to the colonists' situation in that
    a. the British have the superior military.
    b. the colonists have the more virtuous cause.

**B.** (6 points each)
  1. c
  2. b
  3. d

**C.** (4 points each)
  1. c
  2. b
  3. c
  4. a
  5. b

**D.** (15 points; students should answer one of the two)
  1. Answers will vary. Strengths that students might identify include the following:
    a. The fact that the colonists are fighting for their liberty.
    b. The large number of colonists available to fight.
    c. The fact that their cause is just and God always takes the side of the just.

d. The willingness of the colonists to die for
their cause.
e. The rich resources of the land.
f. The fact that the colonists are armed.
g. The possibility that other countries will come to the
aid of the colonists.

Weaknesses that students might identify include the
following:
a. The fact that the colonial leaders are divided.
b. The fact that many colonists believe in the illusion
of reconciliation.
c. The fact that the British have already established
a military presence in the colonies.

2. Answers will vary. Students could say that Henry
believes that revolution is the only course open to
the colonists because
a. the war has already begun.
b. people are already fighting in the North.
c. the British government is prepared to use military
force to quell any opposition.
d. the British crown has refused to be swayed by the
colonists' numerous petitions, pleas, and requests
for aid.
e. liberty is more dear to him than life.

**E.** (15 points) Answers will vary widely, depending on
students' personal experiences, situations, and viewpoints.
Accept any answers that address the concern of the
question and are elaborated by examples or details
from the literature or from life.

## Declaration of Independence

Selection Test, pp. 49–50
**A.** (8 points each) Notes will vary but should include
these examples:
1. We have warned them; We have reminded them; We
have appealed; we have conjured.
2. Jefferson's use of parallelism connects and
emphasizes the idea that the colonists have tried
to communicate with the British. The colonists have
done all that they possibly could to try to negotiate
with the British and to try to make them understand
the colonists' point of view.
3. The use of parallelism gives the sentences a regular
rhythm, which catches the reader's attention. This
rhythm helps to emphasize Jefferson's point: the
colonies do not lightly enter into a separation from
Great Britain. The colonists have tried reason first, but
the British refuse to communicate or compromise.
**B.** (6 points each)
1. d
2. c
3. b

**C.** (4 points each)
1. c
2. a
3. c
4. b
5. b

**D.** (20 points; students should answer one of the two)
1. Answers will vary but should include ideas similar to the
following: Award 4 points per idea, up to 20 points
Britain had
a. refused to approve laws passed by the colonists.
b. refused to pass laws until the colonial assemblies
were suspended or colonists gave up their right
to representation in the legislature ("a right
inestimable to them, and formidable to tyrants
only").
c. tried in many ways to dissolve representative
legislatures.
d. limited immigration.
e. obstructed the administration of justice and
appointed judges to follow orders.
f. deprived the colonists of basic rights, such as trial
by jury.
g. subjected the colonists to harassment by appointed
officials and harsh control under the military.
h. established a large standing army in the colonies
to maintain control.
i. incited insurrection among the colonists and
encouraged both Indians and slaves to rebel
against the colonists.

2. Answers will vary but should include points similar to
the following: Award 6 points per idea, up to 20 points
a. The colonies petitioned for redress to the abuses
by the British government (raising armies against
America; refusing to pass laws to help the colonies;
dissolving representative bodies; etc.). These
petitions were not answered by the British or
they were denied.
b. The colonies warned the British that they were
extending an unwarrantable jurisdiction. They
reminded the British of the history of their
emigration and settlement. Those warnings
and reminders were not acknowledged by
the British government.
c. The colonies appealed to the British government's
sense of justice and asked them not to usurp the
rights that belong to the colonies. These attempts
also were ignored.

**E.** (18 points) Answers will vary widely, depending on
students' personal experiences, situations, and viewpoints.
Accept any answers that address the concern of the
question and are elaborated by examples or details
from the literature or from life.

## Letter to the Rev. Samson Occom/
## Letter to John Adams
Selection Test, pp. 51–52

**A.** (12 points each)
1. Notes will vary but could include points similar to the following:
   a. Wheatley: serious, grateful, humble, hopeful, and angry
   b. Adams: affectionate but angry or annoyed
2. Notes will vary but could include points similar to the following:
   a. Wheatley: thanking the reverend for his letter, getting something off her chest to a fellow philosopher
   b. Adams: getting something off her chest to her husband, persuading a politician of the necessity of recognizing the rights of women

**B.** (6 points each)
1. a
2. c
3. b

**C.** (8 points) Notes will vary but should suggest ideas similar to the following:
   a. A building on fire
   b. The situation in Boston
   c. Both are dangerous situations requiring immediate action.

**D.** (4 points each)
1. a
2. c
3. b
4. b
5. c

**E.** (15 points; students should answer one of the two)
1. Answers will vary but should reflect students' understanding that Wheatley feels that the system of slavery is doomed because
   a. Christianity is bringing order and a greater appreciation of human rights to Africa.
   b. people are endowed by God with a strong desire for freedom.
   c. God will deliver the slaves from slavery.
   d. slavery is absurd, unnatural, and irrational.
2. Answers will vary but could include points similar to the following:
   a. While John Adams is fully occupied with the work of forming a nation, Abigail Adams is not allowed to participate in that work.
   b. Abigail Adams is occupied with running a household and raising their children.
   c. While John Adams has little time to think of his wife or their separation, Abigail Adams has time in which to feel lonely and abandoned.

**F.** (15 points) Answers will vary widely, depending on students' personal experiences, situations, and viewpoints. Accept any answers that address the concern of the question and are elaborated by examples or details from the literature or from life.

## What Is an American?
Selection Test, p. 53

**A.** (40 points) Notes will vary but should suggest ideas similar to the following:
   a. The theme is "Where my bread is earned, there is my country."
   b. The letter emphasizes that America is a land where people can earn their livelihood, and Europe is a place where people can't count on a livelihood.

**B.** (8 points) c
**C.** (4 points each)
1. a
2. a
3. b
4. b
5. c

**D.** (16 points; students should answer one of the two)
1. Answers will vary but should reflect students' understanding that
   a. Crèvecoeur's defense of his new country is based almost entirely on the fact that it provides a living for its citizens.
   b. Crèvecoeur rejects loyalty to European countries almost entirely on the basis that they do not provide a living for their citizens.
2. Answers will vary but should reflect students' understanding that Crèvecoeur probably wouldn't like the idea of "hyphenated" Americans because he thinks
   a. people should identify with the country that feeds them.
   b. very little of considerations such as common language and culture.

**E.** (16 points) Answers will vary widely, depending on students' personal experiences, situations, and viewpoints. Accept any answers that address the concern of the question and are elaborated by examples or details from the literature or from life.

## Lecture to a Missionary
Selection Test, p. 55

**A.** (30 points) Notes will vary. Students could circle the following words and phrases that communicate the tone:
   a. "Brother"
   b. "the Great Spirit has made us all"
   c. "white and red children"
   d. "He has not opened our eyes"
   e. "according to our understanding"

f. "The Great Spirit does right."

g. "He knows what is best for his children"

h. "we are satisfied"

Students could describe the tone as

    a. serious.

    b. respectful.

    c. considerate.

    d. confident.

    e. kindly.

**B.** (15 points each)

  1. b

  2. c

**C.** (20 points; students should answer one of the two)

  1. Answers will vary. Most students will say that the history of relations between the two groups leads Red Jacket to suspect the missionary's motives and message because that history has proven to him that the white settlers are

    a. selfish and greedy in that they have taken over the Indians' country and left the Indians very little of it.

    b. deceitful in that they have lied about wanting only a little bit of the Indians' country.

    c. violent and dangerous in that they have started wars and caused conflicts that have involved the Indians, and they have given the Indians poison (alcohol).

    d. arrogant in that they have always forced their way on the Indians.

  2. Answers vary widely. Students could say that Red Jacket is

    a. coolheaded, in that he doesn't lose patience with the missionary's arrogance.

    b. logical, in that he presents a reasonable, well-supported argument.

    c. modest, humble, or respectful, in that he doesn't attempt to prove the superiority of his religion or humiliate the missionary.

    d. wise, in that he is willing to change his mind if provided with sound reasons for doing so.

Other answers should be supported with appropriate reasons.

**D.** (20 points) Answers will vary widely, depending on students' personal experiences, situations, and viewpoints. Accept any answers that address the concern of the question and are elaborated by examples or details from the literature or from life.

### from Stride Toward Freedom/Necessary to Protect Ourselves

Selection Test, pp. 57–58

**A.** (8 points each) Notes will vary widely but should suggest the following ideas:

  1. Acquiescence: It tells the oppressor that his or her actions are morally right.

  2. Physical violence and hatred: Rather than solving problems, they create greater ones.

  3. Nonviolent resistance: It enables all people to enlist in the struggle for justice.

  4. Support for the idea that Malcolm X condones physical violence and hatred against oppressors includes the following:

    a. He argues that "it's only fair to expect elements to do what is necessary to protect themselves."

    b. He says that his belief in brotherhood doesn't "restrain me in any way from protecting myself."

Other opinions should be supported with appropriate reasons.

**B.** (5 points each)

  1. a

  2. b

  3. b

  4. a

**C.** (4 points each)

  1. a

  2. c

  3. c

  4. b

  5. c

**D.** (14 points; students should answer one of the two)

  1. Answers will vary. Students could say that King means that nonviolent resistance is

    a. aimed at defeating injustice, not those who perpetuate injustice.

    b. intended not to avenge wrongs done by individuals but to overthrow an evil system.

In addition, students could say that King makes this distinction because he

    a. doesn't see injustice as purely a racial matter of white against black.

    b. wants to encourage brotherhood and unity among people of all races.

    c. wants his message to persuade white people to take action, not to alienate them or make them feel that there is nothing they can do about this issue.

  2. Answers will vary widely. Possible answers include the following:

    a. Malcolm X would probably condone most, if not all, violent acts committed in self-defense, including the defense of one's family, community, and property.

    b. Malcolm X would approve of such violence only in those communities in which the authorities have shown an inability or a racist reluctance to perform their lawful duties on behalf of African Americans ("places like Mississippi where the government has proven its inability to protect us").

c. Malcolm X would condone violent acts—by individuals or vigilante committee—in a wide range of situations, including those that go beyond the commonly accepted definition of self-defense.

**E.** (14 points) Answers will vary widely, depending on students' personal experiences, situations, and viewpoints. Accept any answers that address the concern of the question and are elaborated by examples or details from the literature or from life.

### *from* I Am Joaquín/Yo Soy Joaquín
Selection Test, pp. 59–60

**A.** (10 points each) Notes will vary widely. Model answers follow.

1. Determination: The battle that he fights will be a long and difficult one, requiring determination to succeed.
2. His ancestry: The history of his ancestors and knowledge of the battles they fought against forces stronger than them will give him courage.
3. Cultural ties and beliefs shared with other Chicanos: There is strength in numbers and the feeling of belonging to a group.

**B.** (6 points each)
1. d
2. b

**C.** (6 points each) Notes will vary but could suggest ideas similar to the following:

1. Most students will say that it departs because, although the excerpts are long, they do not tell a story or have a traditional plot structure. Students with greater familiarity with the poem as a whole may say that it conforms because it does tell a story and has a plot.
2. Conforms. The subject of the excerpts is a serious one concerning the survival of the Chicano culture in modern America.
3. Many students will say that it departs because it uses informal language. Other students will say that it conforms because the subject is treated in an elevated manner even if the language used isn't all that formal.
4. Conforms. Joaquín is portrayed as a courageous hero whose daring deeds include fighting the Moors and maintaining cultural traditions in modern America among other things.
5. Conforms. Joaquín is presented as a Chicano cultural symbol whose deeds are closely tied to his Chicano heritage.

**D.** (14 points; students should answer one of the two)
1. Answers will vary. Students could describe the choice in terms similar to the following:
   a. whether to place the needs of the soul above the needs of the body.

b. whether to maintain one's cultural identity or adopt the culture of the dominant group.
c. whether to choose economic success over cultural and spiritual survival.

In addition, students should address the issue of the groups of Americans to which the choice applies. Possible points include the following:

   a. The choice applies to all Americans. Most people, regardless of the groups to which they are tied, have hopes and desires that, if pursued, would force them to deviate from the dominant culture and lead a life of alienation and poverty.
   b. The choice applies only to members of a minority group whose cultural ties are endangered by the dominant group. Members of the dominant group do not have to carefully weigh all of their life decisions in terms of cultural survival.

2. Answers will vary. Things associated with "gringo society" include the following:
   a. Confusion and stress (lines 2 and 3)
   b. Rules (line 5)
   c. Scornful attitudes (line 6)
   d. Suppression and manipulation (line 7)
   e. Destruction (line 8)
   f. Neurosis or mental illness (line 21)
   g. Sterilization or death of the soul (line 22)
   h. Full stomach (line 23)
   i. Anguish (line 24)
   j. Mediocrity (line 26)
   k. Lust (lines 40 and 41)
   l. Urban barrios, bigoted suburbs, social snobbery, dejection, exploitation, and racial hatred (lines 48–54)
   m. Absorption (line 86)

Things associated with the society of his ancestors include the following:
   a. Joaquín, himself
   b. Confusion (lines 2 and 5)
   c. Being scorned, suppressed, manipulated, and destroyed (lines 6–9)
   d. Financial poverty (line 10)
   e. Victory of the spirit (line 17)
   f. Struggle (various lines throughout the poem)
   g. Defeating the Moors (lines 34 and 35)
   h. Endurance (various lines)
   i. Being scorned, dejected, exploited, and hated (lines 48–54)
   j. Power, cultural pride, and hope (lines 55–66)
   k. Action (line 72)
   l. Strong spirit, refusal to be absorbed, unbreakable faith, and pure blood (lines 85–91)
   m. Aztecs and Christians (line 92)

**E.** (14 points) Answers will vary widely, depending on students' personal experiences, situations, and viewpoints. Accept any answers that address the concern of the question and are elaborated by examples or details from the literature or from life.

## Unit Two, Part Two Test
pp. 61–62

**A.** (5 points each) Answers will vary but should include points similar to the following:

1. Examples: "Are fleets and armies necessary to a work of love and reconciliation?" "Shall we gather strength by irresolution and inaction?"

2. When a group of people decide to dissolve their political bonds with another group, it is decent and respectful for them to explain their reasons for doing so.

3. Example from Wheatley's letter: ". . . the divine light is chasing away the thick darkness which broods over the land of Africa. . . ." This example of personification suggests that Christianity is spreading to parts of Africa where it had not been practiced before.

4. Red Jacket says that Indians have trusted the white men in the past and have been betrayed. They will not accept the missionary's religion because they see little sense to it, they no longer trust the white men, and they are satisfied with their own beliefs.

**B.** (20 points) Notes will vary. A model answer for "I Am Joaquín" follows.

The speaker feels proud because he (or his people)
   a. has fought many battles and has never lost.
   b. has never surrendered.
   c. has survived many hardships.
   d. is part of a strong, vibrant culture.
   e. sees his people working together to gain their freedom.

**C.** (20 points each; students should answer two of the three)

1. Answers will vary. A model answer for Red Jacket ("Lecture to a Missionary") follows.

Students could point to the following evidence in the selection that Red Jacket would make a good modern-day president:
   a. His strong argument that is based on sound logic
   b. His openness to the possibility of changing his mind if future events should give him cause to do so
   c. His strong commitment to his people and culture
   d. His ability to defend his views without attacking the views of the missionary
   e. His respect for human life and nature
   f. His strong sense of self-respect and dignity

2. Answers will vary. A model answer for Patrick Henry ("Speech in the Virginia Convention") and Abigail Adams ("Letter to John Adams") follows.
Patrick Henry might say that Americans really need
   a. courage, because they are about to go to war against a great military power.
   b. to be realistic, because too many of them think that the war that has already begun can be avoided in some way.
   c. a sense of urgency, because there is a great need to act now.
Abigail Adams might say that Americans really need
   a. leadership, because the Congress is doing very little about the rapidly deteriorating political situation.
   b. to be patriotic, because the battle for independence can be won only if all of the colonists are willing to sacrifice for the new nation.
   c. equality, because it is foolish and hypocritical to grant rights to men that are not granted to women.

3. Answers will vary. A model answer for the tones of "Lecture to a Missionary" and *Stride Toward Freedom* follows.
The tone of "Lecture to a Missionary" and *Stride Toward Freedom* could be described as
   a. respectful or considerate, because both men are very concerned with communicating "revolutionary" ideas and beliefs without offending their audience.
   b. serious, because they take their subjects very seriously.
   c. dignified or confident, because they express their beliefs and ideas in a very straightforward, logical manner.

**D.** (20 points) Notes will vary. A model answer for "Necessary to Protect Ourselves" follows.
African Americans aren't free because
   a. they are oppressed by racists.
   b. in many parts of the country, the authorities can't or won't protect or defend them from those who harm or threaten to harm them and their property.
African Americans can win their freedom
   a. through individual action.
   b. by doing whatever is necessary to defend themselves and their property.

# Unit Three

## A Psalm of Life

Selection Test, pp. 63–64

**A.** (40 points) Notes will vary widely. Students who choose the first quotation might write notes suggesting that both Nin and Carlyle believe that
    a. life should be fully lived.
    b. life is about taking action.
    c. life isn't about avoiding sorrow or seeking enjoyment.
    d. life and death are two very different things, and one's life shouldn't resemble death in any way.
Students who choose the second quotation might write notes suggesting that both Carlyle and Nin believe that
    a. one's life is the sum of one's actions.
    b. the purpose of life is to act.
    c. action is more important than thought.

**B.** (4 points each)
  1. b
  2. c
  3. d
  4. a
  5. c

**C.** (20 points; students should answer one of the two)
  1. Answers will vary widely. Among points with which students might agree or disagree are the following:
    a. There is a meaning to life on earth.
    b. The ultimate goal in life is not happiness.
    c. Life's purpose is found in action and achievement (lines 11 and 12).
    d. Life should be lived in the moment (line 23).
    e. It is possible to make an impact on other lives by example.
  2. Answers will vary widely. Among the type of events students might suggest as appropriate for the poem are the following:
    a. A funeral for a hero, because the poem emphasizes the idea that people can make an impact on others by example.
    b. A graduation or any other "coming of age" ceremony, because the poem offers a philosophy of life from "the Heart of the Young Man" that is especially appropriate for people who are facing important choices about how to lead their lives.
    c. A political rally calling for action, because the poem's emphasis on action and achievement would set the right tone and could inspire the audience to act.

**D.** (20 points) Answers will vary widely, depending on students' personal experiences, situations, and viewpoints. Accept any answers that address the concern of the question and are elaborated by examples or details from the literature or from life.

## The Devil and Tom Walker

Selection Test, pp. 65–66

**A.** (10 points each)
  1. Notes will vary. Students might describe Old Scratch as
    a. casual.
    b. upbeat.
    c. confident.
    d. prepared.
    e. black.
    f. woodsy.
Students might say that the feeling is one of
    a. confidence.
    b. deception.
  2. Notes will vary. Students might describe the mood as
    a. dark.
    b. eerie.
    c. spooky.
    d. somber.
    e. suspenseful.
They might say that the feeling is one of
    a. suspense.
    b. somberness.
  3. Notes will vary. Students might describe Tom as
    a. crazy.
    b. foolish.
    c. worried.
    d. pathetic.
    e. regretful.
    f. desperate.
    g. suspicious.
    h. superstitious.
They might say that the feeling is one of
    a. desperation.
    b. foolishness.

**B.** (4 points each)
  1. a
  2. c

**C.** (4 points each)
  1. Notes will vary. Students might say the narrator's attitude toward Tom is
    a. humorous.
    b. objective.
    c. rather generous.
    d. rather sympathetic.
  2. Notes will vary. Students might say the narrator's attitude toward Tom's wife is
    a. humorous.
    b. not very generous.
    c. not very sympathetic.

3. Notes will vary. Students might say the narrator's attitude toward Old Scratch is
  a. humorous.
  b. objective.
  c. possibly admiring.
  d. somewhat sympathetic.
**D.** (4 points each)
  1. b
  2. c
  3. c
  4. a
  5. a
**E.** (15 points; students should answer one of the two)
  1. Answers will vary. Students might say that the original purpose was to
    a. entertain, because the plot, characters, setting, dialogue, narration, and imagery are colorful, rich, and funny.
    b. enlighten or teach, because the moral of the story is clearly and repeatedly stated.
In addition, students may say that the story still serves its original purpose in that it remains entertaining and has a timeless moral. Students who say the story does not serve the same purpose today should support that answer with a reasonable explanation.
  2. Answers will vary. Students who believe the characters are believable might make points similar to the following:
    a. Tom is greedy, mean-spirited, and hypocritical—human faults that the reader can identify with. These negative qualities are balanced to some degree by his refusal to become a slave trader and, perhaps to a very small degree, by his religious conversion.
    b. Tom's wife is greedy, argumentative, and physically abusive—human faults that the reader can identify with. These negative qualities are balanced to some degree by her courage in going to find Old Scratch.
    c. Old Scratch is believable as a personification of evil.
Students who believe the characters are not believable might say that
    a. the human characters' faults are extremely exaggerated.
    b. they have no redeeming qualities that would make them believable.
    c. Old Scratch—the devil—seems to be the only character to know the difference between right and wrong.
**F.** (15 points) Answers will vary widely, depending on students' personal experiences, situations, and viewpoints. Accept any answers that address the concern of the question and are elaborated by examples or details from the literature or from life.

*from* **Self-Reliance**
Selection Test, pp. 67–68
**A.** (15 points each)
  1. Examples will vary widely but should reflect students' understanding that, in Emerson's view, foolish consistency is based solely on habit, custom, and the expectations of society. Possible examples include most actions that one
    a. does solely out of obligation, fear, or in consideration of one's reputation.
    b. doesn't really want to do.
    c. does to please others.
  2. Examples will vary widely but should reflect students' understanding that, in Emerson's view, wise consistency results from the holding of certain principles which, whether long-lived or transitory, the individual conceives of for himself or herself. Possible examples include most actions that
    a. one does for one's own pleasure or need.
    b. expresses one's individuality.
**B.** (6 points each)
  1. a
  2. c
  3. b
**C.** (4 points each)
  1. c
  2. a
  3. b
  4. a
  5. c
**D.** (16 points; students should answer one of the two)
  1. Answers will vary, but students might say that Emerson's brand of self-reliance would be difficult to obtain because
    a. self-reliance is a life-long goal that requires constant vigilance.
    b. people have to work hard to attain a goal, such as self-reliance, that goes against the conventions of society.
    c. self-reliance requires the leisure to know oneself deeply and fully every day of one's life.
    d. most people are raised to conform and are encouraged to think of the needs of society and other people before their own. It can be very difficult to "un-learn" something that is so deeply ingrained.
  2. Answers will vary. Students may say that it is easier for wealthy people to develop self-reliance because
    a. people with a great deal of money do not have to work hard to support themselves and therefore have more leisure for self-improvement.

b. wealthy people do not have to worry so much about what others think of them. People who are poor need to think about what their boss, landlord, creditor, and so forth, might think of them.

Other students may point out that

a. rich people are often conformists because they have a stake in maintaining the status quo.

b. the poor and disadvantaged often have great integrity and personal courage; they often trust their own insights and views over those of authority figures.

**E.** (16 points) Answers will vary widely, depending on students' personal experiences, situations, and viewpoints. Accept any answers that address the concern of the question and are elaborated by examples or details from the literature or from life.

### *from* Civil Disobedience

Selection Test, pp. 69–70

**A.** (8 points each) Notes will vary but should include points similar to the following:

1. a. An essay is a short, personal work of nonfiction.

 b. This selection from "Civil Disobedience" is a brief, concise work of nonfiction—Thoreau explains his personal ideas about government.

2. a. An essay deals with a single subject.

 b. This essay deals with a single subject: the relationship of the individual to the state.

3. a. The purpose of an essay may be to express ideas and feelings, to analyze, to inform, to entertain, or to persuade.

 b. The purpose of this essay is to persuade readers to accept Thoreau's ideas: "We should be men first, and subjects afterward." He also wants readers to question the principle of majority rule: "But a government in which the majority rule in all cases cannot be based on justice, even as far as men understand it."

**B.** (5 points each)

1. b
2. a
3. d
4. c

**C.** (4 points each)

1. b
2. a
3. c
4. c
5. a

**D.** (20 points; students should answer one of the two)

1. Answers will vary but should include points similar to the following:

Antiwar protesters might have used the following points from Thoreau's essay:

a. The rule of the majority is not always just or right.

b. Soldiers in an unjust war act as agents of injustice, marching against their wills, "ay, against their common sense and consciences."

c. Soldiers should not be machines; they should follow their personal moral sense.

d. Thoreau says that all people who believe a law or government action is against morality should refuse to obey that law or action. Even if they are in the minority, if all just people refuse to obey, then the law or action will have to be changed.

2. Answers will vary but should include points similar to the following:

a. Crittenden's statement is exactly the attitude toward government that Thoreau condemned in his essay.

b. In Thoreau's mind, Crittenden is one of the "machines" or "a mere shadow and reminiscence of humanity." Thoreau feels that if a law causes you to be the agent of injustice to another, you should break the law. To "stand by her [America], right or wrong" means that people ignore their conscience.

**E.** (16 points) Answers will vary widely, depending on students' personal experiences, situations, and viewpoints. Accept any answers that address the concern of the question and are elaborated by examples or details from the literature or from life.

### *from* Walden

Selection Test, pp. 71–72

**A.** (15 points each)

1. Examples will vary widely but should reflect students' understanding that Thoreau would approve of activities such as

a. sitting quietly and thinking.

b. observing nature.

c. writing in a journal.

d. hiking and exploring.

2. Examples will vary widely but should reflect students' understanding that Thoreau would disapprove of activities such as

a. eating more than is necessary.

b. reading the newspaper or watching TV.

c. going to sporting events or parties.

d. writing letters or reading mail.

**B.** (4 points each)

1. c
2. a
3. c
4. d
5. b

**C.** (4 points each)
1. a
2. a
3. b
4. b
5. a

**D.** (15 points; students should answer one of the two)
1. Answers will vary widely, depending on students' personal preferences and tastes. Students who would enjoy the experience might say that sitting quietly with Thoreau and enjoying nature would be
a. pleasant and peaceful.
b. similar to a religious experience.
c. a welcome break from the hustle and bustle of everyday life.
d. enlightening.
Students who would not enjoy the experience might say that
a. Walden Pond would be boring if Thoreau weren't in a talkative mood and perhaps annoying if he were.
b. watching nature is not terribly exciting.
c. Thoreau is so opinionated and judgmental that talking to him would be intimidating and stressful.
2. Answers will vary. Students could say that Thoreau learned
a. about the value of simplicity and the pitfalls of "details."
b. that many people are not truly awake to life and its possibilities.
c. about the deep pleasure and wisdom to be gained from communing with nature at leisure.
d. about the value of intuitive knowledge, or the type of knowledge with which people are born and tend to lose as they mature.

**E.** (15 points) Answers will vary widely, depending on students' personal experiences, situations, and viewpoints. Accept any answers that address the concern of the question and are elaborated by examples or details from the literature or from life.

## Selected Poems by Whitman
Selection Test, pp. 73–74
**A.** (10 points each) Notes will vary but should include points similar to the following:
1. This poem uses a catalog that mentions different workers (mechanics, mason, shoemaker, etc.).
The effect of this catalog is to suggest that
a. each individual is important ("singing what belongs to him or her and to none else").
b. America depends on every one of them.
c. each person contributes to the whole.
d. our country is made up of many different individuals.

2. This poem uses repetition of the word *I* and the verbs *see* and *observe* within lines and throughout the poem.
The effect of this repetition is to
a. call attention to the many depressing things seen by the speaker.
b. drive home the fact that the poet and/or the reader often sees all these things and does not act to stop them.
c. imbue the reader with a deep sense of shame and revulsion at the idea that so much cruelty can be taking place.
d. suggest that many, many people are suffering.
3. This poem uses parallelism to provide structure.
The effect of this parallelism is to
a. establish connections between opposite values, such as I and you, good or bad, young and old.
b. suggest that however different people might be, they have much in common. For example, the speaker connects with the reader at the very beginning ("what I assume you shall assume, / For every atom belonging to me as good belongs to you").
c. suggest different ways of looking at the same thing, especially in part 6 ("I guess . . . Or I guess . . . Or I guess . . .").

**B.** (6 points each)
1. d
2. b
3. d
4. b
5. b
6. c

**C.** (20 points; students should answer one of the two)
1. Answers will vary. Students might say that, by describing the people as "singing," Whitman suggests
a. their contentment, vitality, strength, pride, and individuality.
b. that, like music, work (and workers) can be beautiful, joyous, and uplifting.
c. that each worker, like each voice in a choir, is significant.
d. that the workers' individual contributions blend in the national economy, just as individual voices blend in a choir.
2. Answers will vary. Students might say that the speaker's silence shows that he or she is
a. baffled that such evils can exist.
b. overcome by "all the meanness and agony without end."
c. awed by the enormity of the evils and miseries that exist.
d. profoundly saddened.
e. possibly ashamed.

**D.** (14 points) Answers will vary widely, depending on students' personal experiences, situations, and viewpoints. Accept any answers that address the concern of the question and are elaborated by examples or details from the literature or from life.

## Danse Russe/anyone lived in a pretty how town
Selection Test, pp. 75–76

**A.** (8 points each) Notes will vary widely but should suggest ideas similar to the following:

1. A man who sings and dances and isn't particularly liked by the townspeople (lines 4 and 6).
2. A woman who loves passionately and with all her being (lines 7 and 17–20).
3. Anonymous, spiritually underdeveloped townspeople with dull qualities and routines (lines 5–8 and 33–36).
4. Young townspeople, some of whom are more insightful than their parents but who forget those insights when they grow up (lines 9–12 and 23).
5. The singulars are people with likeable, unusual qualities that set them apart from the plurals, who are anonymous people with predictable, ordinary, or negative qualities.

**B.** (6 points each)
1. b
2. c
3. c

**C.** (12 points) Notes will vary widely. Students who choose the lines from "Danse Russe" (a) might include notes similar to the following:
   a. The sun shines brightly through the morning fog above the trees.
   b. The intensity of the sunlight; the fog's appeal to the sense of touch; the effect of the intense sunlight on the trees; the feeling of power arising from the promise of a new morning.

Students who choose the lines from "anyone lived in a pretty how town" (b) might include notes similar to the following:
   a. People got married. They lived their lives and then they died.
   b. The conformity of those who married, lived, and died; the tragedy of their meaningless lives; the fact that they had dreams that went unfulfilled.

**D.** (15 points; students should answer one of the two)
1. Answers will vary. Students could say that the speaker dances alone because he
   a. can dance freely without worrying about how others might regard what he's doing ("dance naked, grotesquely / before my mirror").
   b. feels that he's at his best when he's alone ("I was born to be lonely, / I am best so!").

   c. can openly take pleasure in his body without the critical eyes of others ("If I admire my arms, my face, / my shoulders, flanks, buttocks").
   d. enjoys the feeling of imagining he's a star, and can tell himself so without fear of being contradicted ("Who shall say I am not / the happy genius of my household?").
2. Answers will vary, but students should recognize that "anyone" has little impact on the lives of the townspeople. Students could say that the townspeople
   a. dislike "anyone" ("women and men (both little and small) / cared for anyone not at all").
   b. regard his burial as little more than a practical matter ("busy folk buried them side by side").

Students could point out that, by contrast
   a. his impact on "noone" is powerful ("anyone's any was all to her").
   b. "noone" loves him passionately ("noone loved him more by more").
   c. "noone" cares about and shares in "anyone's" happiness ("she laughed his joy she cried his grief").
   d. "noone" is finally buried next to "anyone" ("busy folk buried them side by side").

**E.** (15 points) Answers will vary widely, depending on students' personal experiences, situations, and viewpoints. Accept any answers that address the concern of the question and are elaborated by examples or details from the literature or from life.

## Ending Poem/Tía Chucha
Selection Test, pp. 77–78

**A.** (15 points each)
1. Rankings will vary but should place "Ending Poem" somewhere in the left-hand half of the bar. Supportive notes could suggest the fact that the subject of the poem is, basically, a group as well as such specific points as the speaker's emphasis on
   a. the immigration of groups. ("My people . . .")
   b. roots, or ties to ancestors. ("I am the daughter of . . .")
   c. unity with others. ("a child of many diaspora")
2. Rankings will vary but should place "Tía Chucha" somewhere in the right-hand half of the bar. Supportive notes could suggest the fact that the subject of the poem is an individual who does not fit into "normal" patterns of behavior as well as such specific points as the speaker's emphasis on
   a. Tía Chucha's eccentricities.
   b. Tía Chucha's expressiveness.
   c. his desire to see the world "with first eyes."
   d. his learning about a "craving for the new."

**B.** (10 points each)

1. d
2. c
3. b

**C.** (10 points) Notes will vary depending on which quotation students choose and their interpretations. Possible interpretations follow.

"Africa waters . . .": My African heritage is part of who I am and helps to sustain me, but Africa is not, now, my home.

"They have . . .": My ancestors' work was the foundation of great societies.

"Tía Chucha . . .": Tía Chucha's visits were disruptive and upset the routine of family life, but in ways that were more joyous than destructive.

"To me, . . .": Tía Chucha's freedom was like a little bit, or a delicate version of, the wind; she went where she pleased, did what she wanted.

**D.** (15 points; students should answer one of the two)

1. Answers will vary but could include any of the following points:
   a. The speaker's cultural identity was handed down to her. ("A child of many diaspora.")
   b. The speaker is a result of those who went before her. ("They gave us life, kept us going, brought us to where we are.")
   c. The speaker's roots are mentioned throughout the poem.
   d. The speaker sees herself as tied to her ancestors. ("Africa waters the roots of my tree," "Taino is in me," "Europe lives in me.")

2. Answers will vary but could include points similar to the following:
   a. His normal family life was probably relatively structured. (Tía Chucha disrupts things with her visits.)
   b. He knows what is normal and what is abnormal behavior. (He realizes that it is abnormal to run outside naked; he defines his aunt's singing on the bus as "annoying.")
   c. He is capable of appreciating what is valuable in a person. (He wants to be able to see the world in a fresh way, like his aunt, and to "discern the elixir within milk.")
   d. His admiration for his odd aunt is not necessarily obvious to others. (He "secretly" admired her.)
   e. He wants to be worth knowing—to add something to other people's lives. ("I wanted to be one of the prizes. . . .")

**E.** (15 points) Answers will vary widely, depending on students' personal experiences, situations, and viewpoints. Accept any answers that address the concern of the question and are elaborated by examples or details from the literature or from life.

**Gary Keillor**

Selection Test, pp. 79–80

**A.** (14 points each)

1. Notes will vary but could suggest that the event teaches Gary that
   a. he doesn't like to be disregarded, that it makes him angry.
   b. he doesn't know Dede as well (or care for her as much) as he thought he did.
   c. others don't necessarily see him as he sees himself.
   d. he cares what others think of him.

2. Notes will vary but could suggest that the event teaches Gary that
   a. he can be funny.
   b. he enjoys making people laugh.
   c. he feels powerful when he's making people laugh.
   d. an audience can be manipulated by a skillful performer, and a mediocre performer can be destroyed by an audience.
   e. performers need to flexible and quick-thinking.

3. Notes will vary but could suggest that the event teaches Gary that he
   a. can be funny.
   b. enjoys making people laugh.
   c. feels powerful when he's making people laugh.
   d. can change the way people see him.
   e. can be popular and accepted for his talents.
   f. can be insensitive to someone's pain (specifically Bill Swenson's) if he makes others laugh.

**B.** (5 points each)

1. b
2. c
3. a
4. b
5. d
6. d

**C.** (14 points; students should answer one of the two)

1. Answers will vary. Students might say that Gary finds this advice useless because
   a. he wants to be popular with his classmates, not considered different and uncompromising.
   b. people generally go to talent shows to be entertained, not to be uplifted.
   c. it's the sort of advice that's fine for an adult to follow but that doesn't recognize a young person's need to be accepted by his or her peers.

2. Answers will vary. Students might say that Gary's relationship with the other students changes in that
   a. he gains recognition for being funny.
   b. he becomes more popular.
   c. other students begin to see him in a new way.
   Students who find the change positive might say that Gary
   a. finds a way to be accepted and even looked up to by his peers.

b. develops the potential for more friendships and social interaction.

c. discovers his talent and develops his self-confidence.

Students who find the change negative might say that Gary

a. gains his new popularity partly at the cost of humiliating Bill Swenson.

b. gets immediate gratification by entertaining people, but masks his more sensitive self in the process.

**D.** (14 points) Answers will vary widely, depending on students' personal experiences, situations, and viewpoints. Accept any answers that address the concern of the question and are elaborated by examples or details from the literature or from life.

## Unit Three, Part One Test
pp. 81–82

**A.** (5 points each) Answers will vary but should include points similar to the following:

1. The speaker suggests that we can do something great that will be remembered, or make a mark or impression on the world for others to see and be inspired by. Students may also note that making an impression in sand is temporary or short-lived because sand shifts and washes away.

2. They are so greedy that they make bargains with the devil; or, they sell their souls to the devil to gain wealth.

3. Example of an aphorism: "That government is best which governs not at all," from "Civil Disobedience." People should be able to take care of themselves and do what is right without interference from government. "If a man does not keep pace with his companions, perhaps it is because he hears a different drummer," from *Walden*. People have individual beliefs and personalities and should not always be expected to follow the crowd.

4. In "anyone lived in a pretty how town," the speaker's tone is one of indifference and casual observation, as if "anyone" didn't matter and life goes on. (Students might interpret this as cynicism or a criticism of people who are so indifferent and uncaring.) In "Tía Chucha," the speaker's tone is admiring and envious of Tía Chucha's uniqueness, her individuality, and her ability to see things differently.

**B.** (20 points) Notes will vary. A model answer for "The Devil and Tom Walker" follows.

The story criticizes greed because

a. it is what leads Tom Walker and his wife to believe that they can strike a good bargain with the devil.

b. it is what leads people to borrow money from Tom Walker at exorbitant rates, leading to their downfall.

c. it is a trait that we all share to some degree and that causes problems not only for ourselves, but also for society as a whole.

**C.** (20 points each; students should answer two of the three)

1. Answers will vary. A model answer for "Self-Reliance" and "I Sit and Look Out" follows.

"Self-Reliance" is idealistic in that it presents a philosophy of life that

a. is based on the belief that all people are basically good, which fails to account for people who willfully hurt others.

b. stresses individualism and ignores the idea of the "common good," even though this idea is part of the foundation on which democracy is built.

c. might be difficult for those groups in society that are poor and have little means or leisure to reach their potential.

"I Sit and Look Out" isn't idealistic in that the

a. images in the poem are realistic.

b. the speaker merely observes the problems of the world without offering any solutions.

2. Answers will vary. A model answer for "Tía Chucha," "Gary Keillor," and *Walden* follows.

In "Tía Chucha," the insight into love

a. is that loving one's self is more important to one's happiness than being loved by others.

b. is communicated by the speaker's description of his aunt, whose refusal or inability to conform makes her one of the happiest people he knows, despite the fact that her oddness tends to make people avoid or reject her.

In "Gary Keillor," the insight into human nature

a. is that people tend not to see themselves exactly the same as others see them.

b. is communicated when Gary volunteers to participate in the talent show, and Dede Peterson responds by saying, "You?" Gary realizes that Dede doesn't see him as the talented person he sees himself to be.

c. is also communicated by Bill Swenson's not understanding why the audience doesn't find his second number in the talent show as entertaining as he thinks it is.

In *Walden*, the insight into nature

a. is that nature provides the ideal environment for human life.

b. is communicated through the contrast Thoreau draws between what he sees as his relaxed, meaningful way of life followed at Walden Pond and what he sees as the stressful, meaningless way of life followed by people caught up in society.

3. Answers will vary. A model answer for "Danse Russe" and "anyone lived in a pretty how town" follows.

The speaker of "Danse Russe"
   a. is a private, thoughtful man.
   b. is a family man.
   c. relishes solitude.
   d. loves to dance by himself.
   e. is happy.
   f. accepts himself for who he is.
   g. admires his body even though he knows that it is
      "grotesque."
In addition, students should explain how the speaker is
and is not like themselves.
The speaker of "anyone lived in a pretty how town"
   a. is flippant and matter-of-fact.
   b. doesn't seem to admire people very much.
   c. doesn't seem to find much meaning in everyday life.
   d. seems very cynical about modern life.
In addition, students should explain how the speaker is
and is not like themselves.
**D.** (20 points) Notes will vary. A model answer for "I Hear
America Singing" follows.
The theme of the poem might be stated in ways similar to
one of the following:
   a. The strength of the United States depends on the
      ordinary individual.
   b. The common, hardworking people are the heroes
      of the United States.
   c. The spirit of the United States is found in the
      everyday life of the common working person.
The images that communicate the theme are of
   a. the everyday sounds and sights of people at work,
      such as mechanics, carpenters, masons, boatmen,
      deckhands, shoemakers, hatters, woodcutters,
      ploughboys, and women working at home.
   b. the everyday sounds and sights of working people
      relaxing and enjoying themselves.

**The Masque of the Red Death**
Selection Test, pp. 83–84
**A.** (6 points each)
   1. Choices and notes will vary widely. Most students will
      probably choose "selfishness" or "evil" because
      a. Prince Prospero's behavior shows complete
         disregard and lack of compassion for the suffering
         caused by the Red Death.
      b. the Red Death seeks out and kills Prince Prospero.
Other choices should be supported with appropriate
reasons.
   2. Choices and notes will vary widely. Most students will
      probably choose "mortality" or "time" because
      a. a clock keeps time, which, the narrator notes,
         is "flying."
      b. this particular clock is disturbing to the revelers,
         seeming to warn them of their impending doom.

   c. the clock announces the appearance of the Red
      Death at midnight.
Other choices should be supported with appropriate
reasons.
   3. Choices and notes will vary widely. Most students will
      probably choose "revenge" or "fate" because
      a. the Red Death kills all of the revelers.
      b. the revelers are unable to lock out the Red Death.
      c. the revelers show complete disregard and lack of
         compassion for the victims of the Red Death by
         throwing a party in the midst of the plague.
Other choices should be supported with appropriate
reasons.
**B.** (4 points each)
   1. d
   2. d
   3. d
**C.** (6 points each) Notes will vary widely but could
suggest ideas similar to the following.
   1. They seclude themselves from society and create a
      fantasy world of fun and party-going.
   2. The Red Death is terrible and incurable; they fear it;
      they want to live.
   3. They are selfish; they foolishly believe that they are
      superior to the rest of the population and can escape
      death; they lack compassion; they want to live.
   4. Trying to find the cause of the disease; helping ease
      the pain and suffering of the victims; doing whatever
      is possible to prevent the spread of the disease.
   5. Those who are responsible, moral, and
      compassionate, as well as those who realize that
      individuals cannot truly separate themselves from
      the rest of humankind.
**D.** (4 points each)
   1. c
   2. a
   3. a
   4. b
   5. c
**E.** (10 points; students should answer one of the two)
   1. Answers will vary, but most students will find that the
      death of the revelers provokes a feeling of horror. In
      addition, answers should include a point similar to
      one of the following:
      a. Felt sorry. Despite all their precautions, they fell
         prey to the Red Death. No group of people, not
         even the immoral revelers, deserves to die such
         a horrible death.
      b. Felt they deserved their deaths. The revelers
         deserved to share the fate of those who could not
         afford to buy all the precautions that the revelers
         thought would protect them. And, since they never

demonstrated sorrow or concern for those outside the gates of the abbey, it is nearly impossible to have similar feelings for them.

2. Answers will vary widely. Possible answers include the following:
   a. The lesson concerns compassion for those who are less fortunate than ourselves. As with victims of the Red Death, people with AIDS are often treated in ways that fail to recognize their innocence and their humanity.
   b. The lesson concerns the responsibility each of us has for the well-being of other people. Just as with the Red Death, AIDS is a social problem. Individuals must react responsibly and compassionately to protect themselves and others from the disease.
   c. The lesson concerns the dangers of believing in one's own superiority to others. As with the Red Death, AIDS is a public health problem that strikes people from all walks of life. While there are many things individuals can do to protect themselves, in the long run, only a collective effort will effectively combat the spread of the disease.
   d. The lesson concerns the need for authority figures to serve as examples and to lead responsibly in times of crisis. Prince Prospero's irresponsible reaction to the Red Death crisis is similar to that of many politicians and others to the AIDS crisis.
   e. The lesson concerns the futility of trying to protect oneself against disease or death. Prince Prospero and his friends succumb to the Red Death despite great precautions. People today get AIDS despite the fact that they take all recommended precautions and avoid all "unsafe" behavior.
   f. The lesson concerns human ignorance and impotence before nature. The Red Death was incurable, untreatable, and unavoidable. AIDS, although not so easily "caught" as the Red Death, is not absolutely avoidable, only barely treatable (and then at very great cost), and—for the foreseeable future—not curable.

**F.** (10 points) Answers will vary widely, depending on students' personal experiences, situations, and viewpoints. Accept any answers that address the concern of the question and are elaborated by examples or details from the literature or from life.

## The Raven
Selection Test, pp. 85–86
**A.** (10 points each)
   1. Notes will vary but should suggest that the speaker is
      a. gloomy, depressed, thoughtful, weak, and tired.
      b. immersing himself in books in order to forget his grief over the death of his beloved Lenore.

2. Notes will vary but should suggest that the raven
   a. makes the speaker feel uneasy because it arrives mysteriously at midnight on a gloomy winter night and speaks only one ominous word, "nevermore."
   b. makes the speaker realize the hopelessness of trying to forget his sorrows when it answers all of his questions and comments with one word, "nevermore," and refuses to go away.
3. Notes will vary but should suggest that the speaker is
   a. severely depressed, possibly even on the verge of losing his sanity.
   b. sitting in a chair staring at the raven, engrossed in his emotional pain.

**B.** (4 points each)
   1. a
   2. a
   3. c
   4. a
   5. b

**C.** (4 points each)
   1. a
   2. c
   3. c
   4. b
   5. c

**D.** (15 points; students should answer one of the two)
   1. Answers will vary but students could cite numerous details from the poem supporting the ideas that
      a. the speaker's emotional pain will never diminish.
      b. the speaker will never escape his memories of Lenore.
      c. the speaker is without hope.
      d. the speaker has been driven insane by his depression over the death of Lenore.
   2. Answers will vary but students could cite numerous details from the poem supporting the ideas that the raven represents
      a. loss and suffering.
      b. the necessity of loss and suffering in life.
      c. memory of the emotional, painful aspects of life.
      d. the certainty and finality of death.

**E.** (15 points) Answers will vary widely, depending on students' personal experiences, situations, and viewpoints. Accept any answers that address the concern of the question and are elaborated by examples or details from the literature or from life.

## The Fall of the House of Usher
Selection Test, pp. 87–88
**A.** (8 points each) Notes will vary but should include points similar to the following:
   1. Exterior of house:
      a. The House of Usher looks like an old castle or

Gothic mansion. It is described as "melancholy" with "bleak walls" and "vacant eye-like windows."

   b. It shows "excessive antiquity," and "minute fungi overspread the whole exterior." The house is in "extensive decay," with a zigzag fissure running from top to bottom.

2. Interior of house:

   a. The room the narrator enters is large, with windows that are "long, narrow, and pointed" and inaccessible because they are set high in the walls. There is little light, and the room has dark draperies. It is filled with antique, tattered furniture and has an air of gloom.

   b. The underground vault was once used as a dungeon. The vault has been "so long unopened that our torches" were half smothered in its oppressive atmosphere. The vault is small and damp, has no light, and is sheathed in copper.

3. Physical surroundings:

   a. The House of Usher is located in a "singularly dreary tract of country." The narrator stops at the "precipitous brink of a black and lurid tarn," which is surrounded by "rank sedges and white trunks of decaying trees." The "silent tarn" is covered by a "pestilent and mystic vapor."

   b. On the night of the storm, the "clouds hung so low as to press upon the turrets of the house"; "But the under surfaces of the huge masses of agitated vapor . . . were glowing in the unnatural light of a faintly luminous and distinctly visible gaseous exhalation which . . . enshrouded the mansion."

**B.** (5 points each)

1. c
2. b
3. d
4. a

**C.** (4 points each)

1. c
2. a
3. b
4. c
5. c

**D.** (20 points; students should answer one of the two)

1. Answers will vary but should include points similar to the following:

   a. The single effect Poe strives for in the story is fear, or terror: ". . . I must abandon life and reason together, in some struggle with the grim phantasm, FEAR." To unify this single effect, Poe carefully chooses words to describe every character, the details of setting, the actions, and the dialogue.

   b. Examples: the descriptions of the mansion and the landscape are chilling. The reader feels the sense

of gloom, darkness, and despair surrounding every element of the house. This sense of gloom leads to depression and fear. The descriptions of the characters also cause fear: Roderick is a walking cadaver, and Madeline is ghostlike. The dialogue also unifies the effect of fear, as the narrator describes abandoning all reason. Roderick's conversations with the narrator begin to engulf the narrator in fear. He is obviously suffering from anxiety, and the tension in the story builds. At the end, the appearance of Madeline, the living corpse, and the collapse of the house complete the effect.

2. Answers will vary but should include points similar to the following:

   a. The descriptions of Roderick Usher might suggest one who was victimized by a vampire: he was physically weak, could not bear strong light or sounds, and had a "morbid acuteness of the senses." His complexion was pale (cadaverous), and his lips were pallid. He said that the gloom afflicting him "could be traced to his sister."

   b. Madeline is described as "wasting away" (perhaps she had no more victims), and she moved in a trancelike state. In death, she had a "suspiciously lingering smile upon the lip."

   c. Roderick went to great lengths to protect himself from his sister. The vault was deep underground, sheathed in copper, and the door was massive. He screwed down the lid to her coffin, secured the door of iron, and "toiled" to make his way back to the upper portion of the house.

   d. Madeline arose from her coffin at night, when the "blood-red" moon was full, and "fell heavily" upon Roderick. She "bore him to the floor a corpse . . . a victim to the terrors he had anticipated." Vampires often found their victims during a full moon.

**E.** (16 points) Answers will vary widely, depending on students' personal experiences, situations, and viewpoints. Accept any answers that address the concern of the question and are elaborated by examples or details from the literature or from life.

## Dr. Heidegger's Experiment

Selection Test, pp. 89–90

**A.** (6 points each) Examples and notes will vary but should include points similar to the following:

1. a. The description of the portrait in Dr. Heidegger's study foreshadows what will happen to Widow Wycherly. ("a young lady, arrayed in the faded magnificence of silk . . . and with a visage as faded as her dress.")

   b. The widow becomes lovely and youthful again after drinking the water, but her beauty soon fades.

(". . . the widow clasped her skinny hands before her face, and wished that the coffin-lid were over it, since it could no longer be beautiful.")

2. a. The description of the black book and what happens when the maid moves it foreshadows the strange occurrences involving the guests in the experiment. (". . . the skeleton had rattled in its closet, the picture of the young lady had stepped one foot upon the floor, and several ghastly faces had peeped forth from the mirror. . . .")

   b. The black book represents the kind of magic evoked by the water in the vase. After drinking the water, the four guests become young and lively again, but the mirror seems to reflect the same old people, "withered" and "shrivelled."

3. a. The effect of the water in the vase on the 55-year-old rose foreshadows the effects of the water on the four guests.

   b. As the rose regained its "youth" and vitality, so do the four guests. Not long afterward, the rose fades to what it was before, and so do the guests.

4. a. Dr. Heidegger's suggestion that the four guests draw up some rules of conduct before drinking the water suggests that the guests will not act properly.

   b. Once they have taken the water, all four guests essentially revert to being the fools they were when they were young (for example, Mr. Medbourne thinks up a scheme for making money by supplying the East Indies with ice). At the end, it is clear that they have learned nothing from their experience as they plan to find the fountain of youth.

**B.** (5 points each)
1. b
2. a
3. c
4. d

**C.** (4 points each)
1. c
2. b
3. a
4. a
5. b

**D.** (20 points; students should answer one of the two)
1. Answers will vary. Students who think that it is a tribute to science might say that Dr. Heidegger, the only scientist among the characters, is also the only one who
   a. displays any wisdom or common sense.
   b. chooses not to participate in his experiment.
   c. has no interest in repeating the experiment.
Students who think that it is an attack on science might say that
   a. Dr. Heidegger is a quack who consults a statue for advice on his cases.

   b. Dr. Heidegger shows moral irresponsibility in tempting his vulnerable guests to participate in an experiment that he knows will fail and that he, himself, would never participate in.
   c. Dr. Heidegger shows moral irresponsibility in deceiving his guests about the true nature of his experiment, which is based in psychology rather natural science, as he leads them to believe.
   d. Dr. Heidegger's experiment is total folly.
   e. the message of the story is that nature has certain patterns that cannot and should not be altered by science.

2. Answers will vary. Among Dr. Heidegger's reasons for not participating in the experiment are the following:
   a. He knows that the Water of Youth is phony—a device designed to fool his guests and allow him to observe their reactions to its supposed ability to restore youth.
   b. He knows that, as a scientist, he must be able to observe his experiment with objectivity, something he could not do as a participant in it.
   c. He is in no hurry to grow young again. It would simply mean having to grow old again—an experience he prefers not to repeat.
   d. He doesn't believe that it is possible for people to learn from their mistakes and "turn over a new leaf."
   e. He may suspect that the results of drinking the Water of Youth are only temporary or illusory. Either way, the pain of being old again would be too great a price to pay for a few moments of pleasure.
Other reasons should be appropriately supported.

**E.** (16 points) Answers will vary widely, depending on students' personal experiences, situations, and viewpoints. Accept any answers that address the concern of the question and are elaborated by examples or details from the literature or from life.

**A Rose for Emily**
Selection Test, pp. 91–92
**A.** (8 points each)
1. Notes will vary but could suggest the following ideas:
   a. Miss Emily's once grand neighborhood has fallen on hard times.
   b. Her house has survived but is badly decayed.
   c. She is unwilling or unable to keep her house in good repair.
   d. Life has passed her by.
2. Notes will vary but could suggest the following ideas:
   a. Miss Emily was dominated and intimidated by her father.
   b. Her identity can't be separated from that of her father.
   c. She was slender.
   d. She had an innocence about her.

3. Notes will vary but could suggest the following ideas:
   a. Miss Emily is arrogant, cold, and hardened.
   b. She is unhappy and unfriendly.
   c. She is always on guard.
   d. She had lost weight.
4. Notes will vary but could suggest the following ideas:
   a. Miss Emily is cold and unfriendly.
   b. She is an awe-inspiring figure who doesn't invite others into her life.
   c. She leads an isolated existence.
   d. She seems almost not human.

**B.** (6 points each)
 1. b
 2. a
 3. c

**C.** (4 points each)
 1. a
 2. b
 3. c
 4. a
 5. b

**D.** (15 points; students should answer one of the two)
 1. Answers will vary but could include ideas similar to at least two of the following:
    a. The townspeople pity Miss Emily because they know that her father chased off all of her suitors and left her no money, and they believe that she was "ruined" and then abandoned by Homer Barron. Their pity causes them to excuse her arrogance and to feel responsible for maintaining her pride (such as when the Colonel forgives her taxes).
    b. The townspeople dislike Miss Emily because she is arrogant and superior toward them even though she is no longer wealthy. Their dislike causes them to gossip about her and to take some comfort in her misery.
    c. The townspeople are curious about Miss Emily because she is such a mystery to them. Their curiosity leads them to gossip about her, to view her as almost mythical, and to attend her funeral.
    d. The townspeople feel intimidated by Miss Emily because she and her family have been part of the town's elite, and she is a strong woman who tends to get what she wants. Their intimidation causes them to avoid direct dealings with her as when they secretly spread lime around her house rather than ask her to take care of the stench.

Other ideas should be supported with appropriate details from the story.

 2. Answers will vary but could include ideas similar to at least three of the following points:
    a. Miss Emily doesn't fit the stereotype of a murderer.

b. Homer Barron's disappearance isn't all that odd since he is an itinerant worker and he apparently doesn't wish to marry Miss Emily.
c. Miss Emily comes from a well-respected family.
d. Miss Emily's refusal to leave the house after Barron's disappearance isn't all that unusual for her.
e. Miss Emily doesn't receive visitors and keeps only one servant.
f. Tobe, Miss Emily's servant, doesn't have any friends in town, probably wanted to keep his job, and might not have been believed or might have been implicated in the murder if he had gone to the police.
g. The older generation insists that Miss Emily's privacy be kept inviolate.
h. No one in the town has the gumption to directly question Miss Emily about anything.

**E.** (15 points) Answers will vary widely, depending on students' personal experiences, situations, and viewpoints. Accept any answers that address the concern of the question and are elaborated by examples or details from the literature or from life.

## The Life You Save May Be Your Own
Selection Test, pp. 93–94

**A.** (10 points each)
 1. Notes will vary but could include the following:
    a. A car.
    b. Freedom.
    c. To be respected.
    d. To be thought of as a virtuous man.

   Mr. Shiftlet gets
    a. Mrs. Crater's car.
    b. a deep sense that all is wrong with the world.
    c. the hitchhiker's disgust and rejection.
 2. Notes will vary but could include the following:
    a. A live-in son-in-law.
    b. A handyman.

   Mrs. Crater gets
    a. some things fixed around the house.
    b. taken by Mr. Shiftlet.
    c. her daughter taken away from her and lost.
    d. her car stolen.

**B.** (4 points each)
 1. b
 2. a
 3. d
 4. d
 5. a
 6. d

**C.** (6 points each)
 1. Notes will vary but should suggest that Mr. Shiftlet himself doesn't care about young Lucynell and, in fact, abandons her.

2. Notes will vary but should suggest that Mr. Shiftlet suddenly feels lonely and a sense of responsibility to others after he has just stolen Mrs. Crater's car and irresponsibly abandoned his only companion, young Lucynell.

**D.** (4 points each)
 1. b
 2. b
 3. c
 4. b
 5. a

**E.** (12 points; students should answer one of the two)
 1. Answers will vary. Students might say that
    a. Mr. Shiftlet needs to be saved from himself, because he is ruining his life with his lies, thefts, cruelties, and manipulative behavior.
    b. Mrs. Crater needs to be saved from her desperate and desolate circumstances and her own manipulative behavior.
    c. young Lucynell needs to be saved from poverty and from abandonment now and, if she ever finds her way back home, when her mother dies.
    d. the hitchhiker apparently needs to be saved from the problems at home that he is trying to run away from.
 2. Answers will vary. Students might mention that the hitchhiker
    a. blasts through Mr. Shiftlet's hypocrisy.
    b. rejects Mr. Shiftlet's attempt to send him back to his mother, which results in the failure of Mr. Shiftlet's bid to redeem himself for his treatment of young Lucynell and her mother.
    c. helps to establish the theme that one cannot escape the world one creates, that one's own immorality helps to create a world that is immoral, that one cannot allow oneself to be immoral and expect the rest of the world to be moral.

**F.** (12 points) Answers will vary widely, depending on students' personal experiences, situations, and viewpoints. Accept any answers that address the concern of the question and are elaborated by examples or details from the literature or from life.

## Unit Three, Part Two Test
pp. 95–96
**A.** (5 points each)
 1. c
 2. a
 3. b
 4. d

**B.** (20 points) Notes will vary. A model answer for "The Fall of the House of Usher" follows.
Examples of Sensory Details:
    a. white trunks of decayed trees
    b. vacant, eye-like windows
    c. black and lurid tarn
    d. feeble gleams of encrimsoned light
    e. an eye large, liquid, and luminous
Effects: Answers will vary, but accept any responses that address the examples of sensory details and how Poe's language created an overwhelming sense of darkness, dampness, decay, gloom, and death.

**C.** (20 points each; students should answer two of three)
 1. Answers will vary. A model answer for "The Masque of the Red Death" follows.
"The Masque of the Red Death" seems to present the darkest view of the individual because Prince Prospero and his courtiers
    a. fail to demonstrate any compassion for those who are dying outside the gates of the abbey.
    b. lack any redeeming qualities.
    c. foolishly believe themselves more powerful than the Red Death.
    d. are easily vanquished by the Red Death.
 2. Answers will vary. A model answer for "Dr. Heidegger's Experiment" and "The Life You Save May Be Your Own" follows.
In "Dr. Heidegger's Experiment," the writer
    a. criticizes the inability or unwillingness of people to learn or mature from their mistakes.
    b. criticizes the arrogant belief that humans can defy or alter nature.
    c. communicates these criticisms through the characters of the guests, who repeat their past mistakes when they become young again; and through the character of Dr. Heidegger, whose mix of magic and medicine not only fails to heal, but tends to bring about greater misery and destruction.
In "The Life You Save May Be Your Own," the writer
    a. criticizes people for being manipulative, selfish, hypocritical, wretched, and oppressed.
    b. criticizes the human potential for evil.
    c. communicates these criticisms through the characters of Mr. Shiftlet and Mrs. Crater, who, despite their manipulation of each other, fail to get what they truly want.
    d. communicates these criticisms through the plot of the story, which ends with the innocent young Lucynell abandoned, and Mr. Shiftlet fleeing a storm seemingly brought on in answer to his own prayer that the slime be washed from the earth.

In addition, students could say that both writers display
   a. a disturbing view of human nature.
   b. the belief that human nature is seriously flawed.
Some students may feel that O'Connor, unlike
Hawthorne, conveys the belief that there is some hope
of salvation for the human spirit.

   3. Answers will vary. A model answer for Miss Emily
      ("A Rose for Emily") and young Lucynell ("The Life
      You Save May Be Your Own") follows.
Among the similarities that students could discuss are
the following:
   a. The women tend to be victims. (Miss Emily has
      been driven mad; Lucynell is married off and then
      abandoned.)
   b. The women tend to be associated with
      psychological imbalance. (Miss Emily is clearly
      insane; Lucynell may be mentally disabled.)
   c. The women tend to be associated with death.
      (Miss Emily suffers the death of her father, kills her
      lover and sleeps with his body, and dies; Lucynell
      suffers a kind of death through being abandoned
      and is described as an angel.)
   d. The women tend to be associated with beauty.
      (Miss Emily was beautiful; Lucynell is beautiful in
      some of her features and in her innocence.)
   e. The women tend to be associated with obsessed,
      disturbed, or extremely cruel men. (Miss Emily's
      father was cruel and obsessed with controlling her
      life; Lucynell is abandoned by the cruel Mr. Shiftlet.)
Other ideas should be supported with appropriate details
from the selections.

**D.** (20 points) Notes will vary. A model answer for "The
Masque of the Red Death" follows.
In "The Masque of the Red Death,"
   a. Prince Prospero and the revelers die.
   b. the death is literal.
   c. the death communicates the themes that one
      cannot separate oneself from humanity, and that it
      is folly to believe that humankind can overcome
      nature.

# Mid-Year Test
## pp. 97–103

**A.** 1. d
   2. a
   3. c
   4. a
   5. d
   6. c
**B.** 7. a
   8. c
   9. c
   10. d
**C.** Answers may vary but should include points similar to
the following:
11. In the first paragraph, Paine states his views of the case
    against Britain. In the second and third paragraphs, he
    defends the Colonies' right to rebel and prescribes
    what they should become in the future. The final
    paragraph is essentially a summary of his arguments.
12. He relates the anecdote to criticize the attitudes of the
    Tories (who are loyal to Britain), to arouse the reader's
    resentment of the Tories, and to provide a contrast
    between how the Tory parent feels and what patriots
    should feel toward their children.
13. Paine suggests that God and the power of
    righteousness are on the colonists' side, not Britain's.
    Examples: Britain seems to think it has replaced God
    by asserting absolute power over the colonists; God
    would not forsake the colonists who have tried to
    avoid war; God "governs the world" in a fair and
    just manner and would not accept Britain's claims
    to have His support.
**D.** 14. b
   15. a
   16. c
   17. b
**E.** Answers may vary but should include points similar
to the following:
18. Paine believes that the Colonies must be free of
    "foreign dominion," and in the end "the continent"
    will inevitably conquer its enemies. America will be a
    great place because it is isolated from the problems
    of other countries ("remote from all the wrangling
    world"). America could prosper by trading with other
    countries and otherwise leaving them to themselves
    ("she has nothing to do but to trade with them").

19. Paine makes this comparison to depict the Colonies' situation as one of self-defense. He suggests that Britain deserves the same treatment as a common thief, not the kind of reverence that people generally feel toward a monarchy. He also uses this comparison to make his argument personal by appealing to every man's instinct to protect his home and family.
20. Answers will vary widely, depending on students' personal experiences, situations, and viewpoints. Accept any answers that address the concern of the question and are elaborated by examples or details from the literature.

## Writing Exercise Scoring Guide

**4** An **exceptional** paper:
- Has a clear and consistent focus
- Has a logical organization
- Uses transitions effectively to connect ideas
- Supports ideas with details, quotations, examples, and/or other evidence
- Exhibits well-formed sentences varying in structure
- Exhibits a rich vocabulary, including precise language that is appropriate for the purpose and audience of the paper
- Contains almost no errors in usage, mechanics, and spelling

**3** A **proficient** paper:
- Has a relatively clear and consistent focus
- Has a logical organization, although it may be unnecessarily mechanical
- Uses some transition words and phrases to connect ideas, but they do not always clarify connections effectively
- Supports ideas with details, quotations, examples, and/or other evidence
- Exhibits some variety in sentence structures
- Uses vocabulary that is appropriate for the purpose and audience
- Contains a few errors in usage, mechanics, and spelling

**2** A **basic** paper:
- Has a fairly clear focus that may occasionally become obscured
- Shows an organizational pattern, but relationships between ideas may sometimes be difficult to understand
- Contains supporting evidence that may lack effect and so only superficially develops ideas
- Has complete and varied sentences most of the time
- Contains several errors in usage, mechanics, and spelling which cause distraction and some confusion about meaning

**1** A **limited** paper:
- Has a topic but does not include any elaboration, or it only minimally addresses the topic and lacks discernible ideas
- Has only a few simple sentences
- Contains little or no plausible support for ideas
- Shows limited word choice
- Contains numerous and serious errors in usage, mechanics, and spelling which cause confusion about meaning

A paper is unable to be scored if it is
- illegible
- unrelated to the topic
- only a rewording of the prompt
- written in a foreign language
- not written at all

## Revising/Editing

1. c
2. b
3. a
4. d
5. b
6. c

# Unit Four

## from Narrative of the Life of Frederick Douglass, an American Slave
Selection Test, pp. 105–106

**A.** (15 points each) Notes will vary but should include points similar to the following:

1. a. The style of this quotation is mainly objective. The language is unemotional; Douglass reports what happened in specific, factual terms without any real comment or complaint, almost as if he must distance himself from it.
   b. The style is effective here because the event is horrible and dramatic in itself. An objective description has more impact than a subjective description of pain or feelings.

2. a. The style of this quotation is mainly subjective. Douglass uses figurative language and describes how he felt.
   b. This style is effective because Douglass has achieved something emotional; he has revived his spirit and made a bold decision. It is also effective because so much of what preceded this excerpt was described in an objective way; Douglass has at last revealed how he feels about what has happened, and this allows the reader to share in the triumph. Reporting these developments in an objective way would have little impact.

**B.** (5 points each)
1. c
2. b
3. a

**C.** (4 points each)
1. c
2. b
3. c
4. b
5. a

**D.** (20 points; students should answer one of the two)
1. Answers will vary but could include points similar to the following:
   a. At the time the fight takes place, Douglass's spirit has been crushed and he has been without purpose, pride, hope, and self-confidence. Winning an unlikely victory against Covey restores these things to him.
   b. At the time the fight takes place, Douglass is feeling as if he is the brute that white men take him to be. Taking responsibility for his fate by defying Covey's will restores Douglass's humanity to himself.
   c. From that point on, Douglass fights with white men but never again allows one to whip him.

d. From that point on, Douglass is in control of his life to the extent possible under slavery. He never again allows another man to do as he pleases with him.

2. Answers will vary. Students might point out that Douglass
   a. seems to make every effort to learn how to be a good farm laborer, showing that he is extremely responsible, proud, and cooperative.
   b. goes to his owner to ask for his protection from Covey, showing that he is responsible, reasonable, courageous, and very dependent on others for his personal protection.
   c. goes to friends for advice, showing that he is reasonable and eager to find a resolution, and that he is a well-rounded person who has friends.
   d. responds with violence when all else fails, showing that he is reasonable but driven to desperation, remarkably patient, and beginning to take responsibility for his own protection.

**E.** (15 points) Answers will vary widely, depending on students' personal experiences, situations, and viewpoints. Accept any answers that address the concern of the question and are elaborated by examples or details from the literature or from life.

## Stanzas on Freedom/Free Labor
Selection Test, pp. 107–108

**A.** (10 points each) Notes will vary but should include points similar to the following:

1. a. Chains represent slavery.
   b. The speaker associates chains with slavery by saying, ". . . the chain / When it works a brother's pain"; "For your sisters now in chains"; ". . . to break / Fetters for our own dear sake"; "All the chains our brothers wear."

2. a. The speaker's garment is a symbol of freedom.
   b. The garment is made by free labor, not by slaves; it is an "easy garment," which does not "bear / The weight of bondsmen's tears."

3. a. Students may cite "the throne of God" as a symbol of conscience, final judgment, or morality.
   b. The speaker suggests that in the final judgment before God, this garment will not provide any evidence that she has "nerv'd Oppression's hand" by supporting slavery.

**B.** (5 points each)
1. c
2. d
3. c

**C.** (10 points each)
1. Notes will vary widely but could suggest points similar to the following:
   a. Restatement: People who are afraid to speak for

those who cannot defend themselves are trapped by that fear.

    b. Example: Allowing an unpopular fellow student to be humiliated or harassed.

  2. Notes will vary widely but could suggest points similar to the following:

    a. Restatement: People who are afraid to stand with a small minority are trapped by that fear.

    b. Example: Giving in to peer pressure to take drugs or drink alcohol at a party.

**D.** (20 points; students should answer one of the two)

  1. Answers will vary but should reflect students' understanding that the speaker feels that

    a. no one can be truly free while anyone is a slave (lines 3 and 4).

    b. anyone afraid to stand up for what is right is a slave (lines 25–32).

    c. freedom is accompanied by a responsibility to care for, protect, and defend others (lines 21–24).

In addition, students should include a personal response concerning the importance of the message today.

  2. Answers will vary but should reflect students' understanding that the speaker feels that

    a. slavery is sinful.

    b. those who profit in any way from the products of slave labor or who support slavery in any way are as guilty of oppression as those who hold slaves.

Students who take the speaker's message literally will feel that the message is of less importance today than those who apply the message to underpaid or exploited labor.

**E.** (15 points) Answers will vary widely, depending on students' personal experiences, situations, and viewpoints. Accept any answers that address the concern of the question and are elaborated by examples or details from the literature or from life.

## An Occurrence at Owl Creek Bridge

Selection Test, pp. 109–110

**A.** (12 points each)

  1. Notes will vary but could suggest ideas similar to the following:

    a. Third-person omniscient: The reader's attitude is objective, indifferent, or only mildly sympathetic because the narration distances the reader from Farquhar. He is a stranger and the reader may be curious about why he is to be hanged but there is little reason to care about him other than that he is a fellow human being.

    b. Third-person limited: The reader's attitude is sympathetic because the narrator enters Farquhar's mind, sharing with the reader his feelings, concerns, worries, inner experiences, and apparently physical experiences. Farquhar becomes more of an individual

to the reader, making it easier to care about him.

  2. Notes will vary but could suggest ideas similar to the following:

    a. The third-person limited point of view draws the reader into Farquhar's mind, thereby making his escape seem almost as real to the reader as it seems to Farquhar.

    b. Suspense builds as the reader is drawn into Farquhar's harrowing experiences through the third-person limited point of view.

    c. The shift back to the third-person omniscient point of view brings an end to the suspense, allowing for the surprise announcement of Farquhar's death—an event that Farquhar cannot share with the reader because he is dead.

    d. The shift back to the third-person omniscient point of view brings the suspense to an end so abruptly that the reader can appreciate (or even, in a sense, share) the shock of death.

**B.** (8 points each)

  1. b

  2. d

  3. c

  4. d

**C.** (4 points each)

  1. b

  2. c

  3. b

  4. c

  5. a

**D.** (12 points; students should answer one of the two)

  1. Answers will vary widely. Students who believe that Farquhar is a hero might say that

    a. he is motivated by patriotism to attempt to set fire to the bridge.

    b. being a civilian, he is not bound by duty or order to attempt to take action.

    c. he dies for his country.

Students who don't believe that Farquhar is a hero might say that

    a. his actions are motivated by a desire for the excitement of participating in a war, not by patriotism.

    b. he is easily fooled by the Federal scout.

    c. his actions bring about nothing other than his death.

  2. Answers will vary. Students who feel that cutting the ending would have made the story more enjoyable could make points similar to the following:

    a. It would have made a happy ending, instead of a sad and shocking one.

    b. Farquhar didn't deserve to be hanged, since he was encouraged by the Federal scout to burn the bridge and then didn't succeed in doing so.

c. If Farquhar had lived, his daring escape might have earned him the distinction he wanted but was prevented from getting because he was kept out of the army.

Students who feel that changing the ending would have made the story less enjoyable could make points similar to the following:

a. The story works only because Farquhar dies in the hanging; a happy ending would be trite, less believable, and less satisfying.

b. It is easier to believe that Farquhar's thoughts and sensations in section III are the result of tremendously slowed time than that the imagined events could actually occur.

c. The most interesting thing about the story is the presence of many clues to the fact that the events in section III are impossible, clues that a reader ignores until realizing that those events did not actually occur. With a different ending, these clues would become serious flaws in the story.

d. Since Farquhar believed that "all is fair in love and war," he deserved to die, even if he didn't succeed in burning the bridge.

**E.** (12 points) Answers will vary widely, depending on students' personal experiences, situations, and viewpoints. Accept any answers that address the concern of the question and are elaborated by examples or details from the literature or from life.

## A Mystery of Heroism

Selection Test, pp. 111–112

**A.** (6 points each) Notes and examples will vary but should include points similar to the following:

1. The story focuses on common soldiers in battle, rather than on the generals or other leaders or on the battle itself. The plot concerns the ordinary life of the soldiers and their need for water.

2. Crane gives very specific, accurate details to add to the realism of the scenes. He describes how the men looked ("The men of the battery wore white duck trousers, which somehow emphasized their legs . . . "); the horror of death ("One of a 'swing' team was suddenly smitten quivering to the ground . . ."); the landscape (The little meadow's "green and beautiful calm had vanished utterly. Brown earth was being flung in monstrous handfuls.").

3. The effects of natural and social forces can be seen in Collins's natural need for water ("Thunder, I wisht I had a drink.") and the peer pressure he is subjected to ("Well, if yeh want a drink so bad, why don't yeh go git it?"). When his comrades dare him and egg him on, he decides to risk his life to go to the well.

4. The story depicts a battle with bullets and projectiles flying everywhere. When Collins goes to the well and returns safely, the fact that he survives has nothing to do with skill or even courage; it was blind luck.

**B.** (5 points each)
1. d
2. b
3. c
4. a

**C.** (4 points each)
1. b
2. a
3. a
4. b
5. c

**D.** (20 points; students should answer one of the two)
1. Answers will vary but should include points similar to the following:

a. The irony is revealed in the last line: "The bucket lay on the ground empty." Collins is a victim of circumstances over which he has no control. After endangering his own life, it turns out that his great risk was worth nothing because the bucket was empty. All the water had spilled out.

b. Collins struggles with two moral issues. First, in his mind he feels that he cannot be a hero. Heroes are moral men with integrity. He feels he is "an intruder in the land of fine deeds." He is disillusioned when he realizes that "he was, then, a hero. . . . After all, heroes were not much." Second, the reader is not aware of what is in Collins's mind when he runs past the dying officer, but it is obvious that he feels a conflict. He returns to the officer out of instinct or natural reflex, but even that heroic effort fails: he splashes water all over the dying man's face but never actually gives him a drink.

2. Answers will vary but should include points similar to the following:

a. Collins hears the jokes and jeers of his comrades and feels that they are questioning his courage: "Dern yeh! I ain't afraid t' go." Driven by their jeers, the social pressure, and his own pride, he makes a hasty decision to go for the water.

b. Collins begins to realize what he has done when he asks the colonel for permission to go: "Some of the resentment toward his companions, which perhaps had forced him into this affair, was beginning to fade." In the naturalist view of life, Collins had no other choice but to go: pride is an uncontrollable force that "forces" men do strange things.

c. Collins is "vaguely conscious that a chasm, the deep valley of all prides, was suddenly between him and his comrades. . . . He had blindly been led by quaint emotions. . . . " But Collins cannot now refuse to go for fear of shame.

**E.** (16 points) Answers will vary widely, depending on students' personal experiences, situations, and viewpoints. Accept any answers that address the concern of the question and are elaborated by examples or details from the literature or from life.

## Gettysburg Address
Selection Test, pp. 113–114

**A.** (6 points each) Notes and examples will vary but should include points similar to the following:

1. Lincoln uses fairly simple, yet precise words to condense profound ideas into simple statements: "a new nation, conceived in liberty"; "dedicated to the proposition that all men are created equal"; "brave men, living and dead, who struggled here." Lincoln also varies the length of his sentences. The two opening sentences are longer than the brief third sentence. The longer, complex sentences tend to create a relaxed feeling. The shorter sentence that follows grabs the listeners' attention.

2. Lincoln's word choice and sentence length also help to establish his tone: he respects the gravity and emotion associated with the battle. His tone tells the listeners that he respects the men because they not only gave their lives but also advanced the cause of the nation.

3. Lincoln's allusion in the first sentence condenses 87 years of history and instantly gives the listeners an image of the early colonists fighting for freedom and equality. That image—that noble cause—compresses both battles into one. The nation has fought before for freedom and equality, and it will not hesitate to fight again for those ideals.

4. Lincoln uses the element of repetition: "we take increased *devotion* to that cause for which they gave the last full measure of *devotion*"; "[a nation] *conceived* in liberty, and *dedicated* to . . . any nation so *conceived* and so *dedicated* . . ." Lincoln also combines repetition with parallelism, catching the listeners' attention by creating a regular rhythm and connecting the ideas in each phrase: ". . . and that government *of the people, by the people, for the people,* shall not perish from the earth," and ". . . we cannot dedicate—we cannot consecrate—we cannot hallow—this ground.

**B.** (8 points each)
1. d
2. b
3. c

**C.** (4 points each)
1. c
2. a
3. a
4. b
5. c

**D.** (20 points; students should answer one of the two)
1. Answers will vary. A model answer follows.
   a. "Four score and seven years ago our fathers brought forth on this continent a new nation, conceived in liberty, and dedicated to the proposition that all men are created equal." This is a basic creed, or belief, of the nation. People remember this sentence because the allusion to the founding fathers creates a strong, emotional image of the fight for liberty and equality.
   b ". . . and that government of the people, by the people, for the people, shall not perish from the earth." The short, repetitive phrases grab people's attention and reinforce the idea that we are all participants in a democracy; the phrases also echo the Preamble to the U.S. Constitution: "We the people. . . ."

2. Answers will vary but should include points similar to the following:
   a. Lincoln's tone reveals his sincerity to those who fought, to the nation, and to the future. Lincoln believes that those who won America's independence fought a right and just war, just as the Civil War, although horrible, must also be fought to establish and preserve what is right.
   b. He is dedicated to the belief in one nation. He takes this responsibility to the nation seriously, for if he does not, the ideals fought for 87 years before will be lost and gone forever.
   c. He seems very humble standing on this ground. He states that the dedication of the battlefield cannot possibly make the ground more sacred, for it is already sacred with the blood of men who fought for a noble cause and a noble ideal.

**E.** (12 points) Answers will vary widely, depending on students' personal experiences, situations, and viewpoints. Accept any answers that address the concern of the question and are elaborated by examples or details from the literature or from life.

## *from* Coming of Age in Mississippi
Selection Test, pp. 115–116

**A.** (6 points each) Notes will vary but should include points similar to the following:

1. Objective facts immediately establish the accuracy and credibility of the report. For example, Moody states, "Seconds before 11:15 we were occupying

three seats at the previously segregated Woolworth's lunch counter."

2. Moody describes the events in chronological order, beginning before the sit-in actually began, through the sit-in itself, and to the events that followed.

3. One benefit of an eyewitness account is the inclusion of sensory details that add realism to the report. For example, Moody says that her hair was "stiff with dried mustard, ketchup and sugar. . . . My stockings were sticking to my legs from the mustard that had dried on them."

4. Direct quotations from people involved in the event add a sense of immediacy and provide different perspectives on the same event. ("My land, you were in the sit-in, huh?")

5. The inclusion of subjective feelings helps the reader relate to the person reporting the event and makes it more personal. Moody describes her own feelings and reactions to the sit-in. For example, "After the sit-in, all I could think of was how sick Mississippi whites were."

**B.** (6 points each)
1. a
2. b
3. c
4. b
5. d
6. b
7. c

**C.** (14 points; students should answer one of the two)
1. Answers will vary. Students could say that Moody's perception of Mississippi whites changes in that she
   a. comes to view their racism as a disease.
   b. finds that she no longer hates them.
In addition, students might say that her change in perception could be helpful in that it
   a. gives her faith in a possible "cure" for racism.
   b. provides her something positive to focus on.
   c. will probably be more useful to her than anger and hatred would be.
2. Answers will vary. Students may say that Moody is
   a. courageous. (She participates in the sit-in despite the danger.)
   b. determined. (She endures the taunts and attacks of the mob.)
   c. disciplined. (She does not react violently to the violence of the mob.)
   d. assertive. (She takes responsibility for improving her life and that of other African Americans.)
   e. principled. (She works for civil rights because it is the right thing to do.)
   f. independent. (She doesn't allow her mother to dictate her life.)

g. thoughtful and intelligent. (She thinks a good deal about her own actions and motivations and those of the people who oppose her efforts.)
Other ideas should be supported with appropriate reasons.

**D.** (14 points) Answers will vary widely, depending on students' personal experiences, situations, and viewpoints. Accept any answers that address the concern of the question and are elaborated by examples or details from the literature or from life.

**Ballad of Birmingham**
Selection Test, p. 117
**A.** (40 points) Notes will vary. Most students will mark the box labeled
   a. tragic events, because the death by violence of a little girl in a church is tragic.
   b. ordinary people, because there is nothing in the poem to suggest that the little girl and her mother are extraordinary in any way. The mother doesn't even want her daughter to show extraordinary courage by marching for freedom.
   c. theme related to love, adventure, and bravery, because the ballad describes the love between the mother and daughter and the devastating effect of the daughter's death on the mother; the "adventure" of marching through the streets for freedom; and the courage and bravery of people who risk their lives for the cause of freedom.
Students who mark the box labeled "supernatural elements" may interpret the bombing of a church and the little girl's untimely death as involving God, fate, or some other type of supernatural force.
**B.** (10 points each)
1. c
2. a
**C.** (20 points; students should answer one of the two)
1. Answers will vary widely. Students might say that the ballad conveys the idea that freedom
   a. requires sacrifice. (The child is killed over an issue of freedom.)
   b. must be fought for. (The child wants to march the streets of Birmingham for freedom.)
   c. isn't worth dying for. (The child's death is without purpose.)
   d. is worth dying for. (The mother doesn't want the child to march for freedom because it is too hazardous; the people who do march are willing to take the risk of injury or death.)
Other ideas should be supported with appropriate references to the ballad.
2. Answers will vary widely. Students who feel that the little girl is a martyr may say that

a. she supports the freedom march, even though her mother won't let her participate in it.

b. her death is part of the struggle for freedom that is taking place in Birmingham.

Students who don't feel that the little girl is a martyr might say that

a. she doesn't make a decision to sacrifice her life.

b. she has no idea that she is risking her life when she attends church.

Students who feel that the mother is a martyr might say that she loses her daughter and her happiness in the midst of a struggle for freedom.

Students who don't feel that the mother is a martyr might say that she

a. won't allow her daughter to march for freedom.

b. values her daughter's safety more than the struggle for freedom.

c. has no idea that her daughter's life will be sacrificed in church.

**D.** (20 points) Answers will vary widely, depending on students' personal experiences, situations, and viewpoints. Accept any answers that address the concern of the question and are elaborated by examples or details from the literature or from life.

## Unit Four, Part One Test

pp. 119–120

**A.** (5 points each) Answers will vary but should include points similar to the following:

1. Douglass stops Covey from whipping or abusing him physically; Douglass also revives his own spirit, makes himself feel like a man again, and vows never to act like a slave again.

2. In both poems, the speaker's purpose is to protest slavery. In "Stanzas on Freedom," the speaker's purpose is to arouse people who are free to help break the chains that hold others in slavery. In "Free Labor," the speaker explains that she does not support slavery by wearing clothes made by slaves, and she implies that other people should follow her example.

3. Fred Collins risks his life to get water during a battle, but his heroism is a "mystery" because the bucket is empty when he returns, or because he now realizes that heroes are "not much" if he can be one.

4. The mother tries to protect the child from the violence in the streets by sending her to church, but her daughter dies when the church is blown up.

**B.** (20 points) Notes will vary. A model answer for the writer of *Coming of Age in Mississippi* follows.

The writer is motivated to participate in a sit-in by

a. the desire for greater personal freedom.

b. the desire to achieve justice for African Americans.

c. the experience of being looked down upon.

d. impatience with the lack of progress in civil rights.

**C.** (20 points each; students should answer two of the four)

1. Answers will vary. A model answer for Douglass (*Narrative of the Life . . .*) and Collins ("A Mystery of Heroism") follows.

Douglass shows personal responsibility when he

a. stands up to Covey, at great risk to his life, and refuses to allow him to beat or whip him unjustly.

b. seeks help from other sources before resorting to violence against Covey.

c. refuses to allow his legal status as a slave to define him as a human being.

In terms of personal responsibility, Collins

a. asks permission from the captain to leave his post.

b. takes it upon himself to reach the well and get water.

c. returns to the dying officer in the middle of the battlefield, at great risk to himself, to give him water.

Douglass acts more responsibly because his actions are thoughtful and reflect a desire to do the right thing. Collins's actions might be described in the same way, but his motives and purpose are insignificant by comparison. He puts himself at risk because his comrades dare him to, and he risks his life for a drink of water.

2. Answers will vary. A model answer for *Narrative of the Life . . .* and "Ballad of Birmingham" follows.

In *Narrative of the Life . . .* , justice is served because

a. Douglass threatens and beats Covey, the man who has beaten him repeatedly.

b. Douglass puts a stop to the physical beatings, which no person should be forced to endure. Even though he is a slave, Douglass should not be treated with the cruelty and abuse that Covey inflicts on him.

c. Douglass acts in self-defense.

In "Ballad of Birmingham," justice isn't served in that

a. the African Americans of Montgomery are not truly free.

b. an innocent little girl is murdered.

c. even the children are not safe from violence.

d. a sacred place is violated.

3. Answers will vary. A model answer for "Stanzas on Freedom" and "An Occurrence at Owl Creek Bridge" follows.

In "Stanzas on Freedom," the tables are turned by the speaker's

a. suggesting that slavery enslaves so-called free people.

b. pointing out that slavery exists in many forms among so-called free people.

This turning of the tables
  a. surprises the reader, who most probably wouldn't think of himself or herself as a slave.
  b. challenges the reader to reconsider the meaning of freedom and the existence of slavery.
  c. encourages the reader to examine his or her conscience and therefore to feel personal responsibility for slavery.
In "An Occurrence at Owl Creek Bridge," the tables are turned
  a. when Farquhar manages to "escape" from being hanged and make his way back to his home.
  b. when Farquhar is hanged at the moment that his wife's outstretched arms come into his reach.
This turning of the tables
  a. comforts Farquhar in the last moments of his life.
  b. makes Farquhar's death more shocking to the reader.
  4. Answers will vary. A model answer for the daughter ("Ballad of Birmingham") and Douglass (*Narrative of the Life . . .*) follows.
The daughter is most victimized in that she
  a. is murdered.
  b. is an innocent child.
  c. dies in a sacred, supposedly secure place.
  d. can do nothing to defend or protect herself.
Douglass wins the greatest victory in that he
  a. fights a battle that he has little chance of winning, and wins.
  b. risks his life in a struggle for the control of his soul, and wins.
  c. regains his pride, self-confidence, and humanity.
**D.** (20 points) Notes will vary. A model answer for Farquhar ("An Occurrence at Owl Creek Bridge") follows. Farquhar doesn't show this type of real courage in that
  a. his eagerness to be a soldier seems to be based primarily on the desire for excitement.
  b. he has every reason to believe that his plan to set fire to the bridge will work.
  c. there is no reason to believe that he would have acted had he known that he was being set up for failure by the Union scout.

**The Indian and the Hundred Cows/
El indito de las cien vacas**
Selection Test, p. 121
**A.** (20 points each)
1. Notes will vary but should reflect students' understanding that the priest means
  a. for his statement to be taken figuratively.
  b. something more general than the Indian believes, such as "God helps those who help the poor" or "giving to God will bring God's grace on you."

2. Notes will vary but should reflect students' understanding that the Indian believes that the priest means that
  a. a person's donation will earn one hundred times the amount donated.
  b. if one cow is donated, a person will receive one hundred cows in return.
**B.** (10 points each)
  1. c
  2. d
  3. a
**C.** (15 points; students should answer one of the two)
  1. Answers will vary. Students who think that justice is served might say that
    a. the priest is wrong to speak so lightly or casually about making donations to God.
    b. the Indian donates the cow to the church in good faith; he has received the assurance of the priest that he will receive one hundred cows in return.
    c. the Indian receives what he expects to receive.
    d. the priest receives a valuable lesson in return for his loss of the cows.
Students who think that justice isn't served might say that
    a. the Indian has been faithfully attending church for quite some time and should realize by now that not everything that the priest says is meant to be taken literally.
    b. if everyone always took everyone else's statements literally, society couldn't function.
    c. the cows belong to the church, not to the priest. It is the church that loses out.
    d. the Indian's position is unreasonable. He should be made to listen to reason and return the cows.
  2. Answers will vary but could include points similar to the following:
    a. Straightforwardness, plain speaking. (The Indian takes the priest at his word, and the priest pays the price for speaking carelessly in a way that others can easily misinterpret.)
    b. Justice, fairness. (The Indian doesn't allow the priest to take back the cows that were promised to him.)
    c. Self-sufficiency. (When the cows don't show up on their own, the Indian goes and gets them.)
    d. The rights of the individual. (The Indian triumphs over the church.)
    e. Belief in God. (The Indian is a faithful churchgoer.)
Other ideas should be supported with reference to the *cuento*.
**D.** (15 points) Answers will vary widely, depending on students' personal experiences, situations, and viewpoints. Accept any answers that address the concern of the question and are elaborated by examples or details from the literature or from life.

## High Horse's Courting
### *from* Black Elk Speaks
Selection Test, p. 123

**A.** (40 points) Notes will vary but should reflect students' understanding that

    a. High Horse wants the girl.

    b. Red Deer wants (or wants to help) High Horse to get the girl.

    c. the girl wants respect, prestige, and marriage (possibly to High Horse).

    d. the girl's father wants a worthy husband for his daughter.

**B.** (10 points each)

  1. d

  2. c

**C.** (20 points; students should answer one of the two)

  1. Answers will vary. In describing High Horse, students might use such terms as

    a. sweet or good-natured. This makes the reader like him and root for him.

    b. determined, passionate, or sincere. This leads to his doing things that make so much of the folk tale humorous.

    c. uncool. His willingness to risk making a fool of himself gets him into absurd situations.

Other ideas should be appropriately supported.

  2. Answers will vary but could include points similar to the following:

    a. High regard for persistence. (High Horse must show that he will keep trying in order to win the girl.)

    b. An emphasis on marriage as the accepted channel for romantic love. (The parents tie the girl down so she will not be stolen and cannot run away with High Horse.)

    c. The belief that young men must prove their manhood and worthiness as providers in order to marry. (High Horse is accepted by the girl's father only after High Horse brings him the stolen horses.)

    d. The importance of friendship and family ties. (Red Deer, a relative and close friend of High Horse's, helps him to win the girl.)

    e. A respect for the spirit world. (The people fear High Horse when he looks like an evil spirit, but they will not shoot him.)

    f. A love for oral literature. (The telling of the story itself.)

    g. A low regard for other tribes. (Red Deer and High Horse kill the Crow horse guard and steal the horses with no apparent guilt.)

    h. A high regard for women and family. (The girl's parents want the best possible husband for their daughter.)

    i. A low regard for women. (The girl is treated as property to be stolen or bartered by her parents and by High Horse.)

    j. A high regard for traditions and customs. (The rules of courtship and proving one's manhood are clear to and known by all.)

    k. A high regard for self-esteem. (The narrator notes approvingly that the girl refuses to run off with High Horse because she feels she deserves better treatment.)

Other ideas should be supported with appropriate details from the folk tale.

**D.** (20 points) Answers will vary widely, depending on students' personal experiences, situations, and viewpoints. Accept any answers that address the concern of the question and are elaborated by examples or details from the literature or from life.

## *from* The Autobiography of Mark Twain
Selection Test, pp. 125–126

**A.** (7 points each) Notes will vary but should include points similar to the following:

  1. a. Twain expected to be hypnotized and admired by the audience for his performance.

    b. He was the only one who apparently could not be hypnotized, but he was greatly admired for his phony performance anyway.

  2. a. Twain expected that he would be exposed as a fraud if he tried to act on a "mental suggestion" from Simmons.

    b. When he picked up the revolver and rushed into the audience, Simmons took credit for giving him the suggestion and Twain was more admired than ever.

  3. a. Twain did not think he could convince the skeptical Dr. Peake that his hypnotic trance was real.

    b. When he described the fire at the Richmond theater and Peake's mansion, Peake was more convinced than anyone.

  4. a. Twain expected to relieve his conscience when he confessed to his mother, and he expected his mother to believe him.

    b. Instead, Twain's mother told him he was mistaken, that he was too young at the time to know that he actually had been hypnotized, and Twain felt worse than before.

**B.** (4 points each)

  1. b

  2. d

  3. c

**C.** (6 points each)
1. Notes will vary widely but could include the following:
   a. Village or small town.
   b. Rural.
   c. Nineteenth century.
   d. American.
2. Notes will vary but could include the following:
   a. Mischievous boys.
   b. Swindlers.
   c. Local heroes.
   d. Elderly, stiff-backed gentlemen and ladies.
   e. Common, everyday folk.

**D.** (4 points each)
1. b
2. c
3. a
4. c
5. c

**E.** (14 points; students should answer one of the two)
1. Answers will vary. Students could point to such factors as
   a. the townspeople's desire to be entertained.
   b. the fact that not much was known about hypnotism at the time.
   c. the townspeople's gullibility.
   d. Twain's overwhelming desire for recognition.
   e. Twain's vivid imagination.
   f. Twain's strong skills of observation and good memory for detail.
   g. Twain's competitiveness and determination to be better than Hicks.
   h. Twain's ability to withstand physical pain.
   i. Twain's understanding of human nature.
2. Answers will vary but students could point to Twain's
   a. vivid imagination.
   b. strong skills of observation.
   c. good memory for detail.
   d. gutsiness.
   e. understanding of human nature.

**F.** (14 points) Answers will vary widely, depending on students' personal experiences, situations, and viewpoints. Accept any answers that address the concern of the question and are elaborated by examples or details from the literature or from life.

### from Life on the Mississippi
Selection Test, pp. 127–128
**A.** (8 points each) Notes will vary but should include points similar to the following:
1. a. This sentence describes how Mr. Bixby steered the steamboat very close to other boats on the river.

   b. The word *plowed* suggests that water is being thrown up on either side of the boat, just as a plow throws up soil or snow. The reader can see the boat moving quickly and steadily past the other boats. The word also suggests that Twain views Mr. Bixby as competent, confident, and bold, perhaps a bit reckless, in how he pilots the boat.
2. a. This sentence describes Twain's first attempt to steer the steamboat.

   b. The word *claw* suggests desperation and determination. The reader can visualize Twain slowly and carefully dragging himself and the boat along. (Mr. Bixby *plows*, but Twain *claws*.)
3. a. This sentence describes Mr. Bixby's anger.

   b. The word *flaying* suggests that Mr. Bixby was extremely angry and was lashing out at Twain with his reprimands, like a man with a whip who strips the skin from his victim.
4. a. This sentence describes Bixby as a pot boiling over.

   b. The words *boil, overflow,* and *scald* suggest that Mr. Bixby is boiling so furiously that he cannot contain himself. He must relieve the pressure periodically by yelling at Twain.

**B.** (7 points each)
1. d
2. c
3. b
4. a

**C.** (20 points; students should answer one of the two)
1. Answers will vary but should include points similar to the following:
   a. When he first approached Mr. Bixby about becoming a pilot, Twain was young, innocent, and confident that the task would not be too challenging.
   b. He was taken aback when the mate woke him up in the middle of the night ("It was a detail in piloting that had never occurred to me at all"). What he had imagined would be a great adventure was beginning to seem too much like real work.
   c. Because Twain thought that piloting the boat would be easy ("since it [the river] was so wide"), he paid no attention to Mr. Bixby's instruction. Then he had to get a notebook and write down all the information he had to remember.
   d. By the end of his experiences with Mr. Bixby, Twain could no longer appreciate the beauty of the river because he had learned how to read it. What was once something beautiful to see and enjoy had become a "book" he had to read very carefully because it was fraught with dangers. Twain was no longer innocent and naive, and "the romance and beauty were gone from the river."

2. Answers will vary but should include points similar to the following:
   a. Mr. Bixby "*raged and stormed*; . . . the traders sent up a *volley of red-hot profanity*. . . . He *threw open* a window, *thrust* his head out, and *such an irruption* followed. . . . The fainter and farther away the scowmen's *curses drifted,* the higher Mr. Bixby lifted his voice and the *weightier his adjectives grew.*"
   b. This scene suggests that Mr. Bixby was hot-headed and had difficulty controlling his anger. He was "grateful" to have a chance to vent his anger and frustration at someone else.

**D.** (20 points) Answers will vary widely, depending on students' personal experiences, situations, and viewpoints. Accept any answers that address the concern of the question and are elaborated by examples or details from the literature or from life.

## The Notorious Jumping Frog of Calaveras County
Selection Test, pp. 129–130

**A.** (8 points each) Notes will vary but should include points similar to the following:
   1. a. In a tall tale, a character often gets fooled, to the amusement of those who know the truth.
      b. In the story, Jim Smiley gets fooled by a stranger.
   2. a. In a tall tale, the plot is based on exaggeration, and the hero performs or is involved with these far-fetched exaggerations.
      b. In the story, the exaggeration is that Smiley will bet on anything. He has an array of improbable animals capable of incredible feats: an asthmatic horse that always wins the race, a bulldog that fights a dog with no hind legs, and a frog trained to jump on command.
   3. a. In a tall tale, local color is used to present ordinary life and bring a region alive by portraying its typical dress, mannerisms, customs, character types, and dialects.
      b. In the story, Smiley says "Maybe you understand frogs and maybe you don't understand 'em; maybe you've had experience and maybe you ain't only a amateur, as it were."

**B.** (5 points each)
   1. b
   2. b
   3. d
   4. c

**C.** (4 points each)
   1. b
   2. c
   3. a
   4. b
   5. a

**D.** (20 points; students should answer one of the two)
   1. Answers will vary but should include points similar to the following:
      a. The narrator's formal and exaggerated diction creates contrast between him and Simon Wheeler and sets up the narrator as the "straightman"; a pseudo-sophisticated visitor from another region of the country, being taken in by a local tall tale.
      b. Simon Wheeler's casual and informal speech helps to reinforce the nature of this story as a tall tale because it is similar to oral storytelling.
      c. The dialect gives some hints about the way of life of the people speaking and adds local color to the story.
   2. Answers will vary but should include points similar to the following:
      a. Andrew Jackson is described as worthless and ornery, until money was bet on him. "Andrew Jackson would never let on but what *he* was satisfied and hadn't expected nothing else." When he fights the dog without hind legs, Andrew Jackson appears surprised "and then he looked sorter discouragedlike. . . . He give Smiley a look, as much as to say his heart was broke, and it was *his* fault for putting up a dog that hadn't no hind legs for him to take holt of . . ." The image of Jackson fighting the dog with no hind legs is ludicrous. Yet, by giving the dog human qualities of expressions and feelings, the reader can identify with those emotions and feel sympathy for his situation.
      b. Dan'l Webster received an "education" from Smiley and caught flies on command. Once he caught the fly, he would "fall to scratching the side of his head . . . as indifferent as if he hadn't no idea he'd been doin' any more'n any frog might do. You never see a frog so modest and straight-for'ard as he was." When he tried to jump he "hysted up his shoulders—so—like a Frenchman."
      c. By giving the frog a personality (and even shoulders!), Twain makes it easy for readers to identify with the frog and with Smiley, the man who trained him. At the end, the reader is so impressed with both Smiley and his frog that the swindle evokes sympathy for both of them.

**E.** (16 points) Answers will vary widely, depending on students' personal experiences, situations, and viewpoints. Accept any answers that address the concern of the question and are elaborated by examples or details from the literature or from life.

## A Wagner Matinee

Selection Test, pp. 131–132

**A.** (8 points each)

1. Notes will vary. For Clark's view of Boston, students might make notes similar to the following:
   a. Cultured, intellectually exciting.
   b. Pretty, colorful.
   c. Comfortable, secure.
   d. Varied.

For Clark's view of Nebraska, students might make notes similar to the following:
   a. Harsh, dangerous, demanding.
   b. Ugly, desolate.
   c. Monotonous.
   d. Uncultured, wild, backward.

2. Notes will vary. For the frontier farmer's view of Boston, students might make notes similar to the following:
   a. Noisy, crowded.
   b. Dirty, uncomfortable.
   c. Ugly.
   d. Unfriendly.
   e. Closed-in.
   f. Unnatural (or removed from nature).

For the frontier farmer's view of Nebraska, students might make notes similar to the following:
   a. Beautiful.
   b. Free, open.
   c. Demanding, harsh.
   d. Simple.
   e. Challenging.
   f. Rewarding.
   g. Natural (or close to nature).

**B.** (10 points each)
1. a
2. c
3. a
4. c

**C.** (4 points each)
1. a
2. b
3. a
4. a
5. c

**D.** (12 points; students should answer one of the two)
1. Answers will vary, but students might feel that Aunt Georgiana
   a. realizes just how much her choices in life have cost her in terms of self-fulfillment and happiness.
   b. is reluctant to return to her life on the farm.
   c. will probably continue to feel pain and reluctance but may feel them less as she once more becomes involved in the everyday life of the farm.

2. Answers will vary, but students could say that Aunt Georgiana would probably say that
   a. what passes for love in the early stages is often simply infatuation, which fades or dies with time.
   b. even genuine love cannot complete a life that lacks other things that are essential to the soul.
   c. practical considerations affect life more than young, inexperienced people can imagine.

**E.** (12 points) Answers will vary widely, depending on students' personal experiences, situations, and viewpoints. Accept any answers that address the concern of the question and are elaborated by examples or details from the literature or from life.

## The Legend of Gregorio Cortez

Selection Test, pp. 133–134

**A.** (20 points) Notes will vary widely, depending on the quotation students choose to discuss. Possible answers for each quotation include the following:

   a. Carlyle: The narrator emphasizes Cortez's manliness, noting time after time that "He was a man." Cortez never worries about dying but only about living by his code of manhood. It takes greater courage for Cortez to continue his flight than it would to turn himself in.
   b. Sidney: Cortez is presented as a highly skilled person in all areas of his life. These skills, combined with his courage, save his life during his encounters with the sheriffs, Rangers, and courts.
   c. Emerson: Cortez's heroism isn't rational. He doesn't reason through his actions; he acts instinctively, according to his feelings.
   d. Kennan: Cortez's flight to the border is long and filled with danger and hardship. He is able to endure all of it, and doesn't turn himself in until he finds out that others are suffering for his actions.
   e. Senesh: Cortez's life became the basis of many stories and songs. He is a cultural hero whose deeds, the narrator of this retelling seems to feel, are still pertinent to the lives of Mexicans today.
   f. Pearson: The journey to the border is a long one, filled with "dragons" in the form of sheriffs, Rangers, and other enemies. Cortez confronts them, outwits them, and demonstrates the force of his character time and time again. On the way to the border, the ordinary, hardworking family man is transformed into a hero.

**B.** (10 points each)
1. d
2. b
3. d

**C.** (10 points each)
1. Notes will vary widely but should include some of the following:
   a. Modesty.
   b. Cleverness.
   c. Respectfulness.
   d. Skill with animals.
   e. Loyalty.
   f. Respect for nature.
   g. Shrewdness.
   h. Hard work.
   i. Courtesy.
   j. Gentleness.
   k. Honesty.
   l. Peaceableness.
   m. Lawfulness.
2. Notes will vary widely but should include some of the following:
   a. Courage.
   b. Cleverness.
   c. Respectfulness.
   d. Skill with animals.
   e. Loyalty.
   f. Hard work.
   g. Honesty.
   h. Endurance.

**D.** (15 points; students should answer one of the two)
1. Answers will vary. Students could say that Cortez is similar to American tall tale heroes in that
   a. many of his virtues and accomplishments seem greatly exaggerated, such as when it is said that he is the best at everything he does and when he takes on 300 sheriffs at one time.
   b. he embodies certain values of his culture, such as working hard, providing for his family, respecting older people, and preserving the well-being of the community.
   Students could say that Cortez is unlike American tall tale heroes in that
   a. many of his virtues and accomplishments are within the realm of human possibility.
   b. he is, in many ways, the underdog.
   c. he gets in trouble with the law and goes to prison.
   d. his strength of character is more important than his physical and intellectual abilities.
2. Answers will vary. Students might argue that any of the following are responsible for Cortez's downfall:
   a. Fate.
   b. The bigoted sheriff who shoots Román.
   c. Those enemies who poison him.
   d. El Teco, who betrays him.
   e. His strong sense of loyalty, which draws him into conflict with the law and later motivates him to surrender.

**E.** (15 points) Answers will vary widely, depending on students' personal experiences, situations, and viewpoints. Accept any answers that address the concern of the question and are elaborated by examples or details from the literature or from life.

**Unit Four, Part Two Test**
pp. 135–136
**A.** (5 points each)
1. d
2. b
3. c
4. a

**B.** (20 points) Notes will vary. A model answer for "High Horse's Courting" follows.
It is a good thing that the custom of getting the father's permission to marry a young woman is largely a thing of the American past because it
   a. is sexist.
   b. leaves the fate of the young woman in someone else's hands.
   c. doesn't ensure that a marriage will be a good one.
   d. ensures that many people who are in love will be prevented from marrying each other.

**C.** (20 points each; students should answer two of the three)
1. Answers will vary. A model answer for Cortez and the Indian in "The Indian and the Hundred Cows" follows.
Both Cortez and the Indian
   a. represent cultures in conflict with other cultures.
   b. triumph over representatives of the other cultures.
   c. take moral stands in their fight against authority.
   d. are willing to fight to the death for what they think is right.
   e. are hard workers.
   f. live up to the standards set by representatives of the other cultures as well as or better than those representatives do.
   g. use logic to convince others that they are in the right.
   h. are reluctant heroes in that neither seeks trouble.
Cortez and the Indian are different as cultural heroes in that
   a. Cortez has many attributes that set him above his own people, such as his ability to communicate with animals, cover his tracks, and predict the weather, while the Indian seems to be an ordinary person.
   b. the Indian acts on his own behalf, while Cortez acts not only on his own behalf but also that of his family, his people, and, by speaking for justice in the courts, all people whom the law is supposed to protect.
   c. Cortez is far more admirable than the Indian, who is only notable for being naive or simple-minded.

2. Answers will vary. A model answer could include points similar to the following:
   a. Both men use trickery to achieve personal goals.
   b. The trickery of both is humorous.
   c. Both men come to regret their trickery.
   d. Twain uses trickery to his advantage; High Horse is a bumbling failure as a trickster.
   e. Twain's trickery is the most imaginative; High Horse's is the most pathetic.
   f. Twain comes up with his trickery on his own and he works alone; High Horse's trickery is suggested to him by a friend who helps him to carry it out.
3. Answers will vary. A model answer for "The Indian and the Hundred Cows" follows.
   a. The conflict is between the Indian and the priest. The Indian takes the priest's words literally, but the priest meant them figuratively.
   b. In a larger sense, the conflict is between the Christian settlers or missionaries and the Native Americans they try to convert.
   c. When the Indian follows the priest's counsel ("You know that when you make a donation to God, He returns it a hundredfold") and gives the priest a cow, he expects to get one hundred cows back. The priest is presumably talking about acts of faith, but he accepts the cow from the Indian and promises that God will repay him.
   d. When the Indian gets no return for his cow, he takes the priest's herd and refuses to give it back. To him, the priest represents God and may be held responsible.
   e. The Indian expects the priest to keep his promise, and the priest, realizing that he has made a mistake, vows to be more careful with his words in the future.

**D.** (20 points) Notes will vary. A model answer for Aunt Georgiana's life ("A Wagner Matinee") follows.
Before Aunt Georgiana moves to the plains, she
   a. seems to have been happy.
   b. seems to have led a comfortable life.
   c. was able to indulge her love of music.
   d. led a cultured life.
After Aunt Georgiana moves to the plains, she
   a. leads a harsh life of drudgery.
   b. isn't able to indulge her love of music nearly as much as she would like.
   c. is deprived of high culture.
   d. is miserable.

# Unit Five

## Selected Poems by Dickinson
Selection Test, pp. 137–138
**A.** (10 points each) Notes will vary but should include points similar to the following:
   1. a. This is a metaphor comparing hope to a bird.
      b. It suggests that hope is a living thing; that it is a feeling or an emotion rather than a specific idea or thought. It also suggests that because the tune is "without words," an individual can personalize it by making it specific to his or her needs.
   2. a. This is a simile comparing emotional pain to a stone.
      b. It suggests that after emotional pain, a person freezes his or her emotions and becomes as unfeeling as a stone. This permits the person to feel a kind of "contentment," or ease, in the absence of the pain that has been suppressed.
   3. a. This is a personification of death.
      b. It suggests that death will come, whether one is prepared for it or not, and it may come at any time. It also suggests that death might be a relief or an act of kindness ("He *kindly* stopped . . .").
**B.** (5 points each)
   1. a
   2. d
   3. c
   4. b
**C.** (5 points each) Examples and notes will vary but should include points similar to the following:
   1. a. Slant rhymes. From "Success . . .": "Who took the Flag today . . . So clear of Victory."
      b. This inexact rhyme calls attention to the word *victory,* which is the key concept referred to in the next four lines.
   2. a. Use of dashes. From "Much Madness . . .": "Assent—and you are sane— / Demur—you're straightaway dangerous—."
      b. In this example, the dashes isolate and emphasize key ideas, which are also opposites, and they establish causes and effects. If one agress, one is sane; if one disagrees, one is not.
   3. a. Unconventional capitalization. From "I heard a Fly . . .": "And then the Windows failed—and then / I could not see to see—."
      b. The capitalization of "Windows" calls attention to the word. The reader must think about the meaning of this word to interpret the next line. For example, the eyes are sometimes called "windows to the soul," and the speaker, who is describing her own death ("when I died"), "could not see to see" when the "Windows failed."

4. a. Inverted syntax. From "Hope . . . ": "And sweetest—
      in the Gale—is heard— / And sore must be the
      storm—."
   b. Inverted syntax is often used to achieve a certain
      rhyme scheme. In this example, the syntax
      emphasizes the parallel but opposite nature of
      "sweetest" and "sore," and it leads the reader on
      to see what the gale, or storm, is affecting ("the
      little Bird").
**D.** (15 points; students should answer one of the two)
   1. Answers will vary. Students could say that the speaker
      a. has positive feelings toward nature.
      b. believes that nature has entrusted him or her with
         a message.
      c. has tried to communicate that message.
      d. has not had much contact with people in general,
         or society.
      e. feels somewhat neglected by people in general,
         or society.
      f. is concerned that people in general may be
         judgmental about his or her work.
      g. believes that people in general feel positively
         about nature.
   2. Answers will vary. Students could say that the speaker
      a. does not fear death.
      b. is aware that death can come at any time.
      c. is willing to face what comes with death.
      d. sees death as gentle or kind or, at least,
         considerate.
      e. believes in an afterlife.
**E.** (15 points) Answers will vary widely, depending on
students' personal experiences, situations, and viewpoints.
Accept any answers that address the concern of the
question and are elaborated by examples or details
from the literature or from life.

### The Yellow Wallpaper
Selection Test, pp. 139–140
**A.** (10 points each)
   1. Notes will vary. Students who choose quotation *a* could
      say that the imagery suggests that the wallpaper
      a. is old.
      b. is faded enough so that the pattern is difficult, in
         places, to make out.
      c. has a busy and confusing pattern.
   Students who choose quotation *b* could say that the
   imagery suggests that the wallpaper
      a. has an extremely busy pattern.
      b. has some round shapes in it.
      c. contains curving or twisted lines.
      d. contains some small, white-colored parts.
   Students who choose quotation *c* could say that the

imagery suggests that the wallpaper
      a. is firmly affixed to the walls.
      b. contains many round shapes.
      c. contains shapes that look like mushrooms or
         other fungi.
   2. Notes will vary. Students who choose quotation *a*
      could say that the imagery suggests that the narrator
      a. is scornful of the design.
      b. is reacting to the design with more than average
         interest and annoyance.
      c. has begun to form an unpleasant image of a figure
         in the paper.
   Students who choose quotation *b* could say that the
   imagery suggests that the narrator
      a. has begun to read a great deal into what is shown
         in the pattern.
      b. is horrified and disgusted by what she thinks is
         shown in the design.
      c. sees the wallpaper as threatening and dangerous.
      d. seems to believe that the wallpaper has
         supernatural powers.
      e. is becoming, or has become, unbalanced.
   Students who choose quotation *c* could say that the
   imagery suggests that the narrator
      a. believes the wallpaper pattern is a living thing.
      b. sees the pattern as violent and disgusting.
      c. believes the pattern mocks her.
      d. sees the pattern as an enemy.
      e. has become extremely unbalanced.
**B.** (6 points each)
   1. b
   2. d
   3. b
   4. b
   5. c
   6. a
**C.** (4 points each)
   1. b
   2. a
   3. c
   4. b
   5. c
**D.** (12 points; students should answer one of the two)
   1. Answers will vary. Students should note that the
      narrator is losing her sanity. In addition, answers
      could indicate that the narrator sees a woman
      trapped behind the pattern because the narrator
      a. feels trapped by the social conventions of her time,
         her depression, and the restrictions placed on her
         by her husband.
      b. feels repressed in terms of her creativity and sees
         the secretively creeping woman as a projection of
         her own secretive writing.

c. has been discouraged from giving voice to her imagination and "fancies," which then come out in other ways.

d. desperately needs something to occupy her mind, stimulate her intellect, and provide her with a reason to exist.

2. Answers will vary. Students who feel that the narrator's husband is greatly to blame for her breakdown could support this answer by noting that he

a. fails to take her complaint seriously.

b. forbids her to think of her problem as mental illness.

c. refuses to vary the care she gets, despite the fact that her condition is deteriorating rather than improving.

d. refuses to give in to any of her desires, even though many of them would be extremely easy to grant her.

e. is convinced that he knows better than she does what is best for her.

Students who feel that he is not significantly to blame for her breakdown could support this answer by noting that he

a. is trying to help her, not harm her, and takes great pains to calm her.

b. has made many changes in his life in order to do what he thinks is best for her.

c. is limited by the knowledge available at the time about mental problems.

d. is also a victim of the society he lives in.

e. is not aware of how much she is deteriorating, because she hides more and more of her thoughts and feelings from him.

**E.** (12 points) Answers will vary widely, depending on students' personal experiences, situations, and viewpoints. Accept any answers that address the concern of the question and are elaborated by examples or details from the literature or from life.

## The Story of an Hour
Selection Test, pp. 141–142

**A.** (8 points each) Descriptions of events may vary but should be similar to the following:

1. Josephine and Richards tell Mrs. Mallard that her husband has died.

2. Mrs. Mallard weeps and then locks herself in her room.

3. Mrs. Mallard realizes that she is now free.

4. She opens the door to her sister Josephine, and they go downstairs.

5. Brently Mallard walks in the front door.

**B.** (8 points each)

1. a
2. d
3. c

**C.** (20 points; students should answer one of the two)

1. Answers will vary. Students who liked, appreciated, approved of, or were intrigued by the ending could hypothesize that the author chose to end this story in this way because

a. it makes the story complete; the story would just fade out without the concrete conclusion that this surprise ending provides.

b. it reflects a negative view of what is possible for married women, which, at the time, was accurate for many women.

c. it is ironic, and irony is dramatically satisfying.

Students who disliked, or felt dissatisfied by, the ending could hypothesize that the author chose to end the story in this way because

a. it was the easiest way to make a point and to conclude the story.

b. if Mr. Mallard had returned but Mrs. Mallard had survived, Mrs. Mallard would have had to do something about the realization she had had, and the author hadn't created a character capable of that.

2. Answers will vary. Students could note that Mrs. Mallard has difficulty recognizing the realization because

a. she has never had these thoughts before; the concept of freedom and self-assertion are foreign to her.

b. she is aware of the tragedy of what has occurred, so it is hard to realize and accept that there are positive aspects to the situation.

Students could note that Mrs. Mallard fights the realization at first because

a. she feels guilty about feeling happiness so soon after her husband's death.

b. it makes her feel disloyal.

c. she fears losing the self-control she has managed to gain after her hysterical weeping.

**D.** (16 points) Answers will vary widely, depending on students' personal experiences, situations, and viewpoints. Accept any answers that address the concern of the question and are elaborated by examples or details from the literature or from life.

## Seventeen Syllables
Selection Test, pp. 143–144

**A.** (10 points each)

1. Notes will vary but should suggest ideas similar to the following:

a. Mrs. Hayashi: writing haiku causes conflict with her husband, who disapproves of it; writing haiku seems to relieve her inner conflicts about the past and her loveless marriage.

  b. Rosie: she has inner conflicts about Jesus because she isn't sure how she feels about him and about being kissed by him; her mother's sharing the story of her marriage and insisting that Rosie promise not to marry probably increases both this inner conflict and an external conflict involving her parents.

2. Notes will vary but should suggest ideas similar to the following:

  a. Mrs. Hayashi: her husband destroys the prize she won for her haiku.

  b. Rosie: Jesus kisses her; or, her mother forces her to promise not to marry.

3. Notes will vary. Students might suggest that the theme is similar to one of the following:

  a. Marriage (or romance) is a serious undertaking with unpredictable consequences.

  b. Change is difficult, frightening, and sometimes threatening.

  c. Anything worth having is worth fighting for.

  d. People who won't stand up for themselves will get run over.

  e. Children don't necessarily need to learn the same lessons that their parents need to learn.

  f. People shouldn't view others as vehicles to make up for their own mistakes and disappointments in life.

  g. Those who don't learn from history, or a parent's mistake, are condemned to repeat it.

**B.** (5 points each)
  1. c
  2. c
  3. c
  4. b
  5. d
  6. b

**C.** (4 points each)
  1. b
  2. b
  3. c
  4. a
  5. b

**D.** (10 points; students should answer one of the two)

  1. Answers will vary. Students might say that Rosie's mother demands the promise because she

  a. saw her life fall apart after she fell in love.

  b. accepted a hasty marriage to someone she barely knew, a marriage that turned out unhappily.

  c. feels trapped in a relationship that does not allow her to pursue her deepest interests.

  d. feels that her life could be fulfilled if she did not have to consider the needs and temper of her husband.

  e. loves Rosie and wants her daughter's life to be better than her own.

In addition, students might say that Rosie makes the promise because she

  a. tends to say yes, because it is easier, even when she means no.

  b. realizes that at this highly emotional moment they cannot discuss the matter calmly.

  c. does not feel bound by it.

  d. wants to get away from her mother or to bring an end to the discussion.

  2. Answers will vary. Some students may feel that Rosie's father's action is justified because

  a. his wife often ignores him when she is absorbed in haiku.

  b. he has made his feelings on this issue known to his wife.

  c. he sends Rosie back to the house to remind his wife that she is needed at work.

  d. he shouldn't have to remind his wife how important her contribution is on a day when every hand is needed to bring in the tomato harvest.

  e. his wife completely ignores him and her work responsibilities.

Many students will feel that Rosie's father's action is unjustified because

  a. his wife has done nothing cruel to him and does not deserve the hostility and destructiveness of his action.

  b. it is not his wife's fault that he is incapable of understanding her needs or sharing in her fascination with haiku.

  c. his wife hasn't neglected her duties as a wife and mother in fulfilling her personal needs.

  d. he makes no attempt to discuss the issue with her or to accommodate her needs.

  e. he has no right to handle his anger at his wife in a manner that upsets and involves his daughter.

  f. no amount of emotional injury can justify destroying either great art or other people's possessions.

**E.** (10 points) Answers will vary widely, depending on students' personal experiences, situations, and viewpoints. Accept any answers that address the concern of the question and are elaborated by examples or details from the literature or from life.

**Adolescence—III**
Selection Test, pp. 145–146
**A.** (20 points) Notes will vary widely, depending on students' personal responses to the imagery and interpretations of the poem. Model answers for each image follow.

For image "a," students could suggest that the idea of ripening tomatoes represents the girl's growing up. For image "b," students could suggest the idea that the tears in a bowl represent her father's legacy of despair. For image "c," students could suggest that dance dresses and scarred knees represent what once was and what now is.

**B.** (5 points each)
1. a
2. d
3. d
4. b

**C.** (10 points each) Notes will vary but should include points similar to the following:
1. Real World:
   a. Images that appeal to sight include the "dusky rows of tomatoes," "glowed orange in sunlight," "rotted in shadow," "wrapped scarred knees in dresses," and "lipstick stubs / Glittered in their steel shells."
   b. Images that appeal to touch include "Grew orange and softer," "swelling out," "Starched cotton slips," "Lengths of Dotted Swiss."
   c. "Baptized my earlobes with rosewater" appeals to the sense of smell.
2. Imaginary World:
   a. Images that appeal to sight include "he would meet me by the blue spruce," "A carnation over his heart," "father coming toward us," and "his tears in a bowl."
   b. Images that appeal to touch include "At his touch, the scabs would fall away."
   c. "And blood hangs in the pine-soaked air" appeals to the sense of smell.

**D.** (20 points; students should answer one of the two)
1. Answers will vary widely. Students who feel that the speaker's strongest feeling is one of desperation, hopelessness, or defeat could support this view by pointing out that she
   a. associates what is happening to her body (puberty) with ripening and rotting tomatoes (first stanza).
   b. longs for a man to rescue her from her life, love her, and heal her pain (lines 14–20).
   c. can't revel in that romantic vision for long before reality or pessimism intrudes (the change in imagery, mood, and tone introduced in line 21).
Students who feel that the speaker's strongest feeling is one of
   a. pessimism might refer to the speaker's associating puberty with ripening and rotting tomatoes and the intrusion of a violent, sorrowful image into her romantic daydreaming.
   b. longing might refer to the melancholy imagery of the second stanza and the romantic daydreaming of the third stanza.

Other ideas should be supported with appropriate reference to the poem.
2. Answers will vary widely but should include points similar to some of the following:
   a. The first man envisioned is imaginary; the second, a real person.
   b. The first man is the speaker's lover; the second, the speaker's father.
   c. The first man is someone whom the speaker imagines will rescue her; the second, someone who is returning after having abandoned or hurt the speaker in some way.
   d. The first man's arrival is timely and welcome; the second's, an intrusion.
   e. The first man is associated with romance, passion, love, dreams, magic, and healing; the second, with sorrow, reality, violence, suffocation, disappointment, and intrusion.
   f. The first man is associated with the fulfillment of a dream; the second, with an impediment to the fulfillment of a dream.
   g. The first man offers the speaker love, comfort, fidelity, and healing; the second, tears, sorrow, and violence.
   h. The first man comforts the speaker; the second discomforts and threatens her.

**E.** (20 points) Answers will vary widely, depending on students' personal experiences, situations, and viewpoints. Accept any answers that address the concern of the question and are elaborated by examples or details from the literature or from life.

**I Stand Here Ironing**
Selection Test, pp. 147–148
**A.** (6 points each) Examples and notes may vary but should include points similar to the following:
1. Example: The old man living in the back felt compelled to tell the narrator to smile when she spoke to her daughter, because she seldom did.
   Notes: The narrator probably thought she was showing affection ("There were all the acts of love"). But when she compared her treatment of Emily with her treatment of the other children, she realized that she had expected too much of Emily and had not given her enough.
2. Example: Emily was sent to her father's house to live, then sent off to day care, then to a convalescent home; she was also left at home alone before she was old enough to handle it.
   Notes: The narrator clearly did not provide a safe, secure, or stable environment for Emily. Emily hated the day-care center, and she acted stiff and distant when she returned from her father's. She felt no love or sense of security at all at the convalescent center,

where she was not even allowed to keep the letters she received and could not stay with her only friend ("They don't like you to love anybody here"). Students might argue that the narrator had little choice in sending Emily to these places, but she sent her nevertheless.

3. Example: The narrator sometimes brought her collections to Emily in bed so she and Susan could play "Kingdom"; the narrator responded positively to Emily's imitations, encouraged her to perform in the school talent show, and went to see more than one of her performances.
Notes: The narrator does seem to have encouraged Emily to be creative and independent, to develop her own talents, although she does not seem to have expected much from her daughter.

4. Example: The narrator often allowed Emily to stay home from school for no real reason and apparently allowed her to eat rather poorly.
Notes: The narrator does not seem to have taught Emily any kind of self-discipline.

5. Example: Emily had asthma, was often sickly, was too skinny and underdeveloped for most of her childhood, and lost too much weight—to the point where she had to be sent to a convalescent home.
Notes: Emily seems to have had some congenital problems, such as asthma, which her mother could not prevent. But the narrator does not seem to have done much at all toward promoting good health.

**B.** (5 points each)
1. d
2. b
3. c
4. a

**C.** (4 points each)
1. c
2. a
3. b
4. b
5. c

**D.** (15 points; students should answer one of the two)
1. Answers will vary widely. Students may find ample evidence in the story to support the view that both the narrator and Emily were victimized, although they would not be wrong to feel that this is not true of one, both, or, perhaps, neither. Most students will include some of the following examples of what the narrator and/or her daughter were victimized by:
   a. The economic hardships of life during the depression.
   b. The desertion of the family by Emily's father.
   c. The narrator's early motherhood. (Being a teenage mother was hard; having a teenage mother was hard.)

d. The fact that Emily's mother had to work for all of Emily's early childhood.
   e. The inadequacy of good child care.
   f. The beliefs of the time regarding such things as nursing babies and the communicability of disease (the lack of physical closeness between parents and children at the convalescent home).

2. Answers will vary but should reflect students' understanding that the narrator can't account for Emily's success as a comic actress because
   a. Emily's childhood was dreary and unhappy.
   b. Emily doesn't seem to be a happy person.
   c. Emily hasn't been given the opportunity to fully develop her gifts.
In addition, students could say that the narrator makes the comment because she feels that
   a. Emily has a great deal of potential that will probably go untapped or be wasted because the realities of her life—poverty, depression, war, and fear—all have taken their toll on her.
   b. Emily must fight against these forces if she is to succeed and Emily has never been much of a fighter.
   c. she can do little, if anything, to help Emily develop her talents.

**E.** (15 points) Answers will vary widely, depending on students' personal experiences, situations, and viewpoints. Accept any answers that address the concern of the question and are elaborated by examples or details from the literature or from life.

### Unit Five, Part One Test
pp. 149–150
**A.** (5 points each) Answers may vary but should include points similar to the following.
1. Those who do not succeed value that which they lost more than those who attain the prize.
2. The day before she made this wish, Mrs. Mallard dreaded living a long life; now she looks forward to it. But, minutes later, she dies.
3. She dreams about having a man who loves her; or escaping from her current life of hard work, "starched cotton slips," and "scarred knees" to a life of "big-band dresses" and a man with a "carnation over his heart."
4. It allows the narrator to express the things she knows, thinks, and feels about Emily that no one else knows or would understand—and that she does not want to explain to the person who asked about Emily and wants to help.

**B.** (20 points) Notes will vary. A model answer for "'Hope' is the thing with feathers" follows.
The image of a storm bashing a little bird
   a. appeals to the sense of sight, touch, and possibly hearing.

b. might make one think about unfairness, nature's destructiveness, and death.

**C.** (20 points each; students should answer two of the three)

1. Answers will vary. A model answer for Mrs. Mallard in "The Story of an Hour," Mrs. Hayashi in "Seventeen Syllables," and the narrator of "I Stand Here Ironing" follows.

The many similarities among the women in these selections include the following:

a. All of them lead oppressed lives and long for freedom.

b. All of them are married; Mrs. Hayashi and the narrator of "I Stand Here Ironing" also have children.

c. The oppression in their lives is related to their marriages or family responsibilities.

d. Mrs. Hayashi and the narrator of "I Stand Here Ironing" have worked outside the home to support their families.

e. Neither Mrs. Hayashi nor the narrator of "I Stand Here Ironing" seems to have had much free time to pursue her personal dreams and interests.

f. The fate of each woman appears to have been sealed at marriage or upon giving birth to her first child.

g. All of them have regrets.

2. Answers will vary. A model answer for "The Story of an Hour" and "Adolescence—III" follows.

In "The Story of an Hour," Mrs. Mallard

a. Mrs. Mallard who thinks that, at last she is free, suddenly finds her freedom snatched from her.

b. When she learns that she will not have the freedom which she longed for, she dies.

In "Adolescence—III," the speaker

a. loses her immaturity, innocence, or childhood when she begins to go through puberty.

b. seems to become more interested in her appearance, to be less satisfied with her life, to desire a lover to save her, and to be unable to look at life without seeing its darker, more violent aspects.

3. Answers will vary. A model answer for Rosie in "Seventeen Syllables" and Mrs. Mallard in "The Story of an Hour" follows.

Rosie is largely able to determine her own destiny because she

a. is young and has her whole life ahead of her.

b. has grown up in America, where individuality and following one's own dreams is more often encouraged and tolerated than it was in her mother's native country.

c. hasn't made any mistakes in her life that have

limited her options.

d. is responsible, level-headed, and a hard worker, qualities that help people to succeed in life.

e. is not her mother; nor are her mother's problems hers.

f. doesn't seem to take seriously her promise to her mother not to marry.

Mrs. Mallard doesn't have a good deal of ability to control her own destiny because she

a. seems not to have realized how dissatisfied she was with her marriage.

b. dies within an hour of arriving at the important realizations necessary for her to take charge of her life.

**D.** (20 points) Notes will vary. A model answer for the narrator of "I Stand Here Ironing" follows.

Leaving Emily at day care while the narrator went to work

a. allowed the narrator to support her family.

b. deprived Emily of the love and attention she badly needed.

## Chicago/Lucinda Matlock

Selection Test, pp. 151–152

**A.** (20 points) Notes will vary. Students who choose the Saroyan quotation might suggest that Lucinda Matlock would probably agree because

a. Saroyan's statement is another way of saying what Lucinda Matlock says in the final line of the poem, "It takes life to love Life."

b. Lucinda Matlock crowded a great deal of activity into her life and died a satisfied woman. "In the time of [her] life," she lived.

Students who choose the Casanova quotation might suggest that Lucinda Matlock would probably agree because

a. Lucinda Matlock expresses scorn for younger generations' "sorrow and weariness, / Anger, discontent and drooping hopes." She calls them "degenerate."

b. Casanova reflects a similar attitude toward those who do not love life. He says that they are "unworthy of life."

**B.** (10 points each)

1. b
2. a
3. b
4. c

**C.** (20 points; students should answer one of the two)

1. Answers will vary but could include points similar to the following:

a. The city is presented as a young, strong, aggressive, cunning, lively, productive, optimistic, self-confident young man.

b. The epithet conveys the city's strength and its "can-do" attitude.

c. The people of a city might very well find most of the poem's images appealing.

d. The people of a city might very well, like the speaker of the poem, be tired of hearing about the city's negative points and might prefer to think about its positive points.

Other ideas should be supported with appropriate reasons.

2. Answers will vary but should reflect students' understanding that Lucinda Matlock means that people must

a. be strong and vigorous in their everyday lives in order to love life.

b. live each day fully and appreciate all facets of their existence, the challenges as well as the successes, in order to get the most fulfillment out of life.

In addition, students should note that Lucinda Matlock learned this lesson in life. As support, they could note some of the following ideas:

a. She loved life and crowded a good deal of it into her 96 years.

b. She filled her days with dancing, rearing children, housekeeping, nursing the sick, gardening, and savoring nature.

**D.** (20 points) Answers will vary widely, depending on students' personal experiences, situations, and viewpoints. Accept any answers that address the concern of the question and are elaborated by examples or details from the literature or from life.

## Selected Poems by Robinson

Selection Test, pp. 153–154

**A.** (10 points each) Notes will vary but should include points similar to the following:

1. Physical description:

a. Richard Cory is described as a gentleman from "sole to crown." His appearance is regal: "clean-favored, and imperially slim." He appears so regal that he "glitters" when he walks down the street.

b. Miniver Cheevy grows thin.

2. Character's own actions:

a. The apparently perfect Richard Cory with the perfect life commits suicide. His action contradicts what the entire town has believed him to be.

b. Miniver Cheevy weeps, sighs, and mourns because he cannot live in the past. He curses and scorns the present. Rather than face the present and his own alienation and failure, he becomes an alcoholic.

3. Other characters' or the speaker's thoughts and feelings:

a. The townspeople think Richard Cory's life is perfect, and so they all wish they were in his place.

b. The speaker calls Cheevy a "child of scorn" and feels contempt for him.

**B.** (6 points each)

1. b
2. a
3. c
4. d
5. d

**C.** (20 points; students should answer one of the two) Answers will vary but should include points similar to the following:

For "Richard Cory":

a. Richard Cory was not "body-hungry." He was wealthy and could certainly take care of his physical needs.

b. Whatever made him kill himself must have been a hunger of the soul—or inner conflicts that he could not resolve.

c. The townspeople were "body-hungry" (they did not have money to meet their physical needs) but not "soul-hungry" (they may have envied Cory, but that envy did not destroy their lives).

For "Miniver Cheevy":

a. Miniver Cheevy is also not really "body-hungry." He does possess the ability to work and to provide for his physical needs.

b. The source of his alcoholism is a hunger of the soul—an inner dissatisfaction.

c. Like Cory, Cheevy will also kill himself—not with a gun but by drinking.

2. Answers will vary but should include points similar to the following:

a. The philosophy of life suggested in "Richard Cory" is that appearances can deceive. Cory appeared to have the perfect life, yet his inner problems drove him to suicide.

b. Advice to the townspeople might be that you cannot judge a person by appearances and that envy is a futile emotion.

c. The philosophy suggested in "Miniver Cheevy" is that it is important to live in the present, to set goals, to strive to achieve those goals. Cheevy was a failure and alienated himself from everyone and everything in his life. His failure filled him with bitterness, regret, and a need to escape from life. Rather than deal with his inner conflicts, he became an alcoholic.

d. Advice to Miniver Cheevy might be that happiness comes from within; or, appreciate what you have rather than mourning what you do not have.

**D.** (20 points) Answers will vary widely, depending on students' personal experiences, situations, and viewpoints. Accept any answers that address the concern of the question and are elaborated by examples or details from the literature or from life.

## Selected Poems by Dunbar
Selection Test, pp. 155–156
**A.** (15 points each) Notes will vary but should include points similar to the following:
1.  a. A mask symbolizes a false front, disguise, or masquerade. The symbol suggests, "We must hide our feelings, thoughts, and identities. We must hide who we are and what we think."
    b. A heart symbolizes one's deepest feelings and inner thoughts; devotion. The symbol suggests, "Because we must hide what we really think, our inner-selves—our souls—are left bleeding."
    c. Clay symbolizes the earth. The symbol suggests, "Life on earth is vile. It is unbearable because we must deceive."
2.  a. A cage symbolizes a prison, and a bird symbolizes flight and freedom. A "caged bird" is the imprisonment of freedom, which suggests, "I am not free physically or emotionally."
    b. Bars symbolize coldness and obstruction to progress and action; they are made to imprison or exclude. The symbol suggests, "I am exhausted from constantly struggling against everything in this society that physically and emotionally excludes me."
    c. The heart's deep core symbolizes the soul, which suggests, "I pray and plead from my very being, my core, that I might have the freedom to be myself."

**B.** (5 points each)
1. b
2. b
3. b
4. a
5. c
6. c

**C.** (20 points; students should answer one of the two)
1. Answers will vary widely. Students might interpret the speaker's question to mean that
   a. it is impossible for the world to see all the suffering of people who hide that suffering so well.
   b. the world is so "vile" that it would be foolish to expect it to care enough to notice the inner anguish of those who wear the mask.
In addition, students should include a personal response to their interpretation of the speaker's statement.
2. Answers will vary but should include points similar to the following:
   a. Both poems present the pain experienced by African Americans who must struggle against a repressive society. In "We Wear the Mask," the tortured soul cries out. In "Sympathy," the caged bird sings a prayer, or plea, for freedom.
   b. "We Wear the Mask" expresses the problem of identity: The dilemma is how to be an African American and an American in a society filled with stereotypes and negative images. The poet is trying to explain how crippling and torturous it is to live constantly in disguise, to mask one's thoughts and needs.
   c. The poet tries to show white America how this society causes African Americans to hide their feelings and identities. They must wear a mask and "fly back to [his] perch." White America does not accept African Americans as equals in thoughts and feelings.
   d. Both poems try to explain to white America the repression African Americans experience and its detrimental and debilitating effects.

**D.** (20 points) Answers will vary widely, depending on students' personal experiences, situations, and viewpoints. Accept any answers that address the concern of the question and are elaborated by examples or details from the literature or from life.

## Winter Dreams
Selection Test, pp. 157–158
**A.** (6 points each) Notes and judgments will vary but should include points similar to the following:
1. Judy is rude, inconsiderate, and boldly arrogant. She says to her partner that she would have reached the green if her ball had not "hit something." Dexter says nothing during this scene or afterward at the next tee as the other men discuss Judy. He is smitten with her and makes no judgments.
2. Dexter goes to dinner at Judy's and expects to be treated as a formal date, but he is disappointed to find how informal the dinner is. He surrenders to Judy's advances and kisses her, but the reader suspects that she is toying with him. He doesn't seem to care, or doesn't know at this stage, and she treats him with wanton disregard as one of her many boyfriends.
3. Dexter seems to know that Judy will never be faithful to him or fall head over heels in love with him, but he wants her anyway. She is not even considerate enough to give him a definite answer.
4. Judy acts maliciously by exerting her control over Dexter, probably just to prove that she can. She succeeds in breaking up his engagement to Irene, and he doesn't seem to think it is that important. He makes a fool of himself and causes great pain to Irene and her family, with little regard for them.

5. After a month, Judy throws Dexter away once again, proving that she is just as thoughtless and wanton as ever. Dexter does not resent her or even seem to feel great pain, as if he expected this to happen. He has been a fool for Judy, but he still has his "winter dreams," and she is a part of them. He will hold on to the memory and be glad that it happened.

**B.** (5 points each)
1. c
2. d
3. c
4. a
5. b

**C.** (4 points each)
1. c
2. a
3. b
4. a
5. a

**D.** (10 points; students should answer one of the two)
1. Answers will vary but could include ideas similar to the following:
   a. Dexter is so unhappy because he loses his dream.
   b. Losing Judy isn't as painful as losing the dream of Judy.
   c. When he realizes that this illusion has been taken from him, he is devastated.
   d. Besides Judy, he has lost the ability to dream of possibilities, to look forward to the future with youthful idealism.
   e. This loss is more painful because it is more final and because it makes him poignantly aware of the transience of beauty, youth, and idealism.
   f. The theme concerns the fragile, even brittle nature of Dexter's dreams and suggests that such youthful dreams cannot withstand the passage of time. Dexter's dreams, like Judy's beauty and vibrancy, cannot endure.
2. Answers will vary but could include points similar to the following:
   a. Judy seems to want attention and excitement. She gets both out of manipulating the emotions of the men who are attracted to her, including Dexter.
   b. A part of Judy also seems to want the men in her life, including Dexter, to make her feel happy and content. Dexter doesn't, and can't, provide these things for her because happiness and contentment come from within or not at all.

**E.** (15 points) Answers will vary widely, depending on students' personal experiences, situations, and viewpoints. Accept any answers that address the concern of the question and are elaborated by examples or details from the literature or from life.

**America and I**
Selection Test, pp. 159–160
**A.** (5 points each)
1. Notes will vary but could suggest that the
   a. Pilgrims left behind their culture, family, friends, possessions, and homes.
   b. narrator left behind her language, culture, family, friends, possessions, and home.
2. Notes will vary but could suggest that the
   a. Pilgrims expected that their life would be difficult and that they would have to create a new life for themselves.
   b. narrator expected life in America to be a utopia; all that she ever wanted and dreamed of would be handed to her on a silver platter.
3. Notes will vary but could suggest that the
   a. Pilgrims worked hard and remained determined to succeed.
   b. narrator worked hard, kept trying new things, repeatedly asked for help, but finally became alienated and discouraged.
4. Notes will vary but could suggest that the analogy helps the narrator to understand that she
   a. has to think more like the Pilgrims did and to apply herself as they did.
   b. was wrong to expect America to welcome her with open arms and to become discouraged when it did not.
   c. is capable of contributing to the development of American society.

**B.** (6 points each)
1. c
2. c
3. a
4. a
5. c

**C.** (4 points each)
1. a
2. b
3. c
4. b
5. a

**D.** (15 points; students should answer one of the two)
1. Answers will vary, but students should recognize that the narrator found the experience unsatisfactory because
   a. she worked extremely hard and earned no wages.
   b. her employers treated her as if she were inferior to them.
   c. she felt betrayed by the employers whom she trusted.
   d. the experience didn't get her any closer to achieving her goals.

Most students will find her response reasonable because
   a. she believed (or was led to believe) that she would be paid wages for her work.
   b. as a recent immigrant, there were many things she needed and wanted to buy.
   c. her employers clearly took advantage of her naïveté and their power over her.
Students who don't find her response reasonable should support that view with appropriate reasons and reference to the story.
   2. Answers will vary. Students who think she fulfills her desire might say that she has
   a. begun to take responsibility for her fate in America.
   b. overcome great obstacles to become a writer in the English language.
   c. contributed to American society by writing about ghetto life.
   d. discovered a sense of satisfaction in doing work that she loves.
   e. remains aware that there are others who, unlike her, are not able to earn a living doing satisfying work.
Students who do not feel that she has fulfilled her desire should support that view with appropriate reasons and reference to the story.
**E.** (15 points) Answers will vary widely, depending on students' personal experiences, situations, and viewpoints. Accept any answers that address the concern of the question and are elaborated by examples or details from the literature or from life.

## In the American Society
Selection Test, pp. 161–162
**A.** (8 points each)
 1. Notes will vary. A model answer includes the following points:
   a. Ambition: to re-create the Chinese society in the United States.
   b. Reveals: he is traditional and he desires the kind of life that his grandfather led.
 2. Notes will vary. A model answer includes the following points:
   a. Ambition: to join the country club.
   b. Reveals: she identifies herself as American and desires respectability and recognition from others.
**B.** (5 points each)
 1. b
 2. b
 3. c
 4. b
**C.** (8 points each) Notes will vary but should suggest ideas similar to the following:
 1. "His Own Society" focuses on the differences

between Mr. Chang's traditional Chinese culture and American culture, which his wife and daughters have adopted.
 2. "In the American Society" focuses on a party at which Mr. Chang shows that personal dignity is more important than fitting into a culture.
 3. The story would be less effective because the first part offers mostly negative insights into Mr. Chang and his situation. Without those insights, the second part would be less poignant and less meaningful to the reader. The story would also end on a negative note instead of a positive one.
**D.** (4 points each)
 1. b
 2. c
 3. b
 4. a
 5. c
**E.** (10 points; students should answer one of the two)
 1. Answers will vary but could include ideas similar to the following:
   a. The daughters—being young—have adapted more readily to American culture than their father has. They seem to effortlessly understand American customs and nuances that bewilder their father. While Mr. Chang sometimes has difficulty keeping his head "above water," the girls dive in and move around "the American society" with ease.
   b. The theme of the story concerns the difficulties of coming to understand, adapting to, and being accepted by a foreign culture.
 2. Answers will vary but should include ideas similar to the following:
   a. In the beginning, Mr. Chang's optimism, willingness to take risks, and hard work pays off—the restaurant quickly becomes a success.
   b. After the restaurant becomes successful, Mr. Chang takes a greater interest in the employees and begins to demand not only loyalty of them but also personal (and demeaning) favors. His traditional Chinese ideas of the relationship between employer and employee quickly offend his workers, and they begin to quit. Mr. Chang fails to understand why his behavior is offensive.
   c. Soon, the only people who will work for him are those who are Chinese with traditional ideas similar to his own and those whose bad attitudes and ineptitude make them unacceptable to other employers. Business falls off as patrons find the food distasteful and the service incompetent.
**F.** (10 points) Answers will vary widely, depending on students' personal experiences, situations, and viewpoints.

Accept any answers that address the concern of the question and are elaborated by examples or details from the literature or from life.

## Defining the Grateful Gesture/Refugee Ship
Selection Test, pp. 163–164

**A.** (15 points each) Themes and supporting ideas may vary but should include points similar to the following:
1. Theme: The mother is intent on teaching her children to appreciate that food is nourishment for those who work hard, but her intent fails. Instead, she has taught her children guilt and a sense of unworthiness.
   a. ". . . expect us / to be reverent to the sources / of our undeserved nourishment." The speaker has a sense that she does not deserve the food that her mother provides. The mother attacks the speaker's self-worth.
   b. "and to strike a thankful pose / before each lift of the fork / or swirl of the spoon." This is the "grateful gesture" that the speaker makes—something done by way of formality in an attempt to affect her mother's attitude.
   c. "with a sense of realization, or relief, / guilty about possessing appetite." The mother has taught the speaker to feel nothing but guilt and a sense of being unworthy.
2. Theme: The speaker feels that she is neither an American nor a Mexican; she has no identity.
   a. "Like wet cornstarch, I slide / past my grandmother's eyes . . . / The pudding thickens." The grandmother notices the speaker about as much as she notices adding cornstarch to the pudding. They do not talk or share stories.
   b. "Mama raised me without language." The speaker is not fluent in her grandmother's language. Unable to communicate with her grandmother, she loses her cultural roots and history. The speaker may also be suggesting that she did not learn to be comfortable using either language.
   c. "I feel I am a captive / aboard the refugee ship / . . . that will never dock." The speaker is stranded between two cultures and does not feel a part of either one.

**B.** (6 points each)
1. b
2. c
3. d
4. a
5. c

**C.** (20 points; students should answer one of the two)
1. Answers will vary but should reflect students' understanding that the speaker's mother

a. expects her children not only to be grateful for the food that is given to them but also to convey their appreciation for each and every bite.
b. grew up eating meals that provided little more than nourishment ("dinner was not a feast").
c. has known people, such as the Perez family, who survived by finding scraps of food in garbage cans.

Students who think that the mother's expectations are reasonable might say that she only expects her children to be grateful for the things they have that others need and do without, that she never had as a child, or that she herself feels grateful for.

Students who think that the mother's expectations are unreasonable might say that
a. it is unfair to expect children not to take for granted what is common or routine to them. This is hard enough for adults to do.
b. her attitude toward food is learned from her own personal experience. Her children's experiences are quite different. It should not surprise her that her children do not share her attitude.
c. her behavior forces her children to display a false "gesture." They must pretend to feel something that they do not understand fully, which makes them feel guilty for feeling hungry.
d. she seems to resent what her children have as compared with what she had.

2. Answers will vary. Students might describe the mood as
a. isolated.
b. lost and lonely.
c. regretful.

Students might say that one or more of these moods is created by
a. the simile the poet uses in the first line. It creates feelings of loneliness and isolation.
b. her feeling that she was raised without language. She cannot communicate with anyone.
c. her reflection in the mirror. It does not help her connect with any culture. She sees "bronze skin, black hair," but they do not tell her about who she is.
d. the two lines at the end of the poem. The same line is printed in English and then Spanish. The use of two languages reinforces the idea that she does not feel she belongs to either culture.

**D.** (20 points) Answers will vary widely, depending on students' personal experiences, situations, and viewpoints. Accept any answers that address the concern of the question and are elaborated by examples or details from the literature or from life.

## Unit Five, Part Two Test
pp. 165–166

**A.** (5 points each)
1. a
2. c
3. d
4. c

**B.** (20 points) Notes will vary. A model answer for "Chicago" could include the following points:
  a. Unbridled optimism.
  b. Positive.
  c. The people work hard; they are undaunted by obstacles; and they are filled with pride, energy, and joy.

**C.** (20 points each; students should answer two of the three)
  1. Answers will vary. A model answer for Dexter Green in "Winter Dreams" and Lucinda Matlock follows.

The American Dream seems to be an illusion for Dexter Green in that
  a. he has worked hard to become a success, but his success does not seem to satisfy or fulfill him.
  b. he has gone to the best schools, joined the best clubs, bought the best clothes, and seems to have met all the right people, but he has achieved only the business success aspect of the American dream.
  c. he has not found love and does not have a family.
  d. as long as Judy Jones is still beautiful, his "winter dreams" and idealism are alive; when he hears that her beauty has faded, he is crushed. He knows that his own dreams have faded as well, and he can never go back.

The American Dream seems to have been a reality for Lucinda Matlock in that she
  a. was married for 70 years and raised 12 children.
  b. was rewarded for her hard work and devotion to family with a long, full, happy life.
  c. appreciated and made good use of America's natural bounty.
  d. was a very strong person who loved life and had an optimistic attitude.

  2. Answers will vary. A model answer for Mr. Chang in "In the American Society" and the people who wear the mask in "We Wear the Mask" follows.

Mr. Chang represents what it means to be an American in that he
  a. works hard to succeed in business.
  b. remains true to his principles.
  c. bends the rules and challenges authority.
  d. takes responsibility for those less fortunate.
  e. cares little about what others think of him.
  f. tries to be a good person.
  g. is devoted to his family and employees.

The people who "wear the mask" do not represent what it means to be an American in that they
  a. hide their individuality.
  b. avoid risk.
  c. don't demand their right to equal treatment.
  d. have given up on life.
  e. are pessimistic.
  f. view themselves as the victims of a hostile world.
  g. focus more on what the world has done to them than on how they might act on the world.
  h. do little if anything to remedy their problems or improve the conditions that have led them to wear the mask.

  3. Answers will vary. A model answer for Dexter in "Winter Dreams" and the writer in "America and I" follows.

What matters most to Dexter seems to
  a. be holding on to the dream of one day possessing Judy.
  b. provide him with a sense of hope and the feeling that he is still alive and that his life holds wondrous possibilities.
  c. devastate him when he loses it.

What matters most to the narrator of "America and I" seems to
  a. be expressing herself through her work.
  b. control every aspect of her life. Unable to find a creative outlet for her feelings through domestic, sweatshop, and factory work, she becomes alienated from others and disappointed in America.
  c. give her great satisfaction once she is able to achieve it.
  d. make her feel guilty and saddened by the idea that others are not as lucky as she.

**D.** (20 points) Notes will vary. A model answer for Dexter in "Winter Dreams" and "Richard Cory" follows.

Dexter is welcomed or accepted
  a. by the upper classes.
  b. because he works hard to be accepted, appears to share their values and interests, is very wealthy, earns their respect as a businessman, and, in some cases, could be a respectable match for their daughters.

Richard Cory is excluded
  a. from the townspeople.
  b. because he is wealthier and more refined than they are; because they see him as being "above" or superior to them, and, perhaps, because he seems to make no attempt to bridge the gap between them.

# Unit Six

## Selected Poems by Hughes
Selection Test, pp. 167–168
**A.** (15 points each) Notes will vary but should include points similar to the following:
  1. "I, Too"
     a. The theme suggests that someday white America will see African Americans without stereotypes that bring about prejudice and discrimination.
     b. The speaker's tone is assertive, defiant, and confident.
     c. The mood is one of pride, hope, and encouragement, suggesting that someday white America will have respect and appreciation for the beauty and talents of African Americans.
  2. "Harlem"
     a. The theme focuses on what can happen if a dream is not allowed to be fulfilled. It might dry up, fester, stink, crust over, sag, or explode.
     b. The speaker's tone is one of frustration and anger.
     c. The mood is one of seriousness and urgency, suggesting that the dream must be fulfilled. Failing to fulfill the dream may have awful and serious consequences—for the people of Harlem and for others.
  3. "The Weary Blues"
     a. The theme concerns the blues, which are about suffering, surviving, and communicating that story to others.
     b. The speaker's tone is one of respect and appreciation.
     c. The mood is pessimistic, but the speaker's tone adds a more upbeat feeling in appreciation of the music and the musician.
**B.** (5 points each)
  1. a
  2. c
  3. a
**C.** (20 points; students should answer one of the two)
  1. Answers will vary but should include points similar to the following:
     a. The similes are all negative. They describe the dream as dying (drying up, festering, stinking, crusting over, sagging).
     b. The last line is different because it does not complete the pattern of similes used in the other lines. "Or does it explode" *like*–? The reader must complete the simile in his or her own mind.
     c. With the last line, the mood of the poem changes from the dream—and the dreamers—being passive to being active and potentially aggressive.

  2. Answers will vary. Students who feel that the two moods are quite different might include ideas similar to the following:
     a. The musician sings about loneliness, troubles, weariness, lack of fulfillment, and a wish for death.
     b. The mood of the musician's verses is melancholy, depressing, sad, lonely, or pessimistic.
     c. The musician's performance seems to have the opposite effect on the speaker of the poem, who is drawn in, nurtured, enchanted, and carried away by the scene.
     d. The poem's celebration of the blues creates a mood of intimacy, satisfaction, subdued joy, or quiet celebration.
  Students who feel that the two moods are very similar might include ideas similar to the following:
     a. The musician seems to lead the life he sings about. He plays music all night by himself and then goes home where no one appears to have been waiting for him. The blues continue to play in his head while he sleeps like "a man that's dead."
     b. The poem ends with this image, creating a depressing, sad, lonely, or pessimistic mood.
     c. The blues are made up of elements of suffering, survival, and social communication. The speaker is familiar with these emotions and appreciates the musician's talent for playing the blues. The feelings he expresses could be the same as the speaker's feelings.
**D.** (20 points) Answers will vary widely, depending on students' personal experiences, situations, and viewpoints. Accept any answers that address the concern of the question and are elaborated by examples or details from the literature or from life.

## When the Negro Was in Vogue
Selection Test, pp. 169–170
**A.** (20 points each)
  1. Notes will vary but should include points similar to the following:
     a. Hughes's use of words and phrases creates a sarcastic, resentful, and mocking tone.
     b. He describes an "influx" of whites "flooding" into the cabarets. He refers to the whites as "strangers [who] were given the best ringside tables." The word *ringside* suggests a circuslike atmosphere, which apparently was the case: whites sat and stared at the Negroes as if they were "amusing animals in a zoo."
  2. Notes will vary but should include points similar to the following:
     a. Hughes's use of words and phrases creates a tone not only of admiration, pride, and respect for Bentley's talents but also of regret that, to his way of thinking, she "sold out" later.

b. He describes Bentley as "worth discovering." He uses the words *amazing* and *powerful* to describe her music, which has a "continuous underbeat of jungle rhythm" as she plays, "sliding from one song to another." At the same time, he uses words that reveal how critical he is of her choices. She "got famous, acquired an accompanist, . . . along with conscious vulgarity."

**B.** (5 points each)
1. b
2. d
3. a
4. c

**C.** (20 points; students should answer one of the two)
1. Answers will vary but should include points similar to the following:
   a. The mood is one of excitement: Harlem is the center of a cultural renaissance. African Americans are finally being recognized and respected in the arts. The influence of African-American musicians and writers is changing the direction of American culture. With his descriptions of *Shuffle Along* and the artists Gladys Bentley and Josephine Baker, Hughes fills the reader with a sense of pride.
   b. At the same time, the mood conveys a sense of injustice. African Americans still face stereotyping, prejudice, and discrimination. Owners of places like the Cotton Club barred people of their own race from entering. Hughes's use of specific details passes on to the reader the sense that the white audiences were intruders into the culture. They did not contribute to it; they merely came to watch.
2. Answers will vary but should include points similar to the following:
   a. The opening paragraph seems more serious and formal than the last. The first paragraph formally introduces the serious subject—the black Renaissance. He uses the words *scintillating* and *vogue* instead of the more common *clever* and *fad*.
   b. The last paragraph is very casual and warm. He uses the words and phrases *wrote lots of; ate fried fish and pig's foot;* had *liquid refreshment;* he hears *laughter;* and he *feels the floor shaking* as the dancers dance.
   c. His choice of words and phrases in the beginning suggests that he wants to present the subject seriously and make a case for the admirable artists and accomplishments in Harlem at the time. At the end, he is recalling his own memories and expressing personal views of how he felt.

**D.** (20 points) Answers will vary widely, depending on students' personal experiences, situations, and viewpoints. Accept any answers that address the concern of the question and are elaborated by examples or details from the literature or from life.

## My City/Any Human to Another
Selection Test, pp. 171–172

**A.** (8 points each)
1. Notes will vary. Most students will suggest that the question raised is: "What am I going to miss most when it's time for me to die?"
2. Notes will vary. Most students will suggest that the answer is: "Manhattan."

**B.** (5 points each)
1. a
2. d
3. b
4. a

**C.** (8 points each) Notes will vary but should include points similar to the following:
1. Like a Petrarchan sonnet, "My City" has a two-part structure consisting of an octave and a sestet. The octave poses a question and the sestet provides an answer.
2. In the octave of a Petrarchan sonnet, the rhyme scheme generally is *abbaabba*. In the sestet, it is generally *cdecde, cdcdcd,* or a variation. In "My City," the rhyme scheme differs from the Petrarchan model. It is *abbacddc* in the octave and *efefgg* in the sestet.
3. Like the Petrarchan sonnet, "My City" is written in iambic pentameter. Each line has five feet made up of two syllables; the first syllable is unstressed and the second stressed.

**D.** (20 points; students should answer one of the two)
1. Answers will vary. Students might say that the speaker appreciates Manhattan's
   a. liveliness, excitement ("the thrill that comes / From being of her a part").
   b. diversity ("Her shining towers, her avenues, her slums—").
   c. people or overcrowded conditions ("Her crowds").
   d. power ("Her throbbing force").
   Other ideas should be supported with appropriate details from the poem.
2. Answers will vary but should include points similar to the following:
   a. The title states that the poem's words could be spoken by any human being to any other, an assertion of the connectedness of all humanity.
   b. The quoted lines suggest that all are bound together by the experience of grief and suffering; each must be touched by the sorrow of the other, and wear it like a crown.
   c. The crown could suggest the dignity humans achieve in sharing each other's sorrow.

The image of the crown may also suggest to some students the crown of thorns worn by the suffering Christ.
**E.** (20 points) Answers will vary widely, depending on students' personal experiences, situations, and viewpoints. Accept any answers that address the concern of the question and are elaborated by examples or details from the literature or from life.

## If We Must Die/A Black Man Talks of Reaping
Selection Test, pp. 173–174
**A.** (10 points each) Notes will vary but should be similar to the following.
1. If we have to die, let's not be slaughtered like animals.
2. If we have to die, let's do so with honor.
3. We must fight bravely despite the odds against us.
4. We will die proudly because we will die fighting back.
**B.** (8 points each)
1. c
2. c
3. b
4. b
**C.** (14 points; students should answer one of the two)
1. Answers will vary. Students who feel that "If We Must Die" is more relevant to racial issues today might say that
   a. "If We Must Die" recognizes the violent and life-threatening nature of racism to a much greater extent than "A Black Man Talks of Reaping" does.
   b. African Americans and other minority groups are caught in a struggle for existence, and McKay's message is that they must face that fact and fight back.
Students who feel that "A Black Man Talks of Reaping" is more relevant to racial issues today might say that
   a. racism isn't practiced as violently and openly as it once was through oppressive laws and mob action. The battle for equality is being conducted mainly in courtrooms, legislatures, and people's minds.
   b. "If We Must Die" overemphasizes the need of minorities today to protect and defend themselves from physical attack and mob action.
   c. "A Black Man Talks of Reaping" expresses a bitterness similar to that of many people today who have worked hard, have believed in (or tried to believe in) the possibilities for change and justice, and have seen little or nothing result from their efforts.
   d. "A Black Man Talks of Reaping" also reflects the economic injustice that is more clearly a threat to minorities today than is the violence of hate groups.
2. Answers will vary but should include points similar to the following:
   a. In the first stanza, the speaker is saying that despite

his fears of wasted efforts and failure, he has worked hard and saved to gain security.
   b. In the second stanza, the speaker is saying that he has gained very little in comparison to the enormous efforts he has put forth.
   c. In the third stanza, the speaker is saying that both the fruit of his efforts and his ability to continue those efforts has been appropriated or stolen by white Americans. It is no wonder, then, that there is very little for his children: little for them to possess, little means for them to achieve something for themselves, and little joy in their lives.
**D.** (14 points) Answers will vary widely, depending on students' personal experiences, situations, and viewpoints. Accept any answers that address the concern of the question and are elaborated by examples or details from the literature or from life.

## How It Feels to Be Colored Me
Selection Test, pp. 175–176
**A.** (5 points each) Notes and examples of comments from the essay will vary but should include points similar to the following:
1. In contrast, Hurston says, "Not only did I enjoy the show, but I didn't mind the actors knowing that I liked it." The young Zora sat on the gatepost and greeted the Northerners passing through, and sang and danced for them. Hurston's comments emphasize how different she was from the "timid" blacks; she was confident and bold, and she enjoyed herself.
2. "It is a bully adventure and worth all that I have paid through my ancestors for it." Hurston does not feel depressed about slavery and does not need morbid reminders of it; she feels free to enjoy life, and it is "thrilling to think" that she has such opportunities for "glory."
3. "No dark ghost thrusts its leg against mine in bed." Hurston does not feel the oppressive guilt that she suspects her white neighbors feel; she does not suffer from the weight of past injustices.
4. "I dance wildly inside myself; I yell within, I whoop. . . ." Hurston feels the rhythm of jazz intensely and revels in the primal emotions it evokes, but her "white friend" calmly taps his fingers and says the music is good. Hurston realizes the width of the gap between her friend's "whiteness" and how "colored" she really is.
**B.** (10 points each)
1. d
2. c
3. a
4. d

**C.** (4 points each)
1. a
2. b
3. c
4. c
5. a

**D.** (10 points; students should answer one of the two)
1. Answers will vary but should reflect students' understanding of Hurston's implication that, although skin colors may be different, people are pretty much alike on the inside. Students who agree might say that, regardless of skin color, people have similar
   a. physical needs for food, water, shelter, and so on.
   b. emotions such as joy, sorrow, and so on.
   c. problems such as sickness, loneliness, fear, and so on.

Students who disagree might say that, while the color of a person's skin does not matter,
   a. what is inside varies greatly from person to person because of differences in upbringing and life experience, as Hurston demonstrates in her anecdote about the jazz club.
   b. culture has a good deal to do with the values, beliefs, and desires that people have.
2. Answers will vary but should reflect students' understanding that
   a. Hurston's attitude toward slavery is accepting or matter-of-fact.
   b. Hurston feels that slavery "is the price [she] paid for civilization"—it was "worth all that [she has] paid through [her] ancestors for it."
   c. Hurston doesn't feel limited or disadvantaged by the legacy of slavery.
   d. Hurston's critics would likely feel that her attitude is too flippant, selfish, and short-sighted. They would see her attitude as showing too little respect and compassion for the agonies her ancestors suffered under slavery and revealing a shallow understanding of the ways in which slavery continued to affect African Americans of her own time.

In addition, students should include a personal response to Hurston's attitude. Some students may approve of her attitude because it reflects a refusal to be
   a. limited by history.
   b. defined or dictated to by others.
   c. victimized.
   d. dishonest for the sake of political correctness or the feelings of others.

Other students might disapprove of her attitude because it
   a. is shallow and immature.
   b. lacks compassion.
   c. is unrealistic.
   d. is selfish and ungrateful.
   e. belittles other African Americans.

**E.** (10 points) Answers will vary widely, depending on students' personal experiences, situations, and viewpoints. Accept any answers that address the concern of the question and are elaborated by examples or details from the literature or from life.

**My Dungeon Shook: Letter to My Nephew on the One Hundredth Anniversary of the Emancipation**
Selection Test, pp. 177–178

**A.** (30 points) Notes will vary. For quotation *a*, students might suggest that it communicates one or more of the following points:
   a. Conditions in American ghettos are very much like those in London more than 100 years earlier.
   b. Poverty and brutal exploitation are as prevalent in modern society as they were 100 years ago.
   c. Social progress has been slow and conditions for African Americans remain unacceptable.

For quotation *b*, students might suggest that it communicates one or more of the following points:
   a. There is strength to be gained from the example of others.
   b. One's family has a good deal to do with who one is.

For quotation *c*, students might suggest that it communicates one or more of the following points:
   a. Black culture is equal in value to white culture.
   b. African-American culture should be a source of pride and strength.
   c. Baldwin's nephew has something important to communicate to the world.
   d. There is always hope and all things are possible, even when things look very bleak.

For quotation *d*, students might suggest that it communicates one or more of the following points:
   a. African Americans are no freer than they were when the Emancipation Proclamation was issued.
   b. White Americans value their own experiences far more highly than they do those of black Americans.
   c. Racial equality remains a goal rather than a reality.
   d. The United States has a long way to go before racial equality is achieved.

**B.** (5 points each)
1. c
2. a
3. c
4. c

**C.** (4 points each)
1. a
2. b
3. a
4. a
5. b

**D.** (15 points; students should answer one of the two)
  1. Answers will vary. Students might say that, by addressing the open letter to his nephew, Baldwin
     a. adds a personal element, making his thoughts on racism more immediate and moving and allowing him to express his feelings more directly and naturally.
     b. speaks to all young African-American males, a population that was, and still is, especially threatened by the dangers of inner-city life.
     c. powerfully illustrates his ideas about the importance for African Americans of devotion and loyalty to family.
Other ideas should be supported with appropriate reasons or reference to the letter.
  2. Answers will vary. Students who think that Baldwin would hold his nephew most responsible might say that Baldwin
     a. clearly expects great things of his nephew and believes that he has every hope of becoming a good man.
     b. emphasizes how much the family has tried to insulate the nephew from the relentless attack of racism.
     c. makes no excuses for any criminal or morally reprehensible behavior—whether it be that of whites or blacks.
Students who think that Baldwin would hold the system of racism most responsible might say that
     a. because Baldwin believes that his nephew is a good person with unlimited potential, Baldwin would look to outside influences on the boy's life.
     b. Baldwin wouldn't be likely to blame the family, as he emphasizes how much they have loved and tried to protect the nephew.
     c. Baldwin feels that racism creates ghettos, and ghettos destroy hope and limit opportunities. He would probably say that drugs, gangs, and crime appear attractive only to people without hope and opportunity.
Other ideas should be supported with appropriate reference to the selection.

**E.** (15 points) Answers will vary widely, depending on students' personal experiences, situations, and viewpoints. Accept any answers that address the concern of the question and are elaborated by examples or details from the literature or from life.

### Selected Poems by Brooks
Selection Test, pp. 179–180
**A.** (5 points each) Notes will vary but should include points similar to the following:

  1. The repetition of the word *or* emphasizes the idea that the world is filled with simple pleasures.
  2. The use of the period after "No" and after "that" in the same line calls attention to a change in the subject or focus of the poem, from the child's simple pleasures to an explanation of a more complex idea—that the child reaches out without fear and without concern for the consequences.
  3. This alliteration (and internal rhyme) stresses in a kind of humorous way that the child has had many cuts and bruises.
  4. The personification of "Blackness" implies self-awareness and determination.
  5. The repetition of the word *the* emphasizes the idea that black people are a diverse group.
  6. The unorthodox capitalization of "YOU," "COLORED," "NEGRO," "INDian," and other words calls attention to the idea that all black people, despite their diversity, are connected ("our fundamental bone").

**B.** (6 points each)
  1. a
  2. b
  3. c
  4. b
  5. c
  6. a
  7. d

**C.** (14 points; students should answer one of the two)
  1. Answers will vary but should reflect students' understanding that while both the speaker and the child love the same kind of simple pleasures,
     a. the child has yet to learn that reaching often leads to pain and failure. As a result, the child is not afraid to reach for things or take risks (line 10).
     b. the parent has learned this lesson and is, therefore, more reluctant to reach for things.
In addition, students might say that this difference between the speaker and the child makes the speaker feel
     a. glad for the child's fearlessness and hopeful that the child will keep reaching even as he begins to experience limitations and failures.
     b. saddened by his or her lack of the child's faith or courage.
     c. inspired or emboldened by the child's example.
Other ideas should be supported with appropriate reasons or reference to the poem.
  2. Answers will vary. Most students will find that the title is suggestive of both meanings, noting that the poem
     a. puts forth such basic principles as the ideas that black people are powerful, diverse, and connected to each other, and that they need to comprehend what it means to be black and take pride in being black.

b. seems to be specifically directed at those blacks who most need to learn and take to heart these principles and ideas.

c. prepares blacks with the basic knowledge and understanding needed to begin using black strength to strengthen blacks (second stanza).

d. invites or calls on blacks to unite in an effort to use black strength to strengthen blacks.

Students who believe that Brooks intended the title to suggest only one or neither of these meanings should support their views with appropriate reasons and reference to the poem.

**D.** (14 points) Answers will vary widely, depending on students' personal experiences, situations, and viewpoints. Accept any answers that address the concern of the question and are elaborated by examples or details from the literature or from life.

## Thoughts on the African-American Novel

Selection Test, p. 181

**A.** (30 points) Notes will vary. For the novel, answers should reflect an understanding of Morrison's argument that

a. the industrial revolution gave rise to a new class of people, the middle class.

b. the middle class had no art form of its own.

c. the middle class needed an art form that would help it to deal with the social changes that were going on at the time. They needed to know how to behave, what was good, what was bad, and what their responsibilities were.

For the African-American novel, answers should reflect an understanding of Morrison's argument that

a. the African-American traditional art form of music was absorbed into the larger American culture. Because it was no longer a distinctly African-American art form, it had to be replaced with one that would speak directly to the African-American experience.

b. the African-American oral tradition was weakened by social change; as people moved to the city, parents stopped handing down stories to their children.

c. the African-American novel was needed to provide African Americans with information about how to behave, what was good, what was bad, and what their responsibilities were in changing times.

**B.** (15 points each)

1. d
2. d

**C.** (20 points; students should answer one of the two)

1. Answers will vary. Students might say that Morrison

views the role of the African-American writer as that of

a. a teacher or guide. She notes that the African-American novel arose out of a need for guidance during changing times.

b. an inspirational leader. It is important to her that her novels inspire and involve the reader "in the same way that a Black preacher requires his congregation to speak, to join him in the sermon . . . "

Students who believe that Morrison sees her role as being the same as or very similar to that of a white writer might note that Morrison seems to believe that all

a. art forms arise out of similar human needs, such as the need for moral instruction and information.

b. writers have a responsibility to address the needs of their audiences or, at least, an interest in addressing those needs.

Students who believe that Morrison sees her role as being different from that of a white writer should support that view with appropriate reference to the essay.

2. Answers will vary but should reflect students' understanding that Morrison believes that novels should

a. inspire, enlighten, inform, and guide readers.

b. deeply affect readers' emotions.

c. connect to readers' lives.

d. involve and engage readers.

**D.** (20 points) Answers will vary widely, depending on students' personal experiences, situations, and viewpoints. Accept any answers that address the concern of the question and are elaborated by examples or details from the literature or from life.

## Unit Six, Part One Test

pp. 183–184

**A.** (5 points each)

1. a
2. b
3. d
4. c

**B.** (20 points) Notes will vary. A model answer for "Life for My Child Is Simple" could suggest that the strong feeling is hope because the son

a. is fearless.

b. doesn't limit himself.

c. has an optimistic outlook.

d. might retain these feelings, beliefs, and behaviors as he matures.

e. might, as a result, lead a fulfilling life.

**C.** (20 points each; students should answer two of the four)

1. Answers will vary. A model answer for "The Weary Blues" and "My City" follows.

"The Weary Blues" fulfills most of these needs in that
  a. its subject is a blues musician and the effect of his music on himself and on the speaker.
  b. its rhythm imitates the distinctive rhythm of blues music.
  c. the blues musician in the poem pours his heart and soul into the music.
  d. it freely expresses the depression of the blues musician, the cathartic effect on the musician of playing the music, and the thrilling effect of the music on the speaker.

"My City" fulfills most of these needs in that it
  a. celebrates the sights, sounds, and smells of a place.
  b. strongly suggests the gusto or "throbbing force" of that place.
  c. freely expresses "the thrill that comes" from being a part of that place.
  d. freely expresses the speaker's despair at the thought of never again being a part of that place.

2. Answers will vary. A model answer for "I, Too" follows.
Both "How It Feels to Be Colored Me" and "I, Too" express
  a. the defiance of people who refuse to be limited or destroyed by racism.
  b. pride in themselves as individuals and as blacks.
  c. the belief that the people who reject them hurt themselves most of all.
  d. the need to shrug off efforts to restrict or define them.
  e. a sense of humor.
  f. an optimistic outlook on life.

3. Answers will vary. A model answer for "Any Human to Another" follows.
Both "My Dungeon Shook: Letter to My Nephew . . . " and "Any Human to Another" express a
  a. belief in the interconnectedness of all people.
  b. desire for people to come together and share with one another.
  c. belief in the need to sympathize with others.
  d. concern for human dignity.
  e. concern for taking personal responsibility for oneself and for others.

4. Answers will vary. A model answer for Langston Hughes ("The Weary Blues") and Zora Neale Hurston ("How It Feels to Be Colored Me") follows.
Like Morrison in "Thoughts on the African-American Novel,"
  a. Hughes shows an interest in a traditional African-American art form. His poem reflects his interest in the blues, its rhythms, and its effects on those to whom it speaks.
  b. Hurston shows an interest in a traditional African-American art form. Her essay includes an anecdote about the differences between her reactions to jazz and those of her white friends.

  c. Hurston show an interest in oral literature. Her essay has a conversational tone and includes stories from her past.

**D.** (20 points) Notes will vary. A model answer for "Thoughts on the African-American Novel" follows. "Thoughts on the African-American Novel" reflects pride in African Americans and their contributions to American culture in that it
  a. discusses the birth of the African-American novel.
  b. reflects a respect for traditional African-American art forms.

## Selected Poems by Frost
Selection Test, pp. 185–186
**A.** (14 points each)
1. Notes will vary. Students who choose night might suggest that it represents
  a. solitude, in that the speaker is completely alone and seems to prefer that aloneness to the point of avoiding even eye contact with the watchman.
  b. misery, sorrow, unhappiness, or alienation, in that the speaker, who is "acquainted with the night," seems to be feeling all of these things.
Students who choose the watchman might suggest that he represents
  a. society or humanity, in that he is the only person with whom the speaker even remotely comes into contact.
  b. human contact or intimacy, in that the speaker, who is very much alone, avoids making any kind of contact with him.
Other ideas should be supported with appropriate reasons and references to the poem.
2. Notes will vary. Students who choose the wall might suggest that it represents
  a. the barriers to intimacy that people put up between themselves and others, because of suspicion and distrust.
  b. any type of unnatural barriers, such as national borders, cultural barriers, and so on, that prevent people from interacting with one another and serve no purpose necessary to life.
Students who choose the saying might suggest that it represents
  a. tradition or mindless acceptance of tradition, in that the neighbor accepts his father's idea without giving much thought to its relevance to him or to its usefulness.
  b. ignorance, suspicion, and distrust, in that it reflects these feelings and is what causes the neighbor to desire that the fence be mended.
Other ideas should be supported with appropriate reasons and reference to the poem.

3. Notes will vary. Students who choose the boy might suggest that he represents
   a. self-interest, in that he is the only one who seems to care deeply about his death.
   b. the human condition or victimization, in that life is unpredictable and accidents can happen to everyone without warning.

Students who choose the buzz saw might suggest that it represents
   a. fate, in that it is what causes the boy's death.
   b. cruelty and brutality, in that it acts without concern for the innocent boy.
   c. death or the nature of accidents, in that it strikes impersonally and without warning.

**B.** (4 points each)
   1. b
   2. c
   3. c
   4. a
   5. a
   6. b
   7. a

**C.** (15 points; students should answer one of the two)
   1. Answers will vary. Students might say that the darkness is
      a. fear, suspicion, distrust.
      b. ignorance, tradition, or unwillingness to examine values and customs.

In support, students might note that the speaker
      a. says that the darkness in which the neighbor moves is "not of woods only and the shade of trees," suggesting that the darkness is symbolic or metaphorical.
      b. pictures the neighbor as an "old-stone savage," an image suggesting fear, suspicion, and distrust as well as mindless devotion to tradition.
      c. says that the neighbor "will not go behind his father's saying," or will not question or explore whether what was right for his father is right for him.

   2. Answers will vary. Students might say that the poem suggests that accidents
      a. are shocking and surprising (all is calm and it is just about quitting time when the boy's accident occurs).
      b. are confusing and difficult to understand (the speaker isn't sure how the accident happened).
      c. are frightening (the boy seems terrified).
      d. aren't always avoidable (the boy doesn't seem to have done anything to cause the accident).
      e. seem to be a natural part of life (the others go on with their lives as soon as the boy dies).

   f. can be tragic and without meaning (an innocent boy with a long future ahead of him is killed without purpose).

In addition, many students will find that the poem is saying that only the individual is capable of fully realizing and appreciating the value of his or her own life. In support, students might note that
   a. the boy becomes desperate when he sees his life spilling away.
   b. the boy is the only one who really seems to care about his death.
   c. the other people seem indifferent toward the boy's death.

Other students may find that the poem is saying that, however unfeeling it may seem, life goes on, as it must. In support, students might note that
   a. the doctor and other people at the scene are troubled by the boy's death, but there is nothing more that they can do for him.
   b. the continuity of life—the "affairs" of the living—is inevitably more important than the death of one individual.

Other ideas should be supported with appropriate reference to the poem.

**D.** (15 points) Answers will vary widely, depending on students' personal experiences, situations, and viewpoints. Accept any answers that address the concern of the question and are elaborated by examples or details from the literature or from life.

### The Death of the Hired Man
Selection Test, pp. 187–188
**A.** (8 points each) Notes and examples will vary but may include points similar to the following:
   1. a. Mary is particularly sympathetic to Silas and his relationship with the young Harold Wilson. "After so many years he still keeps finding / Good arguments he sees he might have used. / I sympathize. I know just how it feels / To think of the right thing to say too late."
      b. Mary is also sympathetic to Silas and his relationship with his brother and his determination to preserve his pride. "Do you think / If he had any pride in claiming kin / Or anything he looked for from his brother, / He'd keep so still about him all this time?"
   2. a. Mary is kind and thoughtful because she immediately takes in Silas and cares for him when she finds him huddled by the barn door.
      b. Mary makes up a bed for Silas. There is no question in Mary's mind about where Silas will stay. She is aware that he is in bad health, and she intends to help him.

3. a. Mary is persuasive when she urges Warren not to laugh at Silas's plan and not to hurt his feelings.
   b. She works to soften Warren's initial reaction, which is to throw Silas out. "She put out her hand . . . / As if she played unheard some tenderness / That wrought on him beside her in the night. / 'Warren,' she said, 'he has come home to die.'"

**B.** (5 points each)
1. d
2. c
3. d
4. a

**C.** (4 points each)
1. b
2. c
3. b
4. a
5. a

**D.** (20 points; students should answer one of the two)
1. Answers will vary but should include points similar to the following:
   a. Silas is a broken man. He set down no roots when he was younger, jumping from job to job and from farm to farm. Warren gave him work during lean times when all he could pay was room and board and then when it came time for haying (the only thing that Silas could do well), Silas deserted Warren for someone who offered him pocket money. Silas had ". . . nothing to look backward to with pride, and nothing to look forward to with hope. . ." He has probably returned to Warren and Mary's farm because he knows how kind Mary is. She would not turn him away.
2. Answers will vary but may include points similar to the following:
   a. Frost has created striking visual images that help students imagine the scenes.
   b. The poem is a narrative; it tells a story with a beginning, middle, and dramatic conclusion.
   c. The majority of the poem is in dialogue, and it is written in iambic pentameter (as were Shakespeare's plays), which sound much like ordinary speech.
   d. The poem includes several conflicts in the relationships among the characters, which adds interest to the "plot."

**E.** (16 points) Answers will vary widely, depending on students' personal experiences, situations, and viewpoints. Accept any answers that address the concern of the question and are elaborated by examples or details from the literature or from life.

## The End of Something
Selection Test, pp. 189–190

**A.** (20 points each) Notes will vary widely. Model answers follow.
1. Relationship; Nick and Marjorie are in a relationship and it is that which actually comes to an end in the story.
2. Illusion; Nick suggests that Marjorie knows what is wrong with him (and, by extension, that their relationship is ending) but doesn't want to face the reality.

**B.** (10 points each)
1. b
2. b

**C.** (20 points; students should answer one of the two)
1. Answers will vary. Students could say that Hemingway does not directly reveal
   a. the thoughts, feelings, or motivations of any of the characters.
   b. information about the characters' ages and appearances.
   c. how and why Nick and Marjorie fell in love.
   d. exactly what Nick feels "isn't fun any more," why he feels this way, and what Marjorie has to do with his unhappiness.
   e. who Bill is, the nature of his relationship with Nick, and why he appears to know so much about Nick and Marjorie.
   f. exactly what Nick wants in a life apart from Marjorie and what he plans to do next.
   Students might say that they like Hemingway's style because it
   a. is realistic and believable in that many things are left unexplained, just as they are in real life.
   b. made them use their own imaginations to fill in the blanks of the story.
   Students might say that they don't like Hemingway's style because it
   a. is confusing to read or understand without more help from the narration.
   b. leaves too many things unexplained.
2. Answers will vary, but most students will feel that Hemingway attempts to distance the reader because he apparently chose to
   a. use a style that offers very little direct information about, or explanation of, the characters' thoughts and feelings.
   b. use a third-person limited point of view from the perspective of a man who doesn't seem to truly understand what he is feeling, what might make him happy, and what his problem is with the woman in his life.

c. create a tone and mood similar to that felt by the characters in the story.

d. create characters incapable of directly expressing their deepest emotions and, thereby, eliciting the reader's sympathy.

e. create characters who understand each other so completely that they require very few words to communicate their thoughts and feelings to each other.

Students who feel that Hemingway attempted to encourage the reader's sympathy should support that view with reference to the story.

**D.** (20 points) Answers will vary widely, depending on students' personal experiences, situations, and viewpoints. Accept any answers that address the concern of the question and are elaborated by examples or details from the literature or from life.

## The Love Song of J. Alfred Prufrock
Selection Test, pp. 191–192

**A.** (6 points each)
1. Notes will vary. Students could note that the quotation suggests Prufrock
   a. is thoughtful, cautious, and responsible.
   b. wants something more from life.
   c. thinks too much, is too cautious, and assumes too much responsibility.
   d. is insecure, cowardly, and indecisive.
   e. looks for excuses to avoid taking action.
2. Notes will vary. Students could note that the quotation suggests Prufrock
   a. sees himself objectively, is honest with himself, and understands himself.
   b. may have given up on himself.
   c. views himself as ridiculous.
   d. takes refuge in self-mockery.
   e. regrets missed opportunities.
3. Notes will vary. Students could note that the quotation suggests Prufrock
   a. is imaginative.
   b. yearns for something better.
   c. sees himself objectively, is honest with himself, and understands himself.
   d. has given up on himself.
   e. feels left out and thinks he has little to look forward to.

**B.** (4 points each)
1. b
2. c
3. c
4. c

**C.** (6 points each)
1. Notes will vary. Students could suggest that Prufrock characterizes himself as being

a. like John the Baptist, in that he too has suffered, wept, fasted, and prayed.

b. like John the Baptist, in that he has, through his extreme self-consciousness, felt as if his own head had been served up on a platter because of a woman.

c. unlike John the Baptist, in that he lacks courage and strength of character.

2. Notes will vary. Students could suggest that Prufrock characterizes himself as being
   a. like Lazarus, in that his asking his question would be as remarkable and life-affirming as Lazarus's coming back from the dead.
   b. unlike Lazarus, in that he will never do anything so remarkable as to return from the dead.
   c. unlike Lazarus, in that his buried self will stay buried; he cannot bring himself to "tell you all" what he wants to say.

3. Notes will vary. Students could suggest that Prufrock characterizes himself as being
   a. like Hamlet, in that he is indecisive.
   b. unlike Hamlet, in that he lacks qualities that would make him heroic.
   c. unlike Hamlet, in that he is more suited to play a supporting role than a heroic one.

**D.** (4 points each)
1. c
2. b
3. b
4. c
5. b

**E.** (14 points; students should answer one of the two)
1. Answers will vary. Students might say Prufrock finally realizes that
   a. his fear is more overwhelming than his desire to ask the question.
   b. he is not heroic like John the Baptist, Lazarus, or Prince Hamlet.

In describing Prufrock's vision of his future, students might make points similar to the following:
   a. He will play a prudent, timid, dull, and unromantic role in life.
   b. His major decisions will involve such "underwhelming" issues as how to part his hair and whether to eat a peach.
   c. He will grow old and do the sorts of things, such as walking on the beach, that old men do.

2. Answers will vary. Students who think Eliot presents Prufrock as a unique individual might say that
   a. Prufrock is a particular character in a particular social setting, dealing with a particular personal crisis.
   b. Prufrock's inner thoughts and allusions are so peculiar that they make him unique.

Students who think Eliot presents Prufrock as a representative of modern life might say that both Prufrock and the people he associates with (or longs to associate with) demonstrate attributes that characterize many people in modern society, including

    a. pettiness.
    b. boredom.
    c. a judgmental attitude.
    d. preoccupation with trivial matters.
    e. indecisiveness.
    f. lack of courage.
    g. low self-esteem.
    h. excessive concern with others' perceptions of them.
    i. disconnection from tradition.
    j. craving for excitement and adventure.
    k. alienation from the noble or heroic.
    l. passivity, or the inability to commit to direct action.

Students who think Eliot presents Prufrock as both an individual and a representative of modern life might combine elements of the answers above.

**F.** (14 points) Answers will vary widely, depending on students' personal experiences, situations, and viewpoints. Accept any answers that address the concern of the question and are elaborated by examples or details from the literature or from life.

## The Jilting of Granny Weatherall

Selection Test, pp. 193–194

**A.** (10 points each) Notes will vary but should include points similar to the following:

  1. Inside Granny's mind:
    a. Granny senses that death is close, but she is convinced that it isn't time. She has already dealt with the issue of death, has lived, and has put it out of her mind.
    b. She thinks about all the work she still has to do, such as organizing, making sure no food goes to waste, and going through the old letters from George and John.
    c. As she thinks back on her life of hard work, pain and anguish creep into her mind as she remembers being jilted by George. Her memories now seem to open a floodgate. She recalls the details of the day, and they somehow mingle with Hapsy's death. As grief overcomes her, she dies ("blew out the light").
  2. Outside Granny's mind:
    a. The doctor has come to check on her.
    b. Both Cornelia and the doctor know that Granny is dying. (They are whispering in the background.)
    c. Cornelia sends for the other children, and they arrive.
    d. Father Connolly arrives, presumably to deliver last rites and comfort her and her family until the end.

**B.** (5 points each)
  1. a
  2. d
  3. c
  4. b

**C.** (4 points each)
  1. a
  2. b
  3. c
  4. c
  5. a

**D.** (20 points; students should answer one of the two)
  1. Answers will vary but should include points similar to the following:

Psychological insights:
    a. Granny refers to the pain of the "jilting" as "wounded vanity." As the story progresses, it becomes clear that it is more than wounded vanity. This pain has penetrated her very core— who and what she thought she was.
    b. Granny has spent her entire life trying to prove that George was wrong to jilt her. She says she has been happy, has had a wonderful husband, and has been blessed with children. She has had love and has given love. Despite a life devoted to spreading "out the plan of life and tuck[ing] in the edges orderly," the memory of George and that anguish are what surround and consume her in death. This pain overshadows everything else in her life.

Symbolic elements:
    a. Her name, "Weatherall," symbolizes her life. She has weathered all the hard times she had to endure.
    b. She says she must get up and pull down the shades to get some rest, but the shades were not pulled down. She cannot pull the shade down on her memories.
    c. As she faces death, the rosary (a symbol of religion) will not do. She needs something living to comfort her, so she holds on to Jimmy's fingers.
    d. The light from the lampshade represents Granny, and that light (life) is fading. At the end, overcome with grief, she blows out the light and lets go of her life.
  2. Answers will vary but should include points similar to the following:
    a. Her statement describes how she has lived her life and dealt with the sorrows and tragedies she faced. To her, life had to be dealt with by rolling up her sleeves, plunging into work, and refusing to think about the hardship and pain—as she did when she fenced 100 acres by herself ("That changed a woman").

b. Her experience with George was extremely painful. Working so hard that you "almost forgot what you were working for" was a way to block that pain.

**E.** (20 points) Answers will vary widely, depending on students' personal experiences, situations, and viewpoints. Accept any answers that address the concern of the question and are elaborated by examples or details from the literature or from life.

## The Man Who Was Almost a Man

Selection Test, pp. 195–196

**A.** (6 points each)

1. Notes will vary but could suggest that, to Dave, being a man means being
   a. respected, perhaps even feared.
   b. independent.
   c. acting in any way he sees fit.
   d. earning and keeping his own wages.

2. Notes will vary widely. Students who believe that Dave's level of maturity plays an important role in preventing him from being a man could suggest that
   a. his definition of manhood proves his immaturity.
   b. Dave lacks the self-control, integrity, inner strength, and sense of responsibility that it takes to be a mature man.

   Students who believe that Dave's level of maturity does not play an important role in preventing him from being a man will find it difficult, if not impossible, to support that view with reference to the story.

3. Notes will vary widely. Students who believe that Dave's parents play an important role in preventing him from being a man could suggest that
   a. they have raised him.
   b. they apparently have failed to instill in him those things that young men must be taught: self-control, integrity, and responsibility.
   c. beatings and threats are not the way to teach a child anything worth knowing.

   Students who believe that Dave's parents do not play an important role in preventing him from being a man could suggest that
   a. his mother's refusal to allow him to have a gun shows that she does not share his idea of manhood.
   b. their insisting that Dave tell the truth about, and pay for, the mule reveals that they have tried to teach Dave how to be a man.

4. Notes will vary widely. Students who believe that Dave's economic situation plays an important role in preventing him from being a man could suggest that
   a. it severely limits his options; he can work two years to pay for the mule or he can run away.

b. it makes it very difficult for him to achieve something he can take pride in and that others will respect.

Students who believe that Dave's economic situation does not play an important role in preventing him from being a man could suggest that there are many poverty-stricken men in this world who take pride in themselves and live up to their responsibilities.

5. Notes will vary widely. Students who believe that racism and the sharecropping system play an important role in preventing Dave from being a man could suggest that
   a. it is very difficult to learn how to make appropriate moral decisions in an immoral environment.
   b. both systems encourage dependency on white people.

   Students who believe that racism and the sharecropping system do not play an important role in preventing Dave from being a man could suggest that
   a. Dave's problems stem mainly from being treated like a child, a difficulty that he shares with most adolescents of all races and situations in life.
   b. Dave's problems stem mainly from his own failure to learn appropriate, mature behavior or from his own decision to reject that behavior.
   c. being a responsible, moral person may be difficult under such systems, but it is certainly not impossible.

**B.** (5 points each)
   1. b
   2. b
   3. a
   4. a

**C.** (10 points each)
   1. Notes will vary widely. Students might suggest that the consequences for Dave might include
      a. freedom and greater opportunities for happiness and success in life.
      b. being alone in the world, cut off from his family and his home.
      c. being tracked down by the law.
      d. learning to run away from his problems rather than to resolve them.
   2. Notes will vary. Students might suggest that the consequences for Dave's parents might include
      a. public humiliation and scorn.
      b. having to pay off the debt by going hungry, giving up their home and possessions, working longer hours, and putting their younger son to work.
      c. feelings of grief, guilt, and anxiety over his disappearance and having to take on his debt.
      d. the loss of Dave's income.

3. Notes will vary. Students might suggest that the consequences for Hawkins include
   a. the loss of $50.
   b. the loss of a good worker.
   c. nothing.
**D.** (10 points; students should answer one of the two)
 1. Answers will vary but should include points similar to the following:
    a. Wright uses verbal irony by playing on the meanings of the word *man.*
    b. The title could be taken to mean, "The young man who was almost a grown-up man," suggesting the 17-year-old Dave, who was almost of an age at which one is considered an adult.
    c. The title could also be taken to mean, "The male person who blew his chance to become a mature, responsible man," suggesting the opportunities to be responsible and mature that Dave passes by in favor of immaturity and irresponsibility.
 2. Answers will vary widely. Students who feel that the punishment is fair might say that
    a. there is no indication in the story that Hawkins demands more money than the mule is worth.
    b. Hawkins doesn't demand that interest be paid on the debt, even though it will take Dave two years to pay it off.
    c. Hawkins doesn't threaten to call in the law, even though Dave behaved negligently and lied about what he did.
    d. shooting the mule was an accident, but, even so, Dave was behaving irresponsibly and his action resulted in the mule's death, a loss to Hawkins, and his parents' embarrassment.
Students who feel that the punishment is unfair could include points similar to the following:
    a. Dave killed the mule by accident.
    b. In most work situations, employers are expected to absorb the costs of equipment that is accidentally damaged or destroyed by employees.
    c. Hawkins is in a much better position than Dave is to absorb the financial loss that the mule represents.
    d. Hawkins shows no mercy; he is fully aware of what the mule will cost Dave.
**E.** (10 points) Answers will vary widely, depending on students' personal experiences, situations, and viewpoints. Accept any answers that address the concern of the question and are elaborated by examples or details from the literature or from life.

**Mirror/Self in 1958**
Selection Test, pp. 197–198
**A.** (15 points each)
 1. Notes will vary widely, depending on the image or example of figurative language that students choose to discuss. A model answer includes the following points:
    a. Image: "In me she has drowned a young girl."
    b. Tone: calm, matter-of-fact, indifferent, ironic.
    c. Effect: disgust, uneasiness, sympathy, surprise, sorrow, aversion.
 2. Notes will vary widely, depending on the image or example of figurative language that students choose to discuss. A model answer includes the following points:
    a. Image: a doll-like woman "walled in solid by their noise."
    b. Tone: alienated, bitter, disgusted, anguished, ironic.
    c. Effect: uneasiness, sympathy, aversion, pain, disgust, surprise, shock.
**B.** (4 points each)
 1. b
 2. d
 3. a
 4. d
 5. d
**C.** (10 points each)
 1. Notes will vary but should suggest some of the following:
    a. The woman bending over it.
    b. The woman searching in its surface.
    c. The woman's tears and agitation.
    d. The woman coming and going.
    e. The woman's back (as she faces the candle and the moon).
    f. The woman growing old.
 2. Notes will vary but could suggest the following feelings and concerns:
    a. The woman's concern about her appearance.
    b. Her belief that appearance accurately reflects "what she really is."
    c. Her dread of growing old.
    d. Her distress at her appearance.
    e. Her lack of confidence in herself.
    f. Her disgust with herself.
**D.** (15 points; students should answer one of the two)
 1. Answers will vary. Most students will probably say that the woman cannot find what she really is in the mirror because the mirror
    a. can only reflect outward appearances, such as the effects of growing and aging, styles of clothing and grooming, and expressions of emotion, such as tears and laughter.
    b. cannot reflect inner realities, such as loving and being loved, education and intelligence, emotional maturity, satisfaction, fulfillment, disappointment, and disillusionment.

c. cannot feel for the woman, and therefore cannot accurately reflect her importance to others and to the world.

Students may say that the mirror seems to believe that it
  a. truthfully reflects the woman's physical appearance and merely relates its observations of her emotional responses to the mirror's reflections.
  b. understands and reflects the woman's inner self— who she really is.

Some students may add that the mirror shows an egoism ("a little god," "I am important to her") that is part of the irony of the poem.

  2. Answers will vary widely. Students might feel that the speaker's main conflict concerns
    a. her self-image. She pictures herself as a doll or a synthetic human being that walks and talks and is manipulated by people to whom she can't respond in any meaningful way. In the last stanza of the poem, she suggests that, although she should be able to measure up to the standards of the "ideal doll," she cannot. She is even incapable of shedding tears for herself.
    b. her relationship with her husband and children or her role in the family. In the third stanza, she pictures her husband and children as "puppet-masters" who control and manipulate her, but who do not affect her emotionally, other than perhaps to disgust or repel her. The ideal doll to which she compares herself in the last stanza might also be seen as the ideal wife and mother.
    c. society's expectations of women. The speaker seems to be a dissatisfied homemaker whose senses and emotions have been dulled or suffocated by leading a traditional middle-class lifestyle. In lines 31–35, she seems to compare herself to, and despair of her ability to represent, the ideal TV "perfect mother" of the 1950s.

Other ideas should be supported with appropriate reference to the poem.

**E.** (15 points) Answers will vary widely, depending on students' personal experiences, situations, and viewpoints. Accept any answers that address the concern of the question and are elaborated by examples or details from the literature or from life.

## Unit Six, Part Two Test
pp. 199–200
**A.** (5 points each) Notes will vary but should include points similar to the following:
  1. Warren is upset because Silas left him in the lurch the season before by walking out during the haying, and he told Silas he would not hire him again. He does not feel sympathetic toward Silas or particularly compassionate; he doesn't think Silas should be his problem to deal with.
  2. It refers to the end of the relationship between Nick and Marjorie, the end of Nick's love, and/or the end of the mill town's existence.
  3. He most likely wants to make a proposition to one of the women at the party—to ask her for a date or propose marriage to her; but he does not have the self-confidence to put himself on the line and risk rejection.
  4. She realizes that she will never forgive George for jilting her, or that being jilted by George has affected her entire life and caused her more pain than anything else.

**B.** (20 points) Notes will vary. A model answer for "Mirror" and "Mending Wall" follows.
In "Mirror," the image of a young girl drowning in a lake conveys the
  a. idea of aging.
  b. idea that the loss of youth is tragic.
  c. woman's desperation.
  d. woman's grief.
  e. woman's revulsion toward herself and her appearance.
  f. idea that the woman's appearance is terribly important to her identity.
  g. ideas of death and loss.

In "Mending Wall," the saying, "Good fences make good neighbors,"
  a. symbolizes tradition, ignorance, and suspicion.
  b. conveys the ideas that traditions should be relevant and useful or should be discarded; that traditions often result from mindless slavery to habit; and that ignorance and suspicion build unnecessary barriers between people.

**C.** (20 points each; students should answer two of the three)
  1. Answers will vary. A model answer for " 'Out, Out—,' " and "The Love Song of J. Alfred Prufrock" follows.
In " 'Out, Out—,' "
  a. the loss of a boy's life occurs after his hand is cut off by a buzz saw.
  b. the idea of losing his hand deeply affects the boy. He responds with shock, desperation, and fear when he sees "all spoiled."
  c. the loss seems to make the speaker feel regretful.
  d. the loss has little apparent effect on the other people in the poem, who, "since they / Were not the one dead, turned to their affairs" immediately after the boy dies.
In "The Love Song of J. Alfred Prufrock," the loss
  a. is one of hope, opportunity, idealism, or the desire to struggle against fate.

b. occurs when Prufrock decides against asking the "overwhelming question."

c. affects no one but Prufrock and, perhaps, the woman who might have responded favorably to Prufrock's question had he asked it of her.

d. might be seen to have little, if any, effect on Prufrock. Not taking action only ensures that nothing about him or his life will change.

e. might be seen to have a negative effect on Prufrock in that it causes him to accept a lonely, empty, generic existence in which he will not act but will be acted upon.

f. might be seen to have a positive effect in that it relieves him of the pressure he has placed on himself to be someone he is not. He seems to find some peace and contentment in accepting himself for who he is and knowing what the future holds for him, even if they are not what he wants.

2. Answers will vary. A model answer for "The Death of the Hired Man" and "The Love Song of J. Alfred Prufrock" follows.

In "The Death of the Hired Man," the dilemma

a. concerns what to do about Silas, who has returned to the farm and fallen asleep.

b. is difficult because Mary and Warren disagree on what to do. Mary understands that he has "come home to die," but Warren does not want him there. Silas walked out in the middle of a job, and Warren doesn't want him back. Mary, who sees that Silas is in a bad way, is kind to him and wants to help him save his self-respect. Warren does not want to deal with Silas; he would prefer to have Silas go to his own brother who lives 13 miles away. Mary understands that Silas will not go to his brother because he feels his brother is ashamed of him.

c. is resolved when Silas dies.

In "The Love Song of J. Alfred Prufrock," the dilemmas

a. concern fears surrounding love and mortality which separate the speaker from other people.

b. The dilemmas are difficult because they are two of the most complicated and daunting issues of life—how to deal with people of the opposite sex and how to weigh the worth of one's life and accomplishments in view of the fact that it will ultimately end.

c. The dilemmas remain unsolved by the end of the poem, but the speaker seems to forsee an inevitable lonely, disillusioned old age for himself. A solution to the problems might be to just plunge forward into life instead of worrying so much about how he appears to others.

3. Answers will vary. A model answer for "Acquainted with the Night" and "Self in 1958" follows.

"Acquainted with the Night" might appeal to the heart because

a. the speaker is lonely, alienated, and without self-pity.

b. the speaker seems incapable of sharing his thoughts and feelings with anyone except the reader.

c. the simple, beautiful language used in the poem is heartbreaking.

d. the poem elevates the state of isolation in which we all exist to that of the noble state of the tragic hero.

"Self in 1958" might appeal to the intellect because

a. to fully understand the poem, the reader must be familiar with the situation of women in 1958.

b. the poem seems to be a deeply personal one, exposing the troubled life of the poet. It encourages the reader to consider how elements of her life led her to write this particular poem.

c. the comparison of the speaker to a doll demands that the reader come to his or her own conclusions about what the speaker is feeling about herself, her life, and why.

**D.** (20 points)

1. Notes will vary. A model answer for "Acquainted with the Night" might suggest that this characteristic is revealed in that the speaker

a. walks completely alone through life, incapable of making the slightest connection with a single soul.

b. is profoundly isolated from all other living beings.

c. seems indifferent toward his or her isolation.

2. Notes will vary. A model answer for "The End of Something" might suggest that this characteristic is revealed in that the writer

a. used a modified form of the third-person limited point of view.

b. chose to reveal little about the narrator's thoughts and feelings.

c. chose to let the reader fill in the gaps in the story's plot and characterization.

# Unit Seven

## Armistice

Selection Test, pp. 201–202

**A.** (5 points each)

1. Notes will vary but should suggest the following ideas:
   a. The armistice between the two nations comes about when Germany invades France and France is forced to accept Germany's peace terms or be destroyed.
   b. The armistice between the two men comes about when Morris gives in to Leonard's wishes and stops arguing with Gus, and Gus, not wanting to lose Morris's business, leaves the shop.
2. Notes will vary but should suggest the following ideas:
   a. The armistice between the nations terrifies Morris and fills him with despair because it means that the French Jews will be endangered by the Nazis and French democracy has lost out to German fascism.
   b. The armistice between the two men makes Morris uneasy because he doesn't want to hurt his son, but he doesn't feel that he can continue to ignore Gus's hurtful jabs.
3. Notes will vary but should suggest the following ideas:
   a. The armistice between the nations pleases Gus because Germany has forced it on France. Gus admires the Nazi war machine and, like the Nazis, is anti-Semitic.
   b. The armistice between the two men makes Gus uneasy because it reflects a conflict that may cause him to lose Morris's business.
4. Notes will vary but should suggest some of the following ideas:
   a. Both armistices are forced on the "good guys"— France and Morris.
   b. Both armistices are uneasy, unnatural, and unlikely to last long.
   c. Both armistices are between parties that are opposed to each other.
   d. Both armistices bring an end to overt conflict.
   e. Both armistices cover up but do not dissolve the substantial problems that the two parties have with each other.
5. Notes will vary but should suggest some of the following ideas:
   a. The armistice between the nations is brought on by France's helplessness against Germany's violence; that between the men is brought on by Morris's love for his son.
   b. The armistice between the nations affects millions of people; that between the two men is a personal matter.

c. The French and German armistice represents an agreement between a conquering and a conquered nation; the armistice forged by the men is between two equals and signifies neither a win nor a loss for either side.
   d. Revenge and humiliation are important elements of the armistice forced on the French; a child's desire for harmony and the love between a father and child are important elements of the armistice between the men.
6. Notes will vary but could suggest a theme similar to one of the following:
   a. There can be no peace where there is no love.
   b. A true peace cannot be forged between enemies.
   c. A threat to one person is a threat to all of humanity.
   d. Those with the least love in their hearts are the most eager to wage war.

**B.** (5 points each)
   1. d
   2. a
   3. c
   4. d

**C.** (4 points each)
   1. b
   2. b
   3. c
   4. a
   5. a

**D.** (15 points; students should answer one of the two)
   1. Answers will vary. Students who believe that there is just cause for sympathizing with Gus might say that
      a. it makes sense that at the beginning of the war, before Nazi atrocities became widely known, people—especially those of German descent— would admire the strength and power of the German army.
      b. many people sympathized with the hardships the Germans faced after World War I.
      c. Gus's attempts at friendship with Morris are undermined by Leonard for reasons that seem trivial.

Most students will probably feel that there is little reason to sympathize with Gus because he
      a. is a Nazi sympathizer.
      b. is anti-Semitic.
      c. is hostile toward Leonard, who is only a child.
      d. goads Morris about something that he knows Morris feels terrible about.
      e. seems to be lacking in morals.
      f. is ignorant.
      g. is anti-democratic.
      h. thinks of his relationship with Morris primarily in business terms.
      i. is scornful of affection.
      j. wants to have, and use, power against the weak.

2. Answers will vary but could include points similar to the following:
    a. Leonard takes a dislike to Gus, which makes it difficult for Morris to encourage Gus's offers of friendship.
    b. Gus seems to resent and dislike Leonard because of Leonard's interference in his relationship with Morris.
    c. Gus's treatment of Leonard makes Morris feel uneasy about Gus.
    d. Gus's interactions with Leonard reveal Gus to be spiteful, childish, jealous, and eager to lash out at others when hurt.
    e. Morris's interactions with Leonard reveal Morris to be loving, caring, moral, responsible, protective, eager to please, and unselfish.

**E.** (15 points) Answers will vary widely, depending on students' personal experiences, situations, and viewpoints. Accept any answers that address the concern of the question and are elaborated by examples or details from the literature or from life.

## The Death of the Ball Turret Gunner/ Why Soldiers Won't Talk

Selection Test, pp. 203–204

**A.** (10 points each)
1. Notes will vary but could include words similar to the following:
    a. Horrifying, shocking.
    b. Disgusting, gross.
    c. Realistic.
2. Notes will vary but could include words similar to the following:
    a. Unemotional, matter-of-fact.
    b. Cynical.
    c. Ironic.
    d. Bitter.
3. Notes will vary but could suggest some of the following ideas:
    a. The speaker's death is meaningless.
    b. The speaker is bitter about his death.
    c. The speaker's death is meaningful only to him.
    d. The government (or "they" or "the State") fails to recognize and appreciate the sacrifice the speaker has made.
    e. War is brutal.
    f. A dead soldier is just another mess to clean up.
    g. The machinery matters more than the soldier.

**B.** (10 points each)
1. a
2. a
3. b

**C.** (20 points; students should answer one of the two)
1. Answers will vary widely. Students might describe his death as
    a. tragic or ironic, because it occurs just as the speaker leaves the world of innocence and is "born" into the world of experience.
    b. meaningless, because the government (or "they" or "the State") is indifferent toward the speaker's sacrifice.
    c. violent, horrifying, or shocking, because the speaker's body is blown to bits and what is left of it must be washed out of the turret with a hose.
    d. undignified, because what is left of his body is unceremoniously washed out of the turret with a hose.
Other ideas should be supported with appropriate reasons.
2. Answers will vary but should reflect students' understanding that Steinbeck's main premise is that soldiers tend not to talk about their combat experiences because they tend not to remember them. Students who find this idea reasonable might say that
    a. Steinbeck's detailed description of what soldiers experience during combat provides strong logical support for this idea.
    b. their own personal experiences with stressful situations support this idea.
    c. most people tend to feel the need to share painful memories of harrowing experiences. It doesn't make sense that combat soldiers would, as a group, be completely different from everyone else in this respect. Steinbeck is right in feeling that it makes more sense that combat soldiers wouldn't be able to remember their combat experiences than that they wouldn't want to share those experiences.
Students who don't find Steinbeck's hypothesis reasonable might say that
    a. thousands of personal recollections of combat experiences exist in print, film, and other media. Unless all of the sources of these combat recollections are liars or victims of shell-shock, their memories exist in direct contradiction to Steinbeck's hypothesis.
    b. their own personal experiences with stressful situations contradict this idea.
    c. it is more likely that the men of Steinbeck's generation didn't talk about their combat experiences because the men of his generation weren't allowed the luxury of expressing the full range of human emotions without fear of being considered unmanly, especially those emotions central to their combat experiences—terror, doubt, compassion, and despair.

d. Steinbeck should have quoted some soldiers admitting that they don't remember. If this reaction is so common, it must be recognized among those who experience it.

**D.** (20 points) Answers will vary widely, depending on students' personal experiences, situations, and viewpoints. Accept any answers that address the concern of the question and are elaborated by examples or details from the literature or from life.

## Letter from Paradise, 21° 19′ N., 157° 52′ W./ In Response to Executive Order 9066

Selection Test, pp. 205–206

**A.** (10 points each)
1. Notes will vary but could include the following:
   a. Cheerful, happy-go-lucky.
   b. Festive in a "sleazy" way.
2. Notes will vary but could include the following:
   a. Romantic.
   b. Nostalgic.
   c. Satisfied.
   d. Distracted.
3. Notes will vary but could include the following:
   a. Melancholy, depressed, sad, mournful.
   b. Appreciative, grateful.
   c. Sympathetic.
   d. Bittersweet.
4. Notes will vary but could include the following:
   a. Somber, sad.
   b. Bittersweet.

**B.** (10 points each)
1. d
2. d

**C.** (20 points; students should answer one of the two)
1. Answers will vary. Students might describe Didion's attitude as
   a. caring. She mourns their deaths even though they occurred more than 20 years before she wrote the essay and she doesn't appear to have known any of those who died.
   b. respectful. She visits the places where they died and where they are buried, and considers their deaths more profound than John F. Kennedy's.
   c. humble. She is overcome by what happened at Pearl Harbor more than 20 years before her visit.
2. Answers will vary but should include points similar to the following:
   a. The father, when he says that the seeds won't grow where they're going, is suggesting that that place will be barren and hostile not only to the seeds but to the people as well.
   b. Noting that Denise call tomatoes "love apples" establishes the tomato seeds as symbols of love.

c. The speaker gives the tomato seeds to Denise as a symbol of forgiveness for Denise's hurtful accusations, of their friendship and love for each other, and of the hope that Denise will, with time, come to miss the speaker, regret her remarks, and possibly take steps to renew the friendship.

**D.** (20 points) Answers will vary widely, depending on students' personal experiences, situations, and viewpoints. Accept any answers that address the concern of the question and are elaborated by examples or details from the literature or from life.

## Ambush

Selection Test, pp. 207–208

**A.** (15 points each)
1. Notes will vary but should reflect students' understanding that the moment involving the narrator's daughter is difficult because
   a. the narrator has killed.
   b. his daughter is only nine years old.

The moment involving the young soldier is difficult because
   a. the narrator is responsible for keeping watch over the platoon.
   b. the sudden appearance of the young soldier terrifies the narrator.
2. Notes will vary but should reflect students' understanding that the narrator responds to the difficulty posed by
   a. his daughter's question by lying to her and trying to reassure her.
   b. the soldier's sudden appearance by killing him.
3. Notes will vary. Students might suggest that the narrator lies to his daughter because he feels that
   a. she is too young to understand what he has done and why.
   b. it is his duty as her father to put her interests first, and his desire to tell her the truth should come second to her need to feel safe and secure.
   c. telling her the truth wouldn't enlighten her; it would only frighten and upset her.

Students might suggest that the narrator kills the young soldier because
   a. the soldier terrifies him.
   b. the narrator has been trained to respond to the enemy in that way.
   c. the narrator's instincts have been warped by his experiences in Vietnam.

**B.** (5 points each)
1. b
2. a
3. c

**C.** (20 points; students should answer one of the two)
1. Answers will vary. Students who believe that the narrator does the right thing might say that
    a. the daughter is too young to understand what motivated her father to kill the young soldier.
    b. the daughter would only be frightened and upset by what little she would understand about the truth.
    c. the narrator's responsibility as a father is not to the truth; it is to the safety and well-being of his daughter.
    d. the truth might drive a wedge between father and daughter. It is better to wait until she is old enough so that the truth can become a bridge between them.

Students who believe that the narrator does the wrong thing might say that
    a. it is immoral to lie under any circumstances.
    b. the daughter has a right to know that her father is someone who has killed.
    c. if the daughter suspects that the narrator is lying to her or later discovers the truth on her own, she will lose faith in him.
    d. the narrator loses an opportunity to discuss important issues with his daughter and to teach her important lessons about life.
2. Answers will vary widely. Students might describe the narrator's action as
    a. tragic, in that it results in the meaningless death of a young man and haunts the narrator for the rest of his life.
    b. senseless, in that there is no good reason for what the narrator does.
    c. depressing, in that the narrator admits that nothing but fear drove him to kill.
    d. unfair or unjust, in that a young man loses his life without just cause and the narrator, who never would have killed the man under peacetime conditions, must live with the guilt for the rest of his life.
    e. reasonable, in that the narrator has been trained to kill without thinking and is responsible for the welfare of his platoon at the time that he kills the young man.
    f. justifiable, in that the narrator is fighting a war, and the Vietnamese soldier would have done the same if the situation were reversed.

Other ideas should be supported with appropriate reasons or reference to the story.

**D.** (20 points) Answers will vary widely, depending on students' personal experiences, situations, and viewpoints. Accept any answers that address the concern of the question and are elaborated by examples or details from the literature or from life.

## Camouflaging the Chimera/Deciding
Selection Test, pp. 209–210
**A.** (6 points each)
1. Notes will vary but should reflect students' understanding that the "we" in
    a. "Camouflaging" are American soldiers.
    b. "Deciding" are South Vietnamese office workers who work for the Americans.
2. Notes will vary but could suggest that the state of mind of "we" in
    a. "Camouflaging" is one of anxiety, obsession, anticipation, uneasiness, or detachment.
    b. "Deciding" is one of anxiety, fear, sadness, and nostalgia.
3. Notes will vary but could suggest that the "we" in
    a. "Camouflaging" feel this way because they are entirely focused on dissolving into their surroundings and they are preparing to spring an ambush in which they may kill and be killed.
    b. "Deciding" feel this way because they must make difficult decisions quickly under crisis.
4. Notes will vary but could suggest that the speaker in
    a. "Camouflaging" is protected, comforted, and, to a lesser extent, endangered by nature.
    b. "Deciding" is both comforted and saddened by memories of nature.
5. Notes will vary but could suggest that the speaker in
    a. "Camouflaging" is endangered and challenged by war.
    b. "Deciding" is endangered and saddened by the war and her whole life is turned upside down by it.
6. Notes will vary widely. Students who sympathize more with the soldiers in "Camouflaging" might say that the soldiers
    a. are putting their lives on the line for another country's freedom.
    b. seem so vulnerable and desperate.
    c. seem so animal-like and distanced from themselves.

Students who sympathize more with the speaker of "Deciding" might say that
    a. her entire life is turned upside down by the war.
    b. she is forced to leave her home and country behind.
    c. she does not seem to deserve what has happened to her.
**B.** (6 points each)
1. a
2. b
**C.** (6 points each)
1. Notes will vary but could suggest ideas similar to the following:
    a. Camouflaging themselves; blending into the terrain; survival; seeking protection in nature; loss of individuality or personality.
    b. Eeriness, calmness.

2. Notes will vary but could suggest ideas similar to the following:
   a. Long waiting; impatience; endurance; anticipation; obsession; time passing; anxiety.
   b. Tension, suspense, desperation.
3. Notes will vary but could suggest ideas similar to the following:
   a. Childhood; a life largely untouched by war; innocence; happiness.
   b. Contentment, nostalgia.
4. Notes will vary but could suggest ideas similar to the following:
   a. Fear; loss; waiting; the war; destruction; hope; the power of nature to heal; promise.
   b. Guarded hopefulness, confusion, sorrow.

**D.** (14 points; students should answer one of the two)
1. Answers will vary. Most students will feel that the word
   a. chimera refers to the American combat unit described in the poem because, like the mythical chimera, the soldiers are fierce, very dangerous, and emit destructive "fire."
   b. camouflaging refers to the American combat unit because they camouflage their appearance and their movements so that they fit into the landscape and cannot be detected by the VC.

Other students may suggest that
   a. the war itself is the chimera camouflaged by the apparently peaceful landscape.
   b. the American presence in Vietnam is the chimera camouflaged by the apparently good intentions America has in Vietnam.

Other ideas should be supported with appropriate reasons.
2. Answers will vary. Most students will feel that the speaker has decided to leave Vietnam and emigrate to the United States. In support, they might say that
   a. that is what the poet did (and the poem is based on her experiences).
   b. lines 5–7 strongly imply that staying in Vietnam is not a viable alternative for the speaker. Her very survival seems to require that she leave the country.
   c. when the speaker makes up her mind, she is immediately flooded by memories of her childhood. This suggests that she is emotionally preparing herself to take leave of her past.

Students who feel that the speaker has decided to stay in Vietnam should support that view with appropriate reference to the poem.

**E.** (14 points) Answers will vary widely, depending on students' personal experiences, situations, and viewpoints. Accept any answers that address the concern of the question and are elaborated by examples or details from the literature or from life.

## At the Justice Department, November 15, 1969
Selection Test, pp. 211–212

**A.** (15 points each) Notes may vary but should include points similar to the following:
1. Senses Affected: the poem appeals mainly to the sense of sight. The reader can see the ivy-covered bank, the confusion of the protesters, and protesters dragging each other up the bank. The excerpt also appeals to the senses of taste and smell: the "bitter taste" of the gas.
2. What You Visualize: the image is one of confusion. There are bodies everywhere. The poet's use of the words *brothers* and *sisters* creates an emotional appeal of camaraderie. There is a feeling of closeness and unity among the protesters; even though they are strangers, they know they must help one another. The bitter taste applies not only to the taste of the gas but also to the emotion of the moment.

**B.** (10 points each)
1. a
2. c
3. b

**C.** (20 points; students should answer one of the two)
1. Answers will vary. Students might say that the repetition of the word *wanting*
   a. emphasizes the depth of the speaker's desire or need.
   b. emphasizes the difficulty in (or conflict between) her intellect's wanting to be where she is and her body's not wanting to be there, or her body's physical need to be relieved from the effects of the tear gas.
   c. connects the various physical sensations and emotional reactions that the speaker has to being tear-gassed.
   d. emphasizes the importance in the poem of the idea of complete devotion to a cause or of wanting something with all one's being.
   e. creates an urgent or insistent tone and pattern or sound.
2. Answers will vary but should include points similar to the following:
   a. The poet's style helps the reader experience the event, emotionally as well as physically.
   b. Word choice: The poet uses concrete, specific, words that describe things that one knows and understands with one's senses.
   c. Imagery: The reader can see the "brown gas-fog"; see the "street lamps"; see and feel the protesters "stumble hand in hand, blinded, retching." The images create a feeling of suffocation.

d. Sentence length: The two opening sentences are very short and create a sense of physical tension. The longer sentences in the middle of the poem evoke emotions in the reader by creating images that build the emotional turmoil.

e. Rhythm: In lines 5–10, the use of commas creates a rhythm that "stumbles" as the protesters stumble up the bank. The repetition also creates a rhythm that grabs the reader's attention and emphasizes the speaker's commitment to the protest and the other protesters.

**D.** (20 points) Answers will vary widely, depending on students' personal experiences, situations, and viewpoints. Accept any answers that address the concern of the question and are elaborated by examples or details from the literature or from life.

## Unit Seven, Part One Test

pp. 213–214

**A.** (5 points each) Answers will vary but should include points similar to the following:

1. Morris agreed that he would not argue or fight with Gus anymore because it upset his son Leonard, who asked him to stop; Gus ended his hostility because he did not want to lose Morris's business, and perhaps because he realized he went too far by pushing Leonard.

2. At the beginning, the mood is lighthearted and somewhat sardonic as Didion comments on the tourists' behavior. The mood changes when Didion contemplates the sorrow and losses of World War II, the number of people killed, and the fact that such a tragedy happened again in Vietnam.

3. He keeps writing war stories because he killed at least one person in Vietnam during the war and is still trying to resolve the conflicts within himself.

4. She feels strongly about the just cause of the protest—stopping the war—and the suffering caused by the gas makes it feel as if she is sacrificing herself for a righteous goal. However, she is aware that no matter what she suffers during a protest, it does not compare with the death occurring in Vietnam.

**B.** (20 points) Notes will vary. A model answer for an image from "Camouflaging the Chimera" follows.
The image of the men in the combat unit waiting "till something almost broke / inside" them

a. appeals to the sense of touch and, possibly, sight and hearing.

b. might make one think about anticipating dreaded news or events; torture; the illusion of time slowing down; and pounding hearts.

**C.** (20 points each; students should answer two of the three)

1. Answers will vary. A model answer for Morris in "Armistice" and the speaker of "Deciding" follows.
War causes both Morris and the speaker of "Deciding" to

a. feel anxious and sad.

b. recall events from their past.

c. feel a tremendous need to do something about what is happening.

d. come into conflict with loved ones, and to consider their needs against those of family members.

Unlike the speaker of the poem, Morris

a. isn't physically threatened by war.

b. isn't forced by war to leave his home.

Like the speaker of the poem, Morris

a. supports the losing side.

b. fears what the victorious forces will do to his "people."

2. Answers will vary. A model answer for Didion, the writer of "Letter from Paradise . . . ," and "the State" in "The Death of the Ball Turret Gunner" follows.
Didion is admirable in that she

a. is curious, thoughtful, insightful, and compassionate.

b. dares to take a second tour of Pearl Harbor after being too overcome with emotion on the first tour to record the reactions of her fellow passengers.

c. is able to feel deep emotions for strangers who died long ago and, through her writing skills, is able to evoke a similar response in the reader.

d. is willing to explore and bring to public attention feelings and ideas that most people tend to avoid because they are too painful and depressing.

In the poem, the State isn't admirable in that it

a. places common soldiers in inhumane, ghastly situations.

b. is indifferent toward the lives and deaths of common soldiers.

3. Answers will vary. A model answer for Morris in "Armistice" and the narrator of "Ambush" could include points similar to the following:

a. Morris does not at first take personal responsibility for his actions: he loses his temper and lashes out at Gus, who enrages him with his comments about the Nazis and the Jews.

b. The narrator takes personal responsibility for what he believes to have been an immoral act—killing, during wartime, an enemy soldier who posed no immediate threat to him.

c. The narrator acts more responsibly in relation to his daughter by not telling her about killing another man because she was only nine years old; Morris acts responsibly toward his son only after Gus threatens the boy and Leonard starts crying.

d. Morris acts responsibly in a larger sense by feeling such depression and anger over what the Nazis are doing in Europe, while few others in the neighborhood seem to care; the narrator, on the other hand, somewhat tentatively stands up for what is right after taking what he believes to have been a wrong action.

**D.** (20 points) Notes will vary. A model answer for the speaker of "The Death of the Ball Turret Gunner" follows. The State makes the speaker feel bitter and abused because it

a. gave the speaker the impression that his life meant something to it.

b. doesn't appreciate the sacrifice the speaker makes for it.

c. treats his body like garbage.

## Letter from Birmingham Jail

Selection Test, pp. 215–216

**A.** (10 points each) Notes will vary but should include points similar to the following:

1. a. This quotation alludes to events in the New Testament, in which the apostle Paul responds to a call for aid from Macedonia, which was then a Roman province north of Greece.

   b. It probably appeals most to emotion, since he is addressing clergymen.

   c. This allusion is somewhat effective because it places King on a level with the apostles and makes his mission seem righteous, as Paul's mission would have been considered righteous by the Christians.

2. a. The allusion is to Adolf Hitler's systematic suspension of civil rights in Germany during the Nazi regime, including his plan to murder all Jews.

   b. It appeals to emotion, since readers would be familiar with the horrors of the Holocaust.

   c. Alluding to Hitler is a very effective way to support the principles of civil disobedience. The reader's emotions and sense of outrage are stirred. By denying King's actions, the reader then must be accepting Hitler's actions—and the reader knows that is not right.

3. a. The allusion is to President Lincoln at the time of the Civil War.

   b. It appeals to reason.

   c. This allusion is effective because King uses it as an example of an extremist who stood up for what he thought was right, just as King was doing. The comparison with Lincoln gives his own cause more legitimacy.

**B.** (5 points each)
1. d
2. b
3. c

**C.** (4 points each)
1. a
2. c
3. b
4. c
5. a

**D.** (20 points; students should answer one of the two)
1. Answers will vary but should include points similar to the following:

The clergymen had three criticisms of King and his actions:

a. They called King's presence and actions "unwise and untimely."

b. They argued against "outsiders coming in" to Birmingham.

c. They criticized King's willingness to break laws.

King's response to these criticisms:

a. No gain in civil rights has been achieved without concerted legal and nonviolent pressure. King postponed the protest several times in deference to community activities, such as an election. However, he stated, "We have waited for more than 340 years for our constitutional and God-given rights," and the "American Negro" cannot keep waiting.

b. King was invited to Birmingham by a local affiliate; but, of more importance, King is aware that all communities and states are interrelated: "Injustice anywhere is injustice everywhere."

c. King believes that people have a moral responsibility to obey just laws and disobey unjust laws. He then explains the difference and admits that he does support breaking the law, but only if the law is unjust and the violator is willing to accept the penalty.

2. Students may agree or disagree with King's assessment, but accept all responses that make a logical argument and relate to the selection. Answers might also include the following points:

a. The white moderate is more interested in maintaining order and the status quo than in supporting change; even positive change.

b. Racists are easier to fight against because they are often vocal and visible, but moderate people speak neither for nor against a cause..

c. Often a majority of people are moderate, and it is important to convince that moderate majority to support change. If they cannot be motivated, then change is difficult to achieve.

**E.** (15 points) Answers will vary widely, depending on students' personal experiences, situations, and viewpoints. Accept any answers that address the concern of the question and are elaborated by examples or details from the literature or from life.

## Wandering
Selection Test, pp. 217–218
**A.** (20 points each)
1. Notes will vary widely. Students might say that the dialogue reveals that Him
   a. opposes war.
   b. is a pacifist or conscientious objector.
   c. has an international or humanist political outlook.
   d. isn't very patriotic.
   e. thinks for himself.
   f. is true to himself.
   g. believes that he has the right not to be forced to do things he doesn't want to do or doesn't feel are right.
   h. is matter-of-fact about his opinions.
   i. is reasonable.
   j. doesn't believe in killing people.
2. Notes will vary widely. Students might say that the dialogue reveals that He
   a. is patriotic.
   b. is impatient with people who disagree with him.
   c. is used to getting his own way.
   d. expects people to be and feel like him.
   e. supports the military.
   f. is probably a military recruiter or military doctor of some kind.
   g. doesn't take other people's opinions seriously.
   h. doesn't take young people seriously.

**B.** (5 points each)
1. a
2. d

**C.** (4 points each)
1. b
2. b
3. a
4. b
5. c

**D.** (15 points; students should answer one of the two)
1. Answers will vary but should include points similar to the following:
   a. Him's mother seems to have tried to mold him into a young man who would do and think as he was told, who would conform to society's expectations of young men, and who would feel guilty and ashamed of being anyone other than who he was "supposed" to be. When her efforts failed, she became highly critical of Him.
   b. Him's wife seems to have tried to mold him into the husband that she wanted him to be, someone who would provide for the family, stay out of trouble, and not cause embarrassment. Like Him's mother, she tried to make him feel guilty and ashamed of actions that didn't conform to society's expectations and also became highly critical of Him. Some students may note that, unlike Him's mother, Him's wife was slightly more respectful or loving of Him, noting that after his death, his wife calls Him "a lost lamb" and says that he was "handsome" and "gentle."
2. Answers will vary but should include points similar to the following:
   a. To Him, "wandering" is associated with trying to find one's way in life, trying to be a good person, trying to figure things out for oneself, seeking truth, or trying to lead a meaningful life.
   b. To He and She, "wandering" is associated with being "messed up" or "mixed up," being immature or undisciplined, being lost or without goals, being selfish, shirking one's duties, or getting into trouble.
   To account for the characters' different views on "wandering," students might suggest that
   a. Him's values, beliefs, and priorities are quite different from those of He and She.
   b. Him is a nonconformist; He and She are conformists.
   c. Him thinks for himself; He and She don't think for themselves.
   d. Him is self-centered; He and She put others and their communities and country ahead of themselves.

**E.** (15 points) Answers will vary widely, depending on students' personal experiences, situations, and viewpoints. Accept any answers that address the concern of the question and are elaborated by examples or details from the literature or from life.

## The Writer in the Family
Selection Test, pp. 219–220
**A.** (5 points each) Notes will vary but should include points similar to the following:
1. Exposition: Jonathan's father has died. His grandmother is still alive, and his mother resents her and the rest of his father's family.
2. Rising Action: Aunt Frances asks Jonathan to write letters from his dead father to the grandmother. Jonathan struggles with his feelings about writing the letters. Both his mother and brother disagree with what he is doing, and his brother is suspicious of his aunt's motivations.
3. Climax: Jonathan, determined to put an end to writing the letters from his father, writes what his aunt calls a "deliberately cruel and perverse" letter to his grandmother. The climax occurs when Aunt Frances has a

talk with Jonathan. At this point, the reader wonders what is in the letter and what Jonathan will do—until the contents of the letter are revealed at the end.

4. Falling Action: Jonathan learns that his father had a dream for his life: he wanted to be a sailor and travel the world. Suddenly, the connection between the Great Sea Novels, the old ship's telescope, and his father's dream becomes clear. For the first time in Jonathan's life, he sees his father as a person with hopes, dreams, and aspirations.

5. Resolution: Jonathan, feeling guilty about the letter he sent to his aunt, realizes that the letter probably expressed what his father would have really felt. Now Jonathan can begin to come to terms with the feelings he has about his father's life and death.

**B.** (6 points each)
1. b
2. a
3. d

**C.** (4 points each)
1. c
2. c
3. a
4. a
5. b

**D.** (20 points; students should answer one of the two)
1. Answers will vary but should include points similar to the following:
a. Jonathan has never really heard his father's family's opinion of his father and mother. In his conversation with Aunt Frances, he learns that she really loved his father and thought that he was special. His mother has always told him that Jack's family held him back. Now Jonathan begins to see another side to the story of his father's life and wonders if perhaps his mother held his father back.
b. When his mother comes home that night, Jonathan suddenly sees her in a more realistic light and decides she is not as pretty as he thought. For the first time, Jonathan is seeing his mother as a separate person and is beginning to understand that she also had some responsibility for the problems in the family's relationships.

2. Answers will vary but students should understand that Jonathan struggles with both internal and external conflicts:
a. He has an external conflict with his mother over writing the letters. She is upset by Aunt Frances's demands and his compliance, so Jonathan hides the fact that he is writing them.
b. He has an external conflict with his Aunt Frances. He feels that writing the letters is dishonest and does not really want to write them.

c. He has an external conflict with his brother Harold, who makes it clear that Jonathan does not have to write the letters.
d. Internally, Jonathan struggles with whether or not to continue to write the letters. He is influenced by his mother's and Harold's feelings toward his father's side of the family. This influence causes him to write a harsh letter.
e. Jonathan has unresolved feelings about his father. These feelings come out in his dreams. He wonders if his father was just a "nice guy" and his family really did take advantage of him. Jonathan begins to think that maybe his father was not a failure. Perhaps his father just tried to do the best he could once he realized his dream would never be fulfilled.

**E.** (17 points) Answers will vary widely, depending on students' personal experiences, situations, and viewpoints. Accept any answers that address the concern of the question and are elaborated by examples or details from the literature or from life.

**Teenage Wasteland**
Selection Test, pp. 221–222
**A.** (10 points each)
1. Notes will vary widely, depending upon whom students believe is the protagonist of this story. Students might suggest that Donny is the protagonist because
a. the story is about him and his problems.
b. he is involved in every conflict in the story.
c. he undergoes radical change over the course of the story, going from being simply a poor student to being expelled from school to becoming a runaway.
Students might suggest that Donny is an antagonist because
a. Daisy is really the central character of this story.
b. he is in conflict with Daisy, who is the protagonist.
c. he is involved in the story's central conflict, which involves Daisy's concerns about parenting and her desire to help him.
d. he changes very little over the course of the story.

2. Notes will vary widely, depending upon whom students believe is the protagonist of this story. Students might suggest that Daisy is the protagonist because
a. she is the central character in this story, the character about whom the reader knows the most.
b. the story is about her internal and external conflicts over parenting generally and Donny specifically.
c. her outlook on Donny and his problems changes the most. She goes from seeing him as a sweet, chubby-faced boy to seeing him as an emotionally troubled stranger.

Students might suggest that Daisy is an antagonist because she
- a. is in conflict with Donny, the central character of the story.
- b. changes very little over the course of the story.

3. Notes will vary widely, depending upon whom students believe is the protagonist of this story. Students who believe that Donny is the protagonist might suggest that Cal is neither a protagonist nor an antagonist because
- a. Donny is the protagonist.
- b. Cal is supportive of Donny.
- c. Cal isn't in conflict with Donny.

Students who believe that Daisy is the protagonist might suggest that Cal is an antagonist because he
- a. undermines Daisy's efforts to help Donny.
- b. often comes into conflict with Daisy over what is best for Donny.
- c. doesn't help Donny and, in fact, makes things worse for the entire family.
- d. changes very little over the course of the story.

**B.** (5 points each)
1. b
2. d

**C.** (5 points each)
1. Ratings and notes will vary widely. Students might give the best grade to Daisy because
- a. she manages to communicate well with everyone other than Donny and Cal, who make communication difficult.
- b. Donny's grades improve when she begins tutoring him.

Other students might give the best grade to Cal because he communicates well with
- a. Donny.
- b. young people in general.

2. Ratings and notes will vary widely. Students might give the best grade to Daisy because she tries to
- a. get Donny to talk to her.
- b. understand Cal and to follow his advice.
- c. communicate with Donny's principal and teachers.

Other students might give the best grade to Cal because he seems
- a. more open and friendly.
- b. to enjoy the challenge of communicating with troubled kids.

3. Ratings and notes will vary widely. Most students will give the best grade to Cal because
- a. he is confident in his ability to know what is right for Donny and other troubled kids.
- b. Daisy changes her mind often about what is right for Donny, depending on who is talking to her.
- c. Daisy doesn't trust her own judgment of her son's needs or her ability to help him.

Students who give Daisy the best grade should support that view with appropriate reasons.

4. Ratings and notes will vary widely. Students might give the best grade to Daisy because
- a. in order to help Donny, she tolerates Cal's interference with her parental duties and rights.
- b. she repeatedly tries to give Donny what he needs, even when doing so goes against her better judgment.

Other students might give the best grade to Cal because he
- a. seems cool and laid-back.
- b. is tolerant of behavior that upsets other authority figures in Donny's life.
- c. tries to gain greater freedom for Donny.

**D.** (4 points each)
1. b
2. b
3. a
4. a
5. b

**E.** (10 points; students should answer one of the two)
1. Opinions will vary widely but should reflect students' understanding that
- a. although Donny performs best in school when he is under Daisy's tutelage, his self-esteem doesn't improve, and he gets into trouble.
- b. although Donny's self-esteem seems to improve under Cal's tutelage, Donny becomes less interested in his schoolwork, less willing to take responsibility for his actions, and gets into more trouble.

2. Answers will vary. Students might sympathize with Daisy more because she
- a. is better known to the reader.
- b. loves Donny very much.
- c. has tried to be a good mother to Donny.
- d. feels responsible for what has happened to Donny.
- e. doesn't deserve to be treated so badly.
- f. hasn't the confidence to do what she thinks is right for her own son.

Students might sympathize more with Donny because
- a. no one seems to understand him.
- b. his parents do not seem to trust or believe in him.
- c. even his tutor, Cal, gives up on him.
- d. he is unable to get the right kind of help.
- e. he lacks hope and self-confidence.

**F.** (10 points) Answers will vary widely, depending on students' personal experiences, situations, and viewpoints. Accept any answers that address the concern of the question and are elaborated by examples or details from the literature or from life.

## Separating
Selection Test, pp. 223–224

**A.** (10 points each)
1. Notes will vary but should suggest ideas similar to the following:
   a. Joan's plan is for them to tell each of the children individually.
   b. The plan reveals that she is emotionally strong; values the individuality of her children; puts her children's interests ahead of her own; may want to control the situation as much as possible; and that she may wish to punish Richard by making him go through the experience four separate times.
2. Notes will vary but should suggest ideas similar to the following:
   a. Richard's plan is for them to gather the children and tell them all at once.
   b. This plan may reveal that Richard feels guiltier for the separation than Joan does; Richard functions better in group situations than in one-on-one situations; is emotionally weak; and likes to get things over with quickly.
3. Notes will vary but could suggest ideas similar to the following:
   a. Richard's plan is partially implemented when he cries uncontrollably at the dinner table, arousing his children's suspicions, and leading them to ask questions of Joan, who tells them about the separation, all at once and without Richard being present in the room. Richard reveals the news to Dickie by himself later on.
   b. This might reveal that Richard is selfish, untrustworthy, weak, and manipulative, or simply that he lacks self-control; and Joan is more flexible, more in control, and wants to be the one who controls things.

**B.** (5 points each)
1. c
2. c
3. b
4. b

**C.** (4 points each)
1. b
2. a
3. c
4. a
5. b

**D.** (15 points; students should answer one of the two)
1. Answers will vary but could include one of the following ideas:
   a. The story doesn't have any heroes or villains. It is no one's fault that Richard and Joan can't continue their marriage. They love their children and seem to have tried to save their marriage.
   b. The story has both heroes and villains. The children are the heroes; as Richard notes, they accept the news of the separation with humor and courage. The adults are the villains. Both Joan and, especially, Richard put their happiness ahead of their children's.
   c. The story has no heroes but does contain a villain—Richard. He is selfish and weak. He acts as if he has no control over how he behaves at the table and whether he stays in the marriage when, in fact, he does. He lies to his children about the separation being an experiment when, in fact, there is another woman whom he wishes to marry.

Other ideas should be supported with appropriate reasons and reference to the story.

2. Answers will vary. Students who feel that Richard is more concerned with his own happiness could note that
   a. he is leaving his family so that he can marry another woman.
   b. he hasn't been so unhappy in his marriage that he couldn't stick it out at least until his youngest has left the home.
   c. he and Joan don't seem, either to their children or to the reader, to make each other miserable.
   d. he tells his children that they will be fine and that their lives won't be all that deeply affected, as if the breakup of a family were nothing at all. He gives his children unrealistic expectations so that he won't have to deal with their pain.
   e. as the narrator, he focuses almost entirely on how terrible he feels about hurting his children, as opposed to how terrible they are going to feel.

Students who feel that Richard is more concerned with his children's happiness could note that he
   a. has stayed in his unhappy marriage for several years, waiting for his children to grow up.
   b. is overwhelmed with the pain of hurting them.
   c. plans to continue his active role in their lives and to do all he can to make the separation easier on them.

**E.** (15 points) Answers will vary widely, depending on students' personal experiences, situations, and viewpoints. Accept any answers that address the concern of the question and are elaborated by examples or details from the literature or from life.

## Mexicans Begin Jogging/Legal Alien
Selection Test, pp. 225–226

**A.** (20 points each)
1. Notes will vary widely. Notes for one possible theme might suggest the following ideas:
   a. The theme is that Mexicans are becoming more

powerful, or that Mexican Americans are becoming an important force in the United States.

b. The title relates to the theme in that jogging is associated with the leisurely lifestyles of the middle and upper classes. Like the poem, the title suggests that the time is coming when Mexicans (or Mexican Americans) will have the social status associated with jogging instead of the social status associated with running away from the authorities.

Other themes should be supported with appropriate reasons.

2. Notes will vary. Most students will write notes suggesting that the theme concerns the idea that people of bicultural background
   a. aren't fully accepted by either culture to which they belong.
   b. are prejudged, suspected, or rejected by both of their cultures.
   c. are made uncomfortable or unhappy by being prejudged, suspected, and rejected by the cultures to which they belong.
   d. are made to feel as if they do not belong to any cultural group.

In addition, students might suggest that the title relates to the theme in that the title helps to emphasize ideas suggested in the poem, such as the following:
   a. Being bicultural is like being a "legal alien" (one is legal, or a person who belongs or is accepted), but one is also an alien (or a person who doesn't fully belong or isn't fully accepted).
   b. On the surface, bicultural people seem to belong, as a legal alien does, but bicultural people are denied the full status, legitimacy, or validation associated with full citizenship or membership in a group.

**B.** (10 points each)
1. d
2. b

**C.** (20 points; students should answer one of the two)
1. Answers will vary widely. Most students will describe the tone in terms similar to the following:
   a. Ironic.
   b. Amused, mischievous.
   c. Optimistic.

In support, students might point to the following:
   a. The title of the poem.
   b. The irony of the boss's not believing that Soto is an American and pressing a dollar into his hand as he shoves him out the back door.
   c. The amusing, ironic image of Soto running away from the border patrol, which is amusing because he is on the boss's time and doing what the boss wants him to do.

d. The image of Soto, an American, yelling out cheers for icons of American culture as he runs away from the border patrol.
   e. The optimism of the image in the last two lines of the poem, "As I jog into the next century / On the power of a great, silly grin."
   f. The idea of "a great, silly grin" being the source of Soto's power.

Other ideas about tone should be supported with appropriate reference to the poem.

2. Answers will vary. Students might say that
   a. while the grin is genuine, the smile is insincere.
   b. while the grin reveals joy, the smile masks discomfort.
   c. while the grin empowers the one speaker, the smile seems to reflect the other speaker's handing over to others the power to determine her fate.
   d. while the grin seems silly to the one speaker, the smile seems serious to the other speaker.
   e. while the grin reflects the one speaker's optimistic attitude, the smile seems to reflect the other speaker's pessimistic attitude.

Other ideas should be supported with appropriate reasons.

**D.** (20 points) Answers will vary widely, depending on students' personal experiences, situations, and viewpoints. Accept any answers that address the concern of the question and are elaborated by examples or details from the literature or from life.

### Hostage
Selection Test, pp. 227–228
**A.** (12 points each)
1. Notes will vary. Students who feel that Bruno basically conforms to this element of the definition might suggest that, although he is not actually "good," Bruno
   a. has many respectable characteristics such as pride, courage, and self-confidence.
   b. stands out from the other children by being charismatic, being intelligent, having the physique of an adult, being a leader, and by possessing a manner that inspires fear and respect in others.
   c. has a tragic flaw that leads to his downfall. His tragic flaw might be considered an inclination for violence or a deeply buried resentment over his father's murder that explodes in violence. It is this tragic flaw that leads him to use excessive force against the madman.

Students who feel that Bruno differs from this element of the definition might suggest that he
   a. isn't a good person. He is a bully who carries a switchblade, beats up and snubs his classmates, and inspires fear in his teachers.

b. stands out from the other children, but not in ways that one might consider to be signs of genuine superiority in a tragic hero. He is simply bigger, meaner, and gutsier than the other children.

c. has many flaws but doesn't have one single flaw that stands out as "the one" that leads to his downfall.

2. Notes will vary. Students who feel that Bruno basically conforms to this element of the definition might suggest that, after the incident with the madman, he

a. doesn't seem to blame anyone else for what happens to him.

b. behaves as if he hates himself for what he did or has lost all respect for himself.

Students who feel that Bruno differs from this part of the definition might suggest that

a. there is no indication in the story that Bruno comes to understand anything about himself from the incident with the madman.

b. after the incident, Bruno's self-destructive behavior worsens, indicating that he learned little from the incident.

**B.** (4 points each)
1. b
2. b
3. d

**C.** (6 points each)
1. Notes will vary. Students might suggest that, before the incident, Bruno
a. has the physique of a full-grown man.
b. is charismatic.
c. is popular.
d. is feared and respected by the other students.
e. is a school leader.
f. participates in athletics.
g. is self-confident.
h. is feared and mistrusted by the teachers.
i. is considered a "bad boy."
j. is intelligent.
k. seems to hold others in contempt.
l. intimidates, harasses, and beats up other children.
m. is proud.
n. is impulsive.
o. is curious about life.
p. seems to enjoy life.

2. Notes will vary. Students might suggest that, after the incident, Bruno
a. is looked at differently by the community.
b. loses social stature.
c. becomes withdrawn and sullen with everyone.
d. stops going to school as often.
e. resigns his class office.
f. gives up school athletics.
g. is moody, bored, and filled with anger.

h. hates life.
i. seems to hate himself.
j. seems to have given up on himself.

**D.** (4 points each)
1. c
2. a
3. a
4. b
5. c

**E.** (16 points; students should answer one of the two)
1. Answers will vary. Students might say that the narrator's response to the madman is completely passive because she is
a. paralyzed by fear. She doesn't try to escape his grip even though she probably would have succeeded had she tried.
b. taken by surprise. Everything happens so quickly that she doesn't have time to think.
c. naturally shy and passive. She thinks of herself as being practically invisible to other people, not as a powerful person capable of taking matters into her own hands.

Students might say that Bruno's response to the madman is one of unrestrained violence and pure hatred because

a. he grew up in a violent home and was never taught how to control his temper. His mother is rumored to have scarred his face with boiling water in a fit of anger, and his father was known to be a temperamental, paranoid, violent man.

b. his father recently died a horrific death. This may have filled Bruno with rage and, when Bruno sees the madman gripping the narrator, this rage boils over and is directed at the madman.

Other ideas should be supported with appropriate reasons and references to the story.

2. Answers will vary. Most students will say that the main reason people suspect that Bruno's actions are not truly heroic is that Bruno stabs the madman repeatedly, going far beyond what one can reasonably believe would have been necessary. Other students might suggest that suspicion is raised by the fact that Bruno

a. is carrying a switchblade.
b. seems more like a full-grown man than an adolescent.
c. has a reputation for being a "bad boy."

In addition, students should include a personal judgment of Bruno's response to the madman. Some students may sympathize with Bruno, noting that

a. he has grown up with violence and doesn't know any better.
b. he has just lost his father in a particularly gruesome murder.
c. the madman threatens to kill the narrator.

d. the madman threatens someone Bruno knows.

e. the madman fights Bruno.

Students who judge Bruno more harshly might note that

  a. Bruno has no good reason for stabbing the madman once, much less repeatedly.

  b. Bruno repeatedly yells "Die!" to the madman, indicating that he knows what he is doing and wants to do it.

**F.** (16 points) Answers will vary widely, depending on students' personal experiences, situations, and viewpoints. Accept any answers that address the concern of the question and are elaborated by examples or details from the literature or from life.

## Mother Tongue

Selection Test, pp. 229–230

**A.** (10 points each) Notes will vary but should include points similar to the following:

  1. Growing Up:

    a. Tan was ashamed of her mother's English and "believed that her English reflected the quality of what she had to say." Tan supports her feelings by saying that people in stores, restaurants, and banks did not take her mother seriously or seem to give her respect.

    b. Tan was embarrassed because she had to make her mother's phone calls: "I was forced to ask for information or even complain and yell at people who had been rude to her." To support her feelings, she tells the story of having to call the stockbroker to demand a check.

    c. Tan felt that her mother's English may have limited Tan's possibilities in life. To support this statement, Tan explains why she thinks she did better on the math SAT than the English SAT.

  2. As an Adult:

    a. Tan describes her mother's English as a language that relates to family talk. This English is the language of intimacy that she and her husband use.

    b. Tan now knows that her mother's spoken English may be "limited," but her mother's understanding, her thoughts, and her ideas are not (for example, she is an avid reader of journals and books that Tan does not fully understand).

    c. Tan uses her mother as the audience (the reader) for her stories. She feels that her stories express more of her because she uses all the Englishes she grew up with. Tan is proud of her mother's English because it expresses "her intent, her passion, her imagery, the rhythms of her speech and the nature of her thoughts."

    d. Tan knew she had succeeded when her mother said, "So easy to read."

**B.** (6 points each)

  1. a

  2. d

  3. a

  4. d

**C.** (4 points each)

  1. c

  2. b

  3. c

  4. a

  5. b

**D.** (20 points; students should answer one of the two)

  1. Answers will vary but should include points similar to the following:

    a. Tan includes the story to give readers an example of just how her mother's English sounds and how expressive it is.

    b. The story helps the reader understand Tan's later comments about what to call her mother's English—words like *limited* or *broken* affect people's perceptions of her mother and her mother's abilities.

    c. The story helps readers understand one of Tan's points: her mother's English does have intent, passion, imagery, and rhythm, and it shows the complexity of her thoughts.

  2. Students are most likely to conclude that Tan and her mother do have a close relationship and should support their opinion with at least three of the following examples:

    a. Her mother attends her lectures.

    b. Tan, her husband, and her mother go out together.

    c. Her mother relies on and trusts Tan to talk to the doctors about the CAT scan.

    d. Her mother is the audience (reader) for *The Joy Luck Club,* a book about mother-and-daughter relationships.

Students may conclude that Tan and her mother did not have a close relationship if they support this opinion with valid examples.

**E.** (16 points) Answers will vary widely, depending on students' personal experiences, situations, and viewpoints. Accept any answers that address the concern of the question and are elaborated by examples or details from the literature or from life.

## The Latin Deli: An Ars Poetica

Selection Test, pp. 231–232

**A.** (10 points each) Notes may vary but should include points similar to the following:

  1. a. This is a simile.

    b. The stalks of plantains are compared to votive offerings. The image that comes to mind is religious and makes the reader think of a church. In two lines, the poet has expressed how the deli is like a church, or a place where customers can come for comfort and to express their devotion.

2. a. This is a metaphor.

b. The phrase "canned memories" suggests that the cans of products evoke customers' memories of home. At home, they saw and bought the same products. The metaphor emphasizes how homesick the customers feel.

3. a. This is hyperbole.

b. This figure of speech exaggerates the price of coffee from the customer's homeland and suggests a fondness for it, regardless. The customers could go to another store where the prices are much lower, or they could buy a different brand of coffee. Yet they return to the deli because it is the place where they hear their own language and see products from their own countries. The deli is as close to home as they can get.

**B.** (10 points each)

1. b
2. a
3. d

**C.** (20 points; students should answer one of the two)

1. Answers will vary but should include points similar to the following:

a. The woman is the owner, but the use of *presiding* suggests that she also occupies the place of authority. The word creates a much stronger image of the woman's role in the deli.

b. The "*heady* mix of smells" is not only strong but also intoxicating. The word suggests a feeling of giddiness at the delight of such familiar aromas.

c. The word *gaze* means "to stare," but it also implies a fixed attention of curiosity, wonder, or admiration. The image suggests that the customers go to the deli to see someone they admire who looks like the people from their country.

d. The word *hunger* implies more than a desire or physical want; it suggests a deep longing for something.

e. The word *divine* not only means "to guess" but also implies a gift or special power. The image suggests that the owner uses her "special gift" to know just what the customer needs for his or her soul.

f. *Conjuring* means more than "to summon"; it suggests a sense or use of magic, creating an almost mystical atmosphere in the deli.

2. Answers will vary widely but students should include points similar to the following:

a. The speaker sees the deli as almost a church, or a place of comfort, confession, and devotion ("plastic

Mother and Child," "like votive offerings," the "Patroness of Exiles").

b. The speaker sees the owner as a kind of spiritual leader (the "Patroness of Exiles" presides over the counter) with almost mystical powers. She can "conjure" products from places that now exist only in the customers' hearts. The owner is also adept at "divining" their needs. She knows just what to have in her store to satisfy the ache of homesickness in her customers.

c. The speaker seems to sympathize with the customers' homesickness. She understands their need to come to the deli just to see, feel, and smell reminders of home.

**D.** (20 points) Answers will vary widely, depending on students' personal experiences, situations, and viewpoints. Accept any answers that address the concern of the question and are elaborated by examples or details from the literature or from life.

## Straw into Gold

Selection Test, pp. 233–234

**A.** (10 points each) Notes will vary but should include points similar to the following:

1. Sentence Structure: Cisneros uses two rather long sentences and two short ones. The length of each sentence reflects the complexity and the importance of the idea it expresses. For example, one long sentence explains that there were many things that contributed to the author's development. A short sentence explains where she got her "love of wandering."

2. Diction: The writer uses the word *my* five times and *I* four times. This repetition emphasizes the effects of different influences on her, the writer. She begins the first two sentences with *I like to think* and the last two sentences with *from*. This also reinforces the idea that she has given her childhood experiences a lot of thought and evaluated how they have shaped her. The use of repetition gives the passage a regular rhythm, which grabs readers' attention and helps them focus on Cisneros's ideas. The choice of some unusual words and phrases in this excerpt—especially "Mexicanness" and "sappy heart"—calls attention to some important ideas.

3. Tone: The author's tone suggests that, despite some hard times in her childhood, all her childhood experiences made her what she is today—a writer. Her tone, or attitude, is very positive.

**B.** (5 points each)

1. c
2. d
3. b

**C.** (4 points each)
1. a
2. c
3. a
4. c
5. b

**D.** (20 points; students should answer one of the two)
1. Answers will vary but should include points similar to the following:
   a. The concept of turning straw into gold comes from the fairy tale "Rumpelstiltskin" and suggests a seemingly impossible task. It also suggests turning something plain and common into something valuable.
   b. This concept applies to Cisneros herself. When she was a child, she was shy and did not really have any self-confidence. She also lived in poverty and a state of transience for parts of her childhood. Now she is confident and successful, and she implies that she has found a "stable" home in Texas.
   c. It also applies to her work and how she writes. She has taken her childhood experiences and recorded them in stories and other works, thereby turning common "everyday" events into valuable items.
   d. At the end of the essay, she suggests that this process can and does continue: "Along the way there has been straw for the taking. With a little imagination, it can be spun into gold."
2. Notes may vary but should include points similar to the following:
   a. Cisneros's central idea is clearly expressed in two different sentences: "I've managed to do a lot of things in my life I didn't think I was capable of and which many others didn't think I was capable of either." "I've done all kinds of things I didn't think I could do since then." It is also implied in the final sentences: "Along the way there has been straw for the taking. With a little imagination, it can be spun into gold."
   b. The author supports this idea by describing where she came from (she broke with tradition by leaving home before her brothers and without a promise of marriage); things that she did along the way that she did not think she could do (making tortillas, passing the MFA exam); and how she transformed herself and her life to become a successful writer.

**E.** (15 points) Answers will vary widely, depending on students' personal experiences, situations, and viewpoints. Accept any answers that address the concern of the question and are elaborated by examples or details from the literature or from life.

## Unit Seven, Part Two Test
pp. 235–236
**A.** (5 points each)
1. b
2. a
3. d
4. c

**B.** (20 points) Notes will vary. A model answer for *Wandering* might suggest the following ideas:
   a. He and She's ideas of how Him should live and what he should be are contrasted with Him's ideas about his own life.
   b. He and She suggest that Him should follow the traditional American way of life by joining the army, getting a job, settling down, and having a family. Him expresses his feelings that he is opposed to killing, does not want to join the army, and prefers wandering to settling down. Him really is "quite happy" the way he is.
   c. This contrast suggests that people are expected to conform to "normal" ways of life, but what is right for the majority is not right for every individual. He and She cannot believe that Him is happy living the way he does; Him cannot believe that He and She's way of life is "the way people want to spend their lives."

**C.** (20 points each; students should answer two of the four)
1. Answers will vary. A model answer for Martin Luther King, Jr., in "Letter from Birmingham Jail" and Sandra Cisneros in "Straw into Gold" follows:
In "Letter from Birmingham Jail," King does a good job of advancing his political cause in that
   a. he conveys his ideas through carefully reasoned arguments.
   b. he responds point by point to the clergymen's criticisms in a well-structured essay.
   c. his tone is respectful but forceful.
   d. he effectively uses allusions to biblical figures, American presidents, and philosophers to appeal to the reader's reason, and he uses allusions to Hitler, Jews, and freedom fighters to appeal to the reader's emotions.
In "Straw into Gold," Cisneros does not do a good job of advancing her personal cause because she
   a. repeats herself several times during the essay when she tries to explain that she has done many things she never expected she would be able to do.
   b. has a somewhat vain view of her achievements, her travels, and how successful she is.
   c. presents herself as someone who has done something impossible—turning straw into gold—but

turning one's experiences into stories and turning herself into a writer seem hardly as difficult as the metaphorical comparison.

2. Answers will vary. A model answer for "Separating" follows:

There is little the government can do about the issue with which "Separating" is concerned—the breakdown of the family—because the government

    a. can't control the personal choices that individuals make about how to lead their lives. Richard is leaving his family because he is unhappy with his wife and wants to marry another woman.

    b. cannot, by law, outlaw divorce or force fathers to live with their children. The Constitution recognizes a right to privacy, and such laws would overstep the government's boundaries. The government can do nothing to prevent Richard from legally divorcing his wife and leaving his family.

3. Answers will vary. A model answer for "Mother Tongue" and "Legal Alien" follows:

In "Mother Tongue," Tan suggests positive feelings about the bicultural experience by

    a. suggesting that growing up in a bicultural situation gave her an appreciation of different languages and ways of expressing oneself.

    b. explaining that her background helped her to become a writer with a love of language because she defied the assumption that she would study premed or math.

    c. explaining how her mother helped her to become a better writer through her own unique use of English and Tan's appreciation of her mother's understanding, ideas, and thoughts.

In "Legal Alien," the speaker suggests negative feelings about the bicultural experience by

    a. suggesting that she is viewed by Anglos as exotic but inferior.

    b. suggesting that she is viewed by Mexicans as "alien."

    c. explaining that she doesn't feel a part of either culture and is negatively prejudged by members of both.

4. Answers will vary. A model answer for *Wandering* and "Teenage Wasteland" follows:

In *Wandering,* the central conflict

    a. concerns Him's efforts to lead a life that is personally meaningful to him. His efforts are opposed by He and She, who want Him to conform to the type of life that they think Him should lead.

    b. is difficult to resolve because Him's values, desires, needs, and personality are so very different from those of He and She, who do not value compromise.

    c. isn't resolved because Him can't be what He and She want him to be, and He and She refuse to accept Him for who he is.

    d. might be resolved only by Him's removing himself from all of the He's and She's in his life. Him might move to a culture that is more accepting of nonconformity, or Him could become a hermit.

In "Teenage Wasteland," the central conflict

    a. concerns Daisy's efforts to deal with Donny's problems. Daisy would like Donny to communicate more with her, to be a happier person, and to be a good, well-behaved student. Donny doesn't communicate well with her, isn't happy, and isn't a good student.

    b. is difficult to resolve because Daisy doesn't know what Donny needs, Donny doesn't seem to know what he needs, and he avoids communication with Daisy. Donny is going through adolescence, a very difficult, confusing period of life. In addition, Cal lends legitimacy to Donny's excuses and lies.

    c. isn't resolved. Donny runs away from home.

    d. might be resolved simply through the passage of time. As a runaway, Donny will have to grow up fast. He may come to appreciate his family more and be more willing to try to work things out with them.

**D.** (20 points) Notes will vary. A model answer for Richard in "Separating" follows:

Richard feels deeply confused because he

    a. has been wanting to leave his wife for a long time, but now that the day has arrived for him to leave, he isn't sure that is what he wants to do.

    b. wants to leave but doesn't want to face any of the consequences that leaving will have.

    c. the thing that he believes will bring him happiness— leaving his wife for another woman—is causing him to feel grief.

# End-of-Year Test
## pp. 237–248

**A.** 1. d
   2. b
   3. a
   4. d
   5. c
   6. a

**B.** 7. c
   8. a
   9. d
   10. b

**C.** Answers may vary but should include points similar to the following:

11. The psychiatrist interviews a prisoner, Mr. Brock, who calls himself "the murderer." Mr. Brock destroys the radios in the room and on the psychiatrist's wrist. He describes how he destroyed the technology in his car and then disrupted all the communication devices on a bus. He was arrested when he destroyed the technology in his home. The psychiatrist finishes the interview and returns to his office, where technology takes over once again.

12. Bradbury uses mainly personification and sensory images of sound to make the house seem alive, as if it has a mind of its own. He uses allusions to Greek mythology (Medusa, Sirens, Oracles) to suggest that the house has a supernatural power. These images and figurative language help the reader understand how much noise Mr. Brock has to cope with and how the house tries to rules his life, and they make the reader sympathetic to Mr. Brock's reaction.

13. The narrator describes the psychiatrist as living in the kind of world Mr. Brock despises (he uses his wrist radio, listens to music, answers the telephone), especially in the repetition in the last paragraph of the story. The descriptions of the nonstop music and electronic intrusions make the reader react negatively to technology and feel sympathetic to Mr. Brock.

**D.** 14. c
   15. a
   16. b
   17. c

**E.** Answers may vary but should include points similar to the following:

18. Technology that was intended to make life easier is destroying us. Or, people who rebel against the majority will not be tolerated.

19. Students may state that the psychiatrist and Mr. Brock, respectively, represent authority and rebellion, conformity and nonconformity, the majority and the minority, a technological society and humanity.

20. Students may sympathize or agree with either the psychiatrist or Mr. Brock. Accept any answers that address the concern of the question and are elaborated by examples or details from the literature.

## Writing Exercise Scoring Guide

**4** An **exceptional** paper:
- Has a clear and consistent focus
- Has a logical organization
- Uses transitions effectively to connect ideas
- Supports ideas with details, quotations, examples, and/or other evidence
- Exhibits well-formed sentences varying in structure
- Exhibits a rich vocabulary, including precise language that is appropriate for the purpose and audience of the paper
- Contains almost no errors in usage, mechanics, and spelling

**3** A **proficient** paper:
- Has a relatively clear and consistent focus
- Has a logical organization, although it may be unnecessarily mechanical
- Uses some transition words and phrases to connect ideas, but they do not always clarify connections effectively
- Supports ideas with details, quotations, examples, and/or other evidence
- Exhibits some variety in sentence structures
- Uses vocabulary that is appropriate for the purpose and audience
- Contains a few errors in usage, mechanics, and spelling

**2** A **basic** paper:
- Has a fairly clear focus that may occasionally become obscured
- Shows an organizational pattern, but relationships between ideas may sometimes be difficult to understand
- Contains supporting evidence that may lack effect and so only superficially develops ideas
- Has complete and varied sentences most of the time
- Contains several errors in usage, mechanics, and spelling which cause distraction and some confusion about meaning

**1** A **limited** paper:
- Has a topic but does not include any elaboration, or it only minimally addresses the topic and lacks discernible ideas
- Has only a few simple sentences
- Contains little or no plausible support for ideas
- Shows limited word choice
- Contains numerous and serious errors in usage, mechanics, and spelling which cause confusion about meaning

A paper is unable to be scored if it is
- illegible
- unrelated to the topic
- only a rewording of the prompt
- written in a foreign language
- not written at all

## Revising/Editing
1. c
2. a
3. d
4. b
5. c
6. a

# Standardized Test Practice
# Answer Key

## Analogies
1. E
2. A
3. E
4. D
5. C
6. E
7. A
8. B
9. C
10. E
11. A
12. B
13. B
14. C
15. C
16. B
17. D
18. E
19. E
20. A
21. C
22. A
23. B
24. B
25. A
26. E
27. C
28. D
29. B
30. C
31. C
32. B
33. C
34. A
35. B
36. D
37. C
38. D
39. B
40. C
41. D
42. E
43. D
44. C
45. B
46. A
47. B
48. D
49. D
50. E

## Sentence Completion
### Part A
1. D
2. B
3. C
4. E
5. A
6. C
7. C
8. B
9. D
10. E
11. D
12. B
13. A
14. D
15. B
16. B
17. E
18. C
19. C
20. B
21. B
22. A
23. A
24. C
25. D

### Part B
1. C
2. D
3. D
4. A
5. E
6. B
7. B
8. C
9. E
10. A
11. C
12. C
13. D
14. D
15. C
16. A
17. D
18. B
19. E
20. B
21. C
22. C
23. B
24. A
25. E

## Error Identification
1. E
2. A
3. A
4. B
5. C
6. C
7. D
8. C
9. D
10. D
11. E
12. A
13. C
14. A
15. C
16. E
17. D
18. D
19. C
20. E
21. C
22. B
23. B
24. E
25. C
26. D
27. B
28. B
29. C
30. C

## Error Correction
1. B
2. J
3. A
4. H
5. A
6. G
7. B
8. H
9. D
10. G
11. C
12. H
13. D
14. J
15. A
16. F
17. D
18. H
19. C
20. J
21. B
22. H
23. A
24. J
25. C
26. J
27. D
28. F
29. A
30. G

## Revision-in-Context
1. C
2. A
3. B
4. B
5. D
6. B
7. D
8. C
9. A
10. C
11. E
12. B
13. B
14. E
15. D

## Critical Reading
1. C
2. D
3. E
4. A
5. B
6. B
7. D
8. C
9. A
10. E
11. D
12. D
13. C
14. B
15. A
16. B
17. C
18. E
19. D
20. C
21. C
22. A
23. A
24. E
25. B
26. D
27. C
28. C
29. A
30. B